GRAPHICS
in
DESIGN
and
COMMUNICATION

David Anderson

GILL & MACMILLAN

Gill & Macmillan Ltd

Hume Avenue

Park West

Dublin 12

with associated companies throughout the world

www.gillmacmillan.ie

978 0 7171 4247 7

Design in Ireland by O'K Graphic Design, Dublin

Print origination in Ireland by Carole Lynch, Sligo

Artwork by Peter Bull Art Studio

The paper used in this book is made from the wood pulp of managed forests. For every tree felled, at least one tree is planted, thereby renewing natural resources.

For permission to reproduce photographs the author and publisher gratefully acknowledge the following:
1, 2T, 17, 18, 19 © Alamy; Corbis: 213T © Robert Essel NYC, 213B © Joseph Sohm; 137 Courtesy of Hewlett Packard; 24, 25, 49, 50 © Last Resort Picture Library; 212 © Steve Allen/Science Photo Library; 2B © The Art Archive/Museo della Civilta Romana Rome/Dagli Orti.

CONTENTS

PART 2 – COMMUNICATION OF DESIGN AND COMPUTER GRAPHICS

PART 3 – APPLIED GRAPHICS

PART 2

COMMUNICATION OF DESIGN AND COMPUTER GRAPHICS

12 Graphics in Design and Communication

SYLLABUS OUTLINE

Areas to be studied (in an applied context):

• Drawing from a historical perspective. • Design strategies. • Reflection on processes of design. • Design appraisal.
• *Generation of design briefs.* • Interpretation of design briefs. • Ideas sketching. • Design problem-solving.
• Design communication.

Learning outcomes
   Students should be able to:

Higher and Ordinary levels
*   Compare traditional graphic communication methods with electronic methods and appreciate the advantages and disadvantages of both.
*   Understand the steps required to bring a project from situation/brief, to final working drawings.
*   Analyse design as it affects the function, ergonomics and aesthetic qualities of everyday artefacts.
*   Display a knowledge of the rudiments of good design – proportion, colour, materials, ergonomics, safety and value for money.
*   Interpret and analyse given design briefs.
*   Understand the principles of the interpretation of graphic instructions as they apply to the solution of a design brief.

Higher level only
*   *Evaluate design with reference to function, ergonomics and aesthetic qualities.*
*   *Generate design briefs appropriate to given problems.*

Drawing from a Historical Perspective

The Beginnings

Drawing is a means of communication which is understood all over the world. A drawing produced in Ireland will be understood in Japan, in Russia, in Italy and in France. The text accompanying the drawing may not be understood but the graphics will be. Drawings therefore are very powerful and the ability to produce them is a great skill to have.

There are two types of drawings:
(1)   Artistic
(2)   Technical

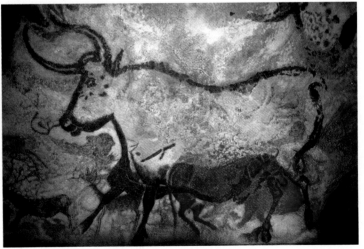

Fig. 12.1

Artistic drawings range from cave drawings (Fig. 12.1), dating back to the Stone Age, to be found in Spain, to modern museum works, to comics etc. These drawings would fall into the 'art' category that we traditionally think of. Technical drawings are drawings used to represent design ideas, or to represent objects to be built or constructed. They are drawn to convey information – that is their function. This is not to say that technical drawings cannot also be works of art. Of course they can, but it is not their primary aim.

The earliest piece of technical drawing which is still in existence is the plan view of a fortress. The drawing, engraved on a stone tablet, dates back to 4,000 BC, to the earliest period of Chaldean art. It can be argued that many of the ancient buildings such as the Temple of Amon in ancient Egypt (Fig. 12.2, 980 BC), the Circus Maximus in Rome, (Figures 12.3 and 12.4), or the Hanging Gardens of Babylon (Fig. 12.5) all required plans to be drawn before they were constructed. No drawings for these exist today, however, but such large building projects could not possibly have been completed without drawings to guide the builders. This argument is even more valid if we factor in the timescale. The Temple of Amon for instance took over 700 years to build. The Roman architect Vitruvius (30 BC) wrote:

Fig. 12.2

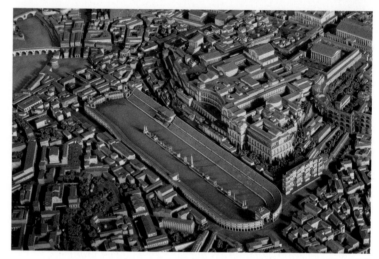

Fig. 12.3

> The architect must be skilful with the pencil, and have a knowledge of drawing so that he readily can make the drawings required to show the appearance of the work he proposes to construct.

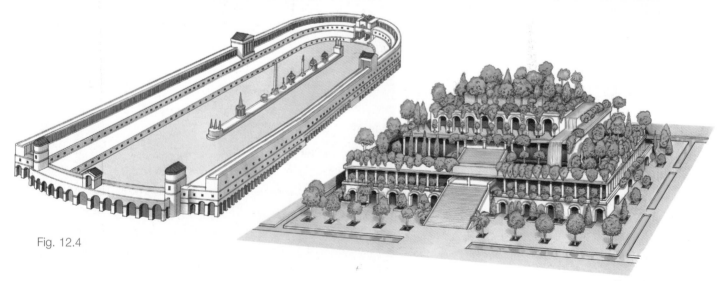

Fig. 12.4

Fig. 12.5

Remnants of bronze compasses have been found and are displayed in our museums. All this evidence points to the fact that technical drawing has been used throughout history in the same way as it is used today – as an aid to design creation and realisation.

The Birth of Geometry

The projection of objects onto imaginary planes to produce views was not developed until the early fifteenth century. Its invention is accredited to two Italian architects, Alberti and Brunelleschi among several others. Several hundred years later, in the eighteenth century, came descriptive geometry. Gaspard Monge (1746–1818) a French engineer began using drawings as a problem-solving tool to help overcome design problems encountered during the construction of military fortifications. His book *Leçons de Géométrie Descriptive* is generally regarded as the first text on the topic.

Up to the turn of the nineteenth century, first-angle projection was the system used throughout the world. The plan was drawn below the front view, the left side view was drawn to the right of the front elevation etc. At this time in the United States of America favour was beginning to lean toward third-angle projection. It has stayed pretty much that way since, with the two systems of projection being used, each finding favour in different parts of the world.

The development of computer graphics and computer-aided drawing is the next big milestone on our timeline. This can be traced back to the Massachusetts Institute of Technology Lincoln Laboratory in the middle of the last century, where Dr Ivan Sutherland developed the **Sketchpad** program. In this program a cathode ray oscilloscope was driven by the Lincoln TX2 computer in such a way that it generated geometrical shapes. Using a light pen, the figures on the screen could be drawn and moved around on the screen. At the time it was an impressive demonstration and was the first real step toward a new type of man–computer communication – communication by graphics.

Huge developments in computing power since Sutherland's Sketchpad program has produced equally impressive development in computer graphics. Computer-aided Drawing or Computer-aided Design (CAD) software is the norm in engineering offices, architects' offices, universities and colleges, and now in secondary schools. These software packages have become powerful enough, adaptable enough and user-friendly enough to take over from the drawing board. In many situations CAD has become the preferred choice.

Which is Better – the T-square or the Tablet?

There is no definitive answer to this question as both traditional methods of drawing and modern electronic methods have different advantages and disadvantages. A brief comparison of each may be useful.

Accuracy

Computer graphics have a uniformly neat and precise appearance, regardless of the individual operator's style. Faults that might be overlooked on a typical hand-drawn drawing are exaggerated by the exactness of the computer plot. Lines that are almost but not quite parallel, corners that are not truly square, and corners where the lines do not meet or lap over, would give a bad appearance to any computer drawing, but might be overlooked on the drawing board. The computer user is more likely, therefore, to produce neat and accurate work than his/her counterpart using a drawing board. Computer-aided drawings are extremely accurate in another way – with respect to distance. To draw a line 100 mm long on a sheet, an accuracy of 0.25 mm would be expected. Using the computer would improve both linear and angular measurement to almost perfection, assuming that the printer/plotter has been calibrated properly.

Tone

Tone of line in any drawing is very important, construction lines being light, outlines heavy and dimensioning somewhere in between. Using such techniques the finished drawing has more impact. It is a drawing skill which many pupils find difficult to develop but is one worth developing. Any drawing lacking such line tone will, more than likely, be both very confusing and very untidy. Computer-aided drawing uses colour and line thickness to achieve the same clarity. An unobtrusive colour, like yellow, could be used for construction lines while a thickened black line could be used for outlines. It should be noted here, however, that with a vast range of colour available to the CAD user, the finished drawing may appear gaudy and distract the eye from the focus of the drawing. It can be difficult to beat a plain black and white drawing for visual impact.

Erasing and Correcting

An area of draughting in which the computer can claim to be far superior is in the correcting of errors in drawings. On a computer a line can be drawn and erased hundreds of times without any detrimental effect to the finished product, the drawing on the screen. If this was tried on a drawing sheet you can imagine the result! Furthermore, line colour and line type, dotted, chain, solid etc., can all be changed with ease on a computer, not so on the drawing board.

Text

An area which is linked to draughtsmanship is that of text on the drawing. There is usually a need to place written material on a drawing, whether it is an integral part of a drawing such as specifications or explanatory notes. Text produced on a drawing board often varies hugely from student to student, often varies in quality from page to page and can be slow to complete. It can be said, however, that text produced by the computer will always be legible, uniform, well spaced and neat, and can be drawn large or very small, see Fig. 12.6. A wide range of text fonts is also available. All dimensioning produced on the computer will be of equally high quality and uniformity. All in all this makes for very neat drawings.

Sabon (serif)

Sabon Regular	....	abcdefghijklmnopqrstuvwxyz!@£$%^&*()
Sabon Italic	....	abcdefghijklmnopqrstuvwxyz!@£$%^&*()
Sabon Bold	....	abcdefghijklmnopqrstuvwxyz!@£$%^&*()
Sabon Bold Italic	....	abcdefghijklmnopqrstuvwxyz!@£$%^&*()

Frutiger (sans serif)

Frutiger Regular	....	abcdefghijklmnopqrstuvwxyz!@£$%^&*()
Frutiger Italic	....	abcdefghijklmnopqrstuvwxyz!@£$%^&*()
Frutiger Bold	....	abcdefghijklmnopqrstuvwxyz!@£$%^&*()
Frutiger Bold Italic	....	abcdefghijklmnopqrstuvwxyz!@£$%^&*()

Fig. 12.6

Speed

One of the great advantages of computer graphics is its speed of execution. With the appropriate software, drawings of high quality can be built up in a matter of minutes. In addition to its speed the computer has a never-ending ability to repeat its work. Repetitive portions of a drawing can be copied instantly, saving time.

The computer is not only very fast in producing drawings but also in storing and retrieving them. During a school year many hours of valuable teaching time are lost while the pupils set up their equipment, find the sheet on which they were working previously or line up a new sheet. Using a computer this time wastage would be reduced considerably. A diagram can be stored on disk by simply giving it a name and can be retrieved by recalling this name. Furthermore, work can be done on a drawing over several days without any problems.

Drawing Manipulation

A thing that most people notice about computer graphics is that they are dynamic. A drawing can be produced on the screen and then can be moved, reflected, scaled, rotated etc. A three-dimensional object can be drawn which can then be viewed from any angle and can be joined to other 3-D objects. This ability to manipulate drawings is a great plus for the computer and helps greatly in the development of spatial perception. Drawing board work on the other hand is static, fixed, difficult to change. The ability to move and change drawings, to view objects from any angle, is a great motivating factor.

Fig. 12.7a

Fig. 12.7b

Fig. 12.7c

Cost

There is simply no comparison between the cost of setting up a traditional drawing station with board, T-square, set-squares etc. and setting up a CAD unit. The price of a graphics software package, coupled with the cost of a computer and a printer or plotter adds up to a huge bill. This cost puts having a CAD facility at home out of reach for most users. Work done at school or at the workplace cannot be brought home to be added to, altered or studied. By printing hard copies of the work this problem is alleviated slightly, but any alterations made on the printed drawings must still be entered into the computer at a later time.

Design

Computers are very well suited to use in the design process. At the beginning of the design process, when ideas have not been properly formed, the initial concepts are usually put down as sketches which are then worked on, modified, adapted and refined. Some of these design ideas will be kept while others will be discarded. The computer can neatly discard unwanted material and store the rest in a library where it can be retrieved later for more modification.

The use of a parts library to help build up a drawing can save a huge amount of time when designing and drawing. A library of bolts, screws, washers, springs, cams, pins etc. means that the computer operator has only to select the required part and insert it in the required place. Repetitive elements can be easily dealt with in this way. Furthermore, new parts can be drawn at any stage and stored in the library for use in future drawings.

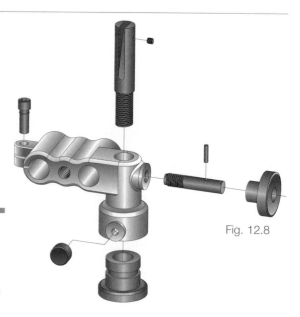

Fig. 12.8

Layers

Layers in a CAD system are like sheets of tracing paper. Each layer can be drawn on and can contain a different part of a drawing build-up. When all the layers are switched on, we see all the drawing. Each individual layer can be switched off at any stage, which removes from the drawing anything drawn on that layer. For example, a drawing contains five layers:

(1)   construction,
(2)   centre lines,
(3)   dark lines,
(4)   text,
(5)   dimensions.

Any construction lines needed are drawn on layer 1, centre lines are drawn on layer 2, outlines and other dark lines on layer 3 etc. Having all layers switched on will show the drawing with construction lines, centre lines, text and dimensions. By switching off layer 1 and layer 5 the drawing will be still seen but without construction lines and dimensions. The advantages of this are obvious. A second example of the plans of a house, for example, would involve the plan itself plus perhaps the electrical system, sewage system, plumbing system, furniture etc. By placing each of these on separate layers, clarity can be maintained by only switching on the relevant layers at any particular time.

CAD/CAM

Computers are not only useful in the design of objects but also in the manufacture of objects. CAM (Computer-aided Manufacture) links a computer to a robot, a lathe, a router or a milling machine. A design created on the computer can then be mass-produced by the machine. There is a direct link between the design process and the manufacturing process.

There is no doubting that computer-aided drawing/design appears to have many advantages over the T-square and drawing board. Yet, at the same time, one is not recommending the abandonment of the traditional method of learning and producing drawings. There is still a huge place for these skills and probably will be for a long time into the future. Some would even argue that learning to draw with a pencil, set-square etc. is an absolute prerequisite to learning to draw using CAD. Whatever your view there is no fear of the drawing board being abandoned for a very long time yet.

The Design Process

Solving a design problem can often be an iterative process. As the solution to the problem evolves you may discover that the route you are taking will be too expensive, will not work or does not meet safety requirements. You then go back to the drawing board and modify/redefine the problem and the solution(s).

Good designs do not appear in a vacuum. A good solution requires a clear methodology or process and a great deal of patience. The Wright brothers did not design a flying aeroplane at the first attempt. They began by conducting tests with kites and then gliders. Before attempting powered flight, they solved the problems of controlling a plane's motion when rising, descending and turning. They didn't construct a powered plane until after making more than 700 successful glider flights.

As has been said earlier, design creation requires a process, a methodology. The methodology described here will have five steps:

(1) Define the problem.
(2) Gather relevant information.
(3) Generate multiple solutions.
(4) Analyse and select a solution.
(5) Test and implement the solution.

When working through these five steps you may find at any stage that you need to go back one step or more. The solution chosen may prove unworkable for any number of reasons and may require the redefining of the problem, collecting more information or generating different solutions. This is a continuous, iterative process until a satisfactory solution is reached.

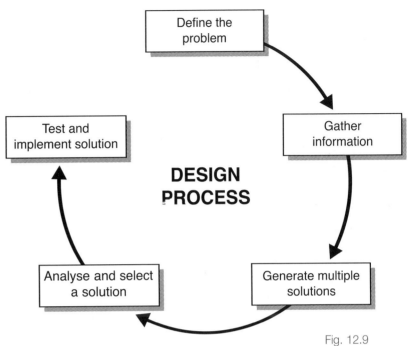

Fig. 12.9

Step 1: Define the Problem

The solution to a design problem begins with a clear, unambiguous definition of the problem. This can be presented in the form of a design brief to the designer. More often, the design problem begins as a vague, abstract idea in the mind of the designer and must be honed and clarified to become more specific. The definition of the problem may also evolve as the design process is worked through. By working toward a solution a more complete understanding of the problem is developed. The definition of the design problem usually requires an analysis of the following three steps:

(1) Identify and establish the need.
(2) Develop a problem statement.
(3) Establish criteria for success.

(1) IDENTIFY AND ESTABLISH THE NEED

Design activity always occurs in response to a human need. You need to recognise the need for a new or improved product, system or machine. The success of the new design ultimately depends on how well the designer captures this need and responds to it. If the final design does not adequately address the original need, then the design is not a solution to the design problem.

(2) DEVELOP A PROBLEM STATEMENT

Once the need has been established, the problem statement needs to be formulated in clear and unambiguous terms. It should address the need, yet be broad enough not to exclude certain solutions. A broad definition allows a wide range of alternative solutions to be looked at before a specific solution is focussed on. The temptation at this point in the design process is to develop a preconceived mental picture of the solution, thus excluding many potentially innovative solutions. A problem statement should be concise and flexible enough to allow for creative solutions.

(3) ESTABLISH CRITERIA FOR SUCCESS

Criteria for success are the attributes the final design must possess in order to be considered a good design. These criteria should be included in the problem statement to provide direction toward the solution. The criteria are preliminary at this stage and may need to be redefined or modified as the design process develops. Again the preliminary criteria must not be too specific so they allow flexibility through the design process.

At this stage we have a design brief.

Step 2: Gather Pertinent Information

Before going any further in the design process, information relating to the problem needs to be gathered. Do not be tempted to skip over this step as effort spent now will pay dividends later. Research on work done on similar designs, false starts and mistakes by other designers can all help to save time. It often helps to try to find answers to the following questions:

* What are the existing solutions to the problem?
* What is wrong with the way the problem is currently being solved?
* What is right about the way the problem is currently being solved?
* What are the cost restraints on the design?
* Do safety factors need to be considered?
* Are there environmental issues?
* Are aesthetics important?

There are many places to search for the answers to these questions. Books and the library are still the primary source of information. Periodicals, journals and specialist magazines are also a good source. The Internet is becoming increasingly important. Just as important as these resources is human discussion. The designer is ill-advised to work in solitude. By discussing the problem with peers and colleagues many of the answers sought can be found quickly. Furthermore new questions may be posed which will help refine and define the design problem and thus produce a better design solution.

Step 3: Generate Multiple Solutions

The next step in the design process begins with creativity. Start with existing solutions to the problem and then tear them apart – find out what is wrong with these solutions and focus on how to improve on their weaknesses.

Psychological research has found no correlation between intelligence and creativity. People are creative because they make a conscious effort to think and act creatively. You can, however, boost your creative ability by being:

* curious and tolerant of the unknown,
* open to new experiences/ideas,
* willing to take risks.

As mentioned earlier, a design team will probably produce a more creative solution to a problem than will an individual working in isolation. A team will possess more knowledge and different ways of looking at the problem than an individual. Team members learn from each other and one member's ideas will often stimulate another more creative idea from someone else on the team. Teams will generate more ideas than an individual and can better evaluate and judge these ideas to determine the best one.

STRATEGIES FOR GENERATING CREATIVE SOLUTIONS

There are two recognised techniques that aid the generation of creative ideas:
- Brainstorming.
- Sketchstorming.

Brainstorming: This is a group activity. It usually takes place over a short period of time, approximately 30 minutes, and should involve between 3 and 15 people. It is a technique of generating many ideas with the hope that a few good ideas will develop into something workable.

During a brainstorming session the members should:
- Accept everything. There should be no criticism or evaluation of ideas. All members are equal and each member's ideas are of equal importance.
- Welcome the outlandish. New ideas are born only when the freedom to hatch them exists. There are no 'dumb' ideas.
- Stress the importance of quantity. Encourage the generation of as many ideas as possible. As the number of ideas increases so do the chances that a really good idea will emerge.
- Build on and combine old ideas. Examine how existing solutions can be improved or combined into a new solution.
- Record everything. One person in the group should write down all ideas.

Sketchstorming: Sketchstorming is the visual equivalent of brainstorming. Since many solutions are typically presented in visual rather than verbal or written form, it makes sense to record initial ideas in sketch form. The sketches are not detailed but are rather quick, two-dimensional representations of what your mind is seeing.

Step 4: Analyse and Select a Solution

A decision must now be made as to which solution to implement. This is a highly subjective step and is best made by a group. Before deciding which design solution to implement, each alternative solution must be examined against the selected criteria defined in Step 1.

Every design problem is unique and requires different types of analysis but the following types of analysis apply to most problems:
- Functional analysis.
- Ergonomics.
- Aesthetic qualities.
- Safety analysis.
- Strength and mechanical analysis.
- Environmental impact.

Functional Analysis: The chosen design must function properly and consistently. A design solution that does not solve the problem as set out in Step 1 of the process is a failure even if it satisfies all other criteria. A design that functions erratically is also a failure. Economy, good appearance, durability etc. of a design are all irrelevant if the product does not function properly. A good example would be the invention of the ballpoint pen during World War II. The pen was invented to solve the problems inherent with the fountain pen, i.e. the need to constantly refill with ink and the messiness of this operation. The early pens depended on gravity for the ink to flow to the roller ball. The pens only worked in an upright position and the ink flow was often inconsistent. The ink flow was often too heavy and therefore left blotches and smudges, at other times the flow was too light leaving gaps in the writing. The pens also tended to leak and this ruined people's clothes. It was not until an elastic ink was developed in 1949 that a better flow was produced. This flow was more dependent on capillary action than gravity.

The first ballpoint pens failed the functionality analysis and in spite of fulfilling the other design criteria, were a design failure until this basic problem was overcome.

Ergonomics: Ergonomics is the human factor in design. It is the study of how people interact with machines. People

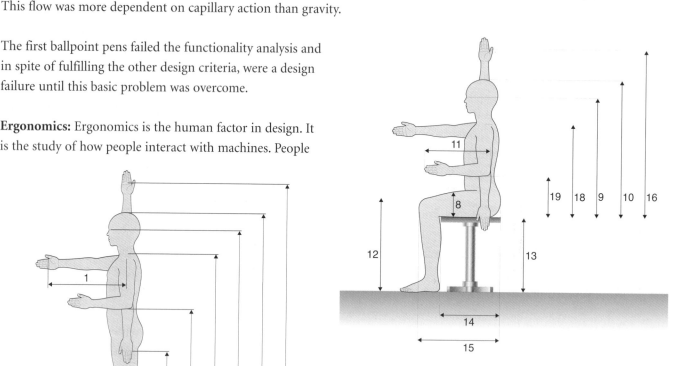

Anthropometric data – Sitting

Table 2 Seated at work

Measurement (units in centimetres)	Males			Females		
	95	50	5	95	50	5
8 Thigh clearance	17.8	14.5	13.7	17.5	13.7	10.7
9 Seated eye height	84.3	78.5	72.6	78.5	73.4	67.6
10 Seated stature	96.8	90.7	84.1	90.7	85.1	78.5
11 Elbow to fingertip	51.3	48	44.2	46	42.2	38.6
12 Knee height	61.7	56.9	51.8	57.2	52.3	47.8
13 Seat height	51.3	46.7	41.7	46.7	42.4	38.1
14 Seat length	54.9	49.5	44.2	53.6	48	42.9
15 Upper leg length	64.3	59.4	54.1	62.5	56.9	51.8
16 Seated overhead reach	142	129	115	131	120	109
17 Hip breadth	39.4	35.6	31.8	42.2	38.1	34
18 Seated shoulder height	65.8	59.4	52.6	61.7	55.6	49.3
19 Seated elbow height	30.2	24.4	19.1	28.2	23.4	18
20 Elbow breadth	50.5	41.7	35.1	49	38.4	31.5
21 Arm span	193	178	166	172	161	149
22 Elbow span	102	94.5	86.6	91.9	85.1	78

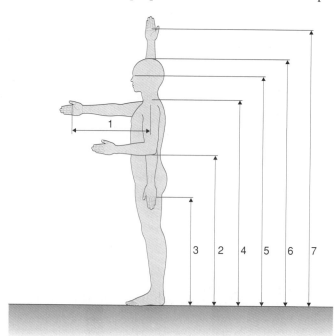

Anthropometric data – Standing

Table 1 Standing at work

Measurement (units in centimetres)	Males			Females		
	95	50	5	95	50	5
1 Forward reach	88.4	82.6	76.2	79	71.1	64
2 Standing elbow height	122	113	103	111	104	96.3
3 Standing knuckle height	83.1	78	72.4	78.5	72.6	66.8
4 Standing shoulder height	155	145	135	145	52.6	124
5 Standing eye height	175	165	154	160	151	141
6 Standing stature	187	176	164	174	163	152
7 Standing overhead reach	225	212	198	207	196	184

Fig. 12.10a

Fig. 12.10b

may occupy a space inside or around the design, they may operate and provide power for the design, they may have to control its function. A design solution can be considered to have satisfied the ergonomic criteria if the design fits, or is comfortable for, the people who will use it. The handle of a cordless drill for example must fit the hand of the people using it. The tool should not be heavy or cumbersome or else it will put strain on the user. A computer desk must be designed to have the keyboard at a good height for typing while at the same time holding the monitor at eye level. Failure to meet either of these ergonomic criteria will lead to finger and wrist strain when typing and/or back strain.

The proportions of people, their weight, height, reach, circumference etc. are called **anthropometrics**. Many studies and surveys have produced anthropometric data which can be accessed easily on the Internet or from books. A successful design needs to be checked against the people who will eventually use it.

Fig. 12.11 shows two designs for pliers. The pair in Fig. 12.11a are of a familiar, conventional design which makes good economic and practical sense. It is made from two identical parts and so will minimise production costs, and is also very functional.

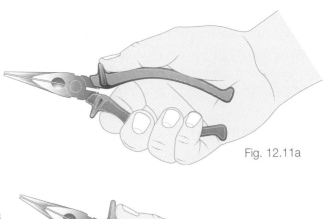

Fig. 12.11a

Well, the pliers appear to have reached the end of their design evolution. If we now consider the design shown in Fig. 12.11b, this pair looks awkward and is made from two very different halves. Yet trials have shown that these pliers are more comfortable to use than their classical predecessors. The reason for this is because the design is based on studies of the anatomy of the hand and wrist, particularly studying how the muscles and tendons work. The older design requires a bending of the wrist when using them and this causes unnecessary strain.

Fig. 12.11b

Aesthetics: Aesthetics is about looking good to the user. The best design in the world, if not pleasing to the eye, will never become hugely popular. When looking at aesthetics we must consider shape, proportion, size, colour, texture etc. It must be remembered that what is aesthetically pleasing to one person may not be aesthetically pleasing to the next. Aesthetics will effect the final shape of the design. In many cases the actual working parts of a design are encased in an aesthetic housing which serves no purpose except that of beautifying the product. Aesthetic considerations will also have a major part to play in material choice for the design. Properties sought may include a particular surface texture or quality finish, a certain visual appearance, colour, degree of transparency, be self-finishing etc.

Safety analysis: Because litigation has become common in today's environment it is of utmost importance that any proposed new design is safe. There are essentially three ways of approaching the problem of safety in a design. The first of these is to design safety directly into the product. Determine all potential risks when the artefact is functioning properly and also if there is failure of some or several elements of the design. Ask: 'What if?', and design in fail-safes and protection to protect against such a scenario.

There are some products that are inherently dangerous and for these we use the second method of designing for safety. Machinery that involves rotating parts cannot be completely safe, here the designer must include safety shields placed around the moving parts and automatic kill-switches that turn a machine off if there is potential for injury.

The third method of designing for safety is to use warning labels describing risks and dangers. Warning labels are the weakest way to implement safety in design.

Strength and mechanical analysis: It is important that the component parts of a design are looked at both individually and as a unit to assess their mechanical strength. The parts must be both strong enough to perform their function and strong enough to continue to function over the proposed lifetime of the product. Furthermore each part, or group of parts, must be able to resist the wear and tear of everyday use which will include being knocked and dropped. The sizes and cross-sections of various elements of the design may need to be calculated. Modern computer software allows the simulation of moving parts, can calculate fluid flow through an object, can determine the heating of engine parts due to friction or combustion, can determine stresses on roof struts or building foundations. For designs which may be mass-produced such computer modelling is essential and very cost-effective, but for the smaller-scale operation it is often the case that prototypes are made and tests are physically performed on these prototypes.

Environmental impact: 'Green' design has become an increasingly important factor. There are three strands to the 'green' design idea. Firstly, the production of the product should not entail wastage of resources, emission of toxins into the environment or the legacy of useless by-products. Secondly, during the working life of the product it should use energy efficiently and should not adversely effect the environment in which it is working. Thirdly, the product should have a long working life and at the end of this working life should be mostly biodegradable or recyclable. In general, although there is increased interest in the development of genuinely green designs, it is often difficult to find solutions which are feasible, credible and generally acceptable when compared to the more traditional, less green, designs.

What we are looking for in any design is the reduction to a minimum of the environmental impact of the product. The designer should therefore:
- increase the efficiency in the use of materials, energy and other resources,
- minimise damage or pollution from chosen materials,
- minimise any harm to the environment caused by the use of the product,
- ensure that the life of the product is as long as possible,
- take full account of the effects of the end-disposal of the product,
- ensure that the packaging, appearance and instructions encourage environmentally friendly use,
- minimise nuisances such as noise or smell,
- minimise potential hazards.

Step 5: Test and Implement the Solution

The final stage of the design process is implementation, which involves the testing, construction and manufacture of the solution. It is often at this stage that problems are identified which were not clear at earlier stages in the design process.

Prototyping and modelling: It may well be worthwhile to build a working prototype of the design. This is particularly true if it is intended to produce the design in large numbers. Such a prototype can be tested and modified before full-scale production begins. The prototype should be made using the same materials as the intended final product and should be tested under real conditions and extreme conditions. Feedback from these tests will often suggest minor improvements in the design.

For designs which will not be mass-produced, e.g. large, one-off designs; bridges; buildings; one-off furniture or designs which involve the use of expensive materials such as individual jewellery pieces; it is not practical to use prototypes. Here models and mock-ups are used. By using cheap and more easily worked materials, costly mistakes can be avoided. For larger projects, scaled models are used. The main interest with a scaled model is usually visual appearance. Information on shape, size, proportion, spatial organisation, colour etc. all becomes clearer with the use of a model.

In addition to prototyping and modelling the designer may also have access to 3-D CAD models. It is now possible to use CAD software to create 3-D models of the design's geometry and to use these models to analyse factors such as strength, stresses, weight etc. Using feedback from this analysis the designer can quickly modify the model to reflect the results. This process can be repeated many times to produce a superior product in a short period.

Drawing: The designer thinks about many different properties during the early stages of design and generally uses sketches to explore geometrical arrangement, visual appearance, possibilities for construction and assembly, relative motion of parts etc. At later stages in the design process more precise information is required incorporating exact shape and dimensions. These drawings carry annotations and symbols relating to the material's properties and assembly of parts. Before the chosen design is manufactured, a set of working drawings needs to be produced. These working drawings will include component or single-part drawings and also assembly drawings. The single-part drawings, as the name suggests, serve to describe individual components, usually using multi-view orthographics. The assembly drawings show how the

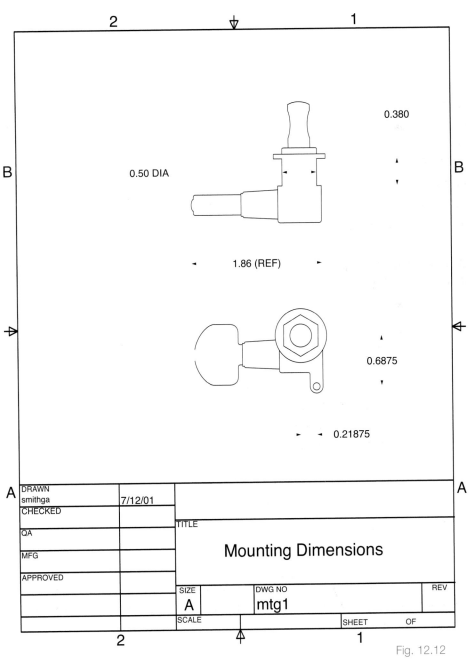

Fig. 12.12

components are put together. Both kinds of drawing are annotated with details of dimensions, tolerances, materials to be used, finishes of surfaces and manufacturing techniques. Most assembly drawings will be accompanied with a parts list, setting out the types and numbers of components needed for the complete assembly.

The CAD software used to model a 3-D design will usually have the ability to produce component drawings, assembly drawings and a parts list from the actual 3-D model. A change in the model will produce a corresponding change in the computer-generated working drawings.

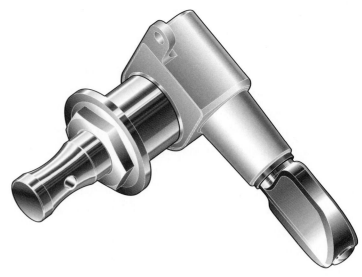

Fig. 12.13

Worked Example 1

DEFINING THE PROBLEM

Consider the statement 'Design a better mousetrap' and use this to develop a problem statement.

It is obvious that the statement given is not an adequate problem definition to start the design process. It expresses a vague dissatisfaction with existing mousetraps and therefore establishes a need. The designer must take this statement of need and through research, identify what is lacking in existing mousetrap designs. Perhaps through investigation the designer discovers that existing mousetraps are inadequate because they provide no protection from the deadly hantavirus carried by mice. A better mousetrap therefore is one that does not expose humans to this virus. From the research, the problem definition is modified to read 'Design a mousetrap that allows for the sanitary disposal of the trapped mouse, minimising human exposure to the hantavirus'.

It is best at this stage to keep the problem definition broad as this allows a wide range of alternative solutions. To define the better mousetrap problem as 'Define a mousetrap that sprays the trapped mouse with disinfectant' would be to make a problem statement that is very clear, yet too specific. This statement will exclude many potentially innovative solutions. Criteria for success should be stated at this stage. A preliminary list of criteria should include the following:

- The design must be cheap to produce.
- The design must be safe to operate.
- The design should be environmentally friendly.
- The design should be aesthetically pleasing.
- The design must be simple to operate.
- The design must be disposable.
- The design must kill the mouse humanely.

Our problem definition should incorporate these criteria.

Design a stylish mousetrap that allows for the sanitary disposal of the trapped mouse, minimising human exposure to any bacterial or viral agents being carried on the mouse. The trap should be cheap to produce, disposable and made from biodegradable materials. It must be easy to operate and kill the mouse humanely.

Worked Example 2

GENERATE MULTIPLE SOLUTIONS

Design a simple, easy-to-use, portable device to crush aluminium drinks cans. The device must be safe, strong and durable and be cheap to produce.

On looking at this problem statement we must devise several potential solutions.

Design idea 1

- Foot-operated release mechanism.
- Heavy crushing plate guided by upper guide bar and lower track.
- Spring provides crushing power.

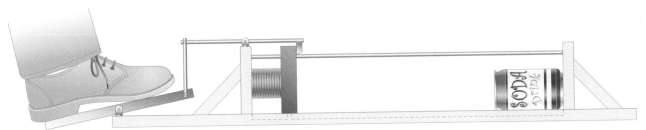

Fig. 12.14

Design idea 2

- Foot provides crushing power.
- Crushing plate runs on four guide bars.
- Spring returns plate back to top.

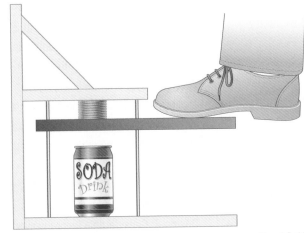

Fig. 12.15

Fig. 12.16

Design idea 3
- Heavy plate uses gravity to crush can.
- Plate runs on four guide bars.
- Plate must be wound back into position.

Design idea 4
- Arm-powered using law of the lever.
- Two guide bars for crushing plate.
- Spring returns arm to start position.

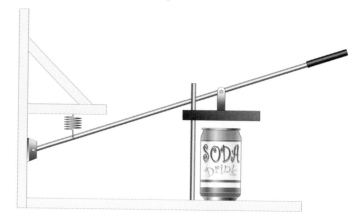

Fig. 12.17

ANALYSE AND SELECT A SOLUTION

The first design uses the energy of the spring to produce kinetic energy, moving the plate at speed to crush the can. The second idea uses direct force to crush the can, speed is not an issue. The third design uses gravity on the heavy plate, which falls at speed to crush the can. The fourth design uses the law of the lever to reduce the force needed to crush the can.

We must now look at the problem statement and rate each potential solution against the criteria given.

Functionality	All four designs will crush the drinks can.
Simplicity	All four designs are simple. Design 2 is probably the easiest to build with Design 4 running closely behind. Design 1 is slightly more complex as the crushing plate must be able to run freely in a horizontal direction on the guide tracks. Also, the trigger-release mechanism involves extra work. Design 3 with the heavy crushing plate and the pulley system will need a lot of parts.
Portability	Design 1 and 3 will be the least portable because of the need in the design for a heavy crushing plate which will add considerably to the weight of the devices. Design 2 would be the most compact design.
Ease of Use	Design 1: It may be difficult to reload the crushing plate back to its start position. The spring will need to be quite strong. Design 2: Very simple to use. Quick also. The operator may need to be over a certain size to provide enough force to crush the can. Design 3: Considerable work involved in loading plate up to the top. Design 4: Force needed to crush can is reduced because of the lever action.

Cheap to Produce	All four designs are cheap to produce. Designs 1 and 3 have the most parts so would probably cost slightly more.
Strong and Durable	All four ideas are strong and durable.
Safety	Because the plates in Designs 1 and 3 depend on speed and mass to crush the can they are potentially dangerous. Furthermore, when reloading the crushing plate in Design 1 there is a risk of injury. When the crushing plate is falling in Design 3 the cranking handle will rotate quickly, another potential hazard. Designs 2 and 4 have negligible risk of injury.

Taking an overview of this analysis Design 4 appears to best fulfil the criteria.

Design as it Affects the Function, Ergonomics and Aesthetic Qualities of Everyday Artefacts

Fig. 12.18a

When a product becomes commonplace, reaching a wide clientele, it is generally because it satisfactorily meets a need. Satisfying a need is not enough, however. There are many other criteria that need to be reached as we have seen earlier in the chapter. Frequently a balance needs to be struck between these criteria, so that the complete satisfying of one of the criteria needs to be compromised to help satisfy another.

So what makes a good design? When looking at any design to see if it is 'good', there are many areas that can be measured and quantified: size and ease of use for a given sector of the population, efficiency and safety of the mechanism for its task, strength and durability of its parts and so on. There are, however, other factors and parameters to consider, which are matters of more subjective judgment. These factors rely more on individual preferences and are difficult to quantify. In the case of a chair, comfort or aesthetic appeal may come into this category. A designer that ignores these areas and concentrates on the more easily measured ones may end up with a very credible solution to a design problem – but one that nobody wants.

Is every object that sells well a good design? Not quite. There are two main ways in which something that sells well may prove to be a bad design: when it fails to fulfil its purpose or fulfils it only for a short time; and where it is dangerous to the user. The object sells well,

Fig. 12.18b

perhaps because it is more aesthetically pleasing than other designs aimed at the same market, or because of a good advertising scheme, or because it is cheaper than its rivals etc. In the long term, however, the product's sales will diminish because of these shortcomings.

When designing a product, it is vital to weight the criteria for success. Depending on this weighting a design may be successful even if it is more aesthetically pleasing than functional.

Fig. 12.18c

Take for example the designing of a chair. This is an object that has been designed and redesigned many, many times. An easy chair, one for relaxing in when watching TV, will be soft, reclined, generally low. It will not be elegant, the emphasis is on function and good ergonomics, not on appearance. A dining room chair will be more straight-backed, less padded, generally of highly polished wood, and will have good ergonomics for sitting while using your hands. There will be a strong emphasis on aesthetic appeal, hence the large amounts of wood on show, high polish, perhaps fretwork and/or carvings, inlay, expensive upholstery materials. A kitchen chair will be of strong, sturdy construction, made from less-expensive wood, will not be upholstered and therefore will be easily kept clean. It will have

Fig. 12.18d

Fig. 12.18e

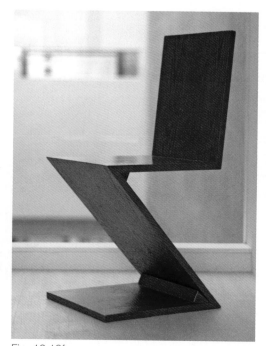

Fig. 12.18f

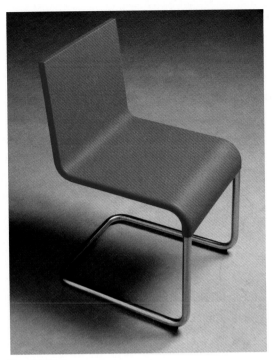

Fig. 12.18g

good ergonomics for sitting straight at a table, for using your hands and will generally be plain. A chair for your hall will generally have an emphasis on elegance and aesthetics rather than functionality. It is a chair that will not be sat on for long periods and will not be that comfortable. A plastic patio chair will have good ergonomics and needs to be weather-resistant, cheap and easily formed. Aesthetics are important but not to the same extent as in a dining-room chair.

The Rudiments of Good Design

It may be very difficult to define a good design but there are some basic rules to follow in order to achieve a good design. These are:

- proportion, • colour, • materials, • ergonomics, • value for money.

Proportion

Proportion is a comparison between one part of an object and another. This comparison is usually between an object's height and width but can be a comparison between any two parts of the whole or a comparison between a single part of an object and the whole.

If the sizes of an object, or the component parts of that object, look right and are in harmony, then they are in good proportion. There is no set formula or exact rule to follow to produce a design that is in good proportion. It is a matter of visual judgment and therefore is very difficult to define.

One shape that is accepted as being in good proportion is the **golden rectangle**. This rectangle was discovered by the ancient Greeks and has sides in the ratio of 1:1.618. This rectangle has a pleasing shape and is used extensively as a framework for design. What is interesting about the golden rectangle is that each time a square is cut off the end, the remaining rectangle is a golden rectangle, Fig. 12.19. This removing of squares can continue giving smaller and smaller golden rectangles. This will not work for any other rectangle.

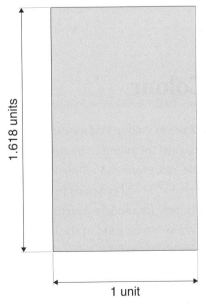

1.618 units

1 unit

Fig. 12.19

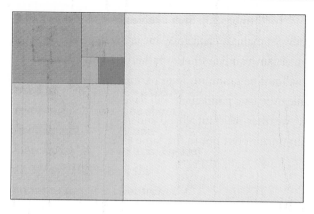

Fig. 12.20

It is important to realise that a design that does not fit into the strict proportions of the golden rectangle is not necessarily a design that is out of proportion. If this was the case we would be restricting our freedom to form too much. For example, consider the three vases in Fig. 12.21. Each is a good design, but the overall height to width ratio varies on each. The second vase fits into a golden rectangle and would generally be chosen as the most elegant of the three but there are cases where design one or three would be more suitable choices.

Even though each vase is different, the ratio of the divisions in the heights are the same, as is the ratio of the divisions in the widths. In this respect all three vases are proportionally the same.

Finally, the apparent size of an object is influenced by the relative size of other objects in its environment. A bungalow can sit nicely in the country surrounded by its garden. Place this bungalow in among high-rise buildings and it is suddenly completely out of proportion.

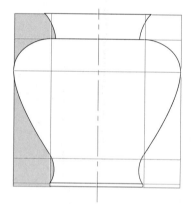

Fig. 12.21a

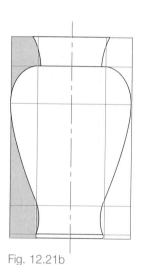

Fig. 12.21b

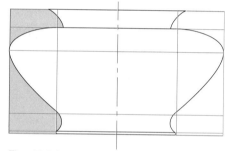

Fig. 12.21c

Colour

Choice of colour(s) does effect people's reaction to design. Toys designed for young children will usually have the four bright colours blue, red, green and yellow, see Fig. 12.22. Furniture designed in the period style will generally be upholstered in muted colours while furniture for modern apartments etc. will use brighter colours. Each of these can be good in their own right, what is important is that the colours chosen for a design are in harmony with each other and that the colours of the design are in harmony with its proposed surroundings.

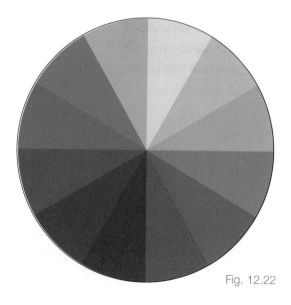

Fig. 12.22

Colours which are close together on the colour wheel go well together. Colours from opposite sides of the colour wheel are complementary colours and are in contrast with each other.

By using colours from close together on the colour wheel for the individual elements of a design, the whole design can be tied together and unified.

Materials

It is very important for a designer to know the full range of materials which are available for their design. Furthermore, s/he must understand the main properties of these materials.
It is useful to divide materials into five classes:

- Metals, e.g. steel, aluminium, copper, brass, tin etc.
- Ceramics, e.g. pottery, glass, cement etc.
- Polymers, e.g. plastics, rubbers etc.
- Composites, e.g. fibreglass, reinforced plastics, wood etc.
- Textiles, e.g. polyester, wool, cotton etc.

Each of these materials have their own individual set of properties: strength, stiffness, hardness, electrical conductivity, ductility and malleability.

When the designer is selecting materials for the component parts of the design, account must be taken of what the component is expected to do, under what conditions it must perform and how it must look. A material is selected for the component so that the properties of the selected material will match the work that the part must do. The selection process is not always as simple as this, however. A good designer must carefully consider the performance properties of each material as well as:

- processing properties of each material,
- economic properties of each material,
- aesthetic properties of each material,
- environmental impact of using each material.

Processing properties
Some materials are easy to shape, cut, mould, bend and cast, while others are not. When selecting a material for a design the processing properties can be vital. The best material from a performance point of view, may often be a bad choice from a processing point of view.

Economic properties
The prices of materials vary enormously. This will obviously have an influence when making choices of materials. For high-performance or luxury items price may be a small constraint but for domestic products and budget items, price is one of the major factors to

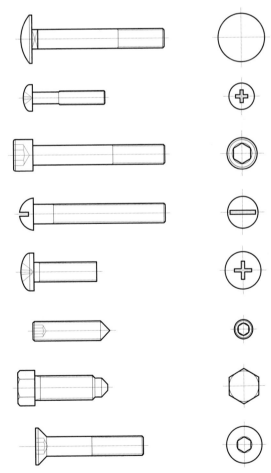

Fig. 12.23a Using standard fittings in a design saves money in manufacture.

consider. The cost of the final product can be reduced by designing around standard forms and sizes. By using pre-processed components the labour and manufacturing costs of the design are kept to a minimum.

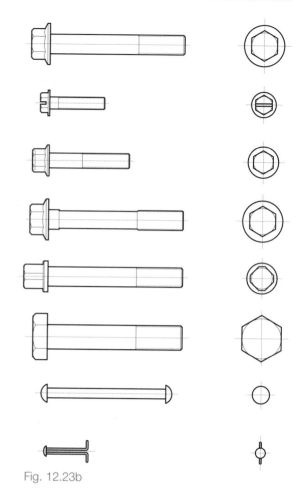

Aesthetic properties

When there is a choice between several products which all have the same function, it is often aesthetics which decide which product is purchased. Chrome, stainless steel, burnished copper are all materials which have a high aesthetic quality for kitchen appliances. Plastic which can be highly coloured has good aesthetic qualities for children's toys.

Environmental properties

Increasingly, environmental impacts are playing a part in designers' choices of materials. These impacts include the energy consumed and pollution produced in the extraction and processing of raw materials and in the final processing into a product, the effect of chosen materials on the life of the product and the potential for recycling and final disposal at the end of the product's life.

Ergonomics

Any part of a design which is used by humans must be ergonomically designed. Good design takes the user as the central point of reference and it is the user who is encouraged to evaluate

Fig. 12.23b

the final product. The word ergonomics comes from the Greek *ergos*, meaning work, and *nomos*, meaning laws. Ergonomics = the laws of work. Using anthropometric tables of measurements, the designer can aim to accommodate ninety-five per cent of the potential user population. Using the designed product will be a comfortable experience and prolonged use of the product will not cause strain or pain.

Value for money

Brilliant design alone will not be sufficient to sell a product. The product must be perceived to present value for money or the consumers will not buy it in quantity. At all times, costs should be kept to a minimum. Often the preferred choice of material will have to be rejected for a compromise, e.g. a cheaper material.

Graphic Instructions and the Design Brief

During the process of working from a design brief through to the final design solution, the designer will make use of drawings as a means of communication. Initially these drawings will be quick sketches. The sketches are an attempt to place on paper the internal mental picture which the designer has constructed and manipulated in his/her head. This mental model may not be crystal clear and the process of sketching on paper helps to clarify some areas. When there are a multitude of ideas, sketching helps to record these ideas. Without these sketches as a record, good ideas can be lost. An internal mental picture in a designer's mind is of no use to a team of designers. It has been said earlier that designing is best done as a team effort. Sketching is a great way of communicating ideas in a team forum. The sketch of a design solution from one designer can be taken up and worked on by another team member and maybe progressed a little further toward a good solution. Furthermore the sketch might inspire a flash of creativity from another designer.

Fig. 12.24

The person who designs the solution to a design brief is rarely the same person who is given the job of producing the artefact. Rough sketches of the object are not good enough at this stage. Working drawings are produced which communicate or show graphically the exact size and shape of the design solution. Working drawings show someone else what your idea looks like and exactly how to produce it. Information is also given on materials used, how the pieces fit together and how the solution operates.

The working drawings (detail drawings and assembly drawings) must be drawn clearly and according to accepted conventions and standards. They give enough unambiguous information so that the parts can be produced repetitively by different people and be exactly the same.

Detail drawings and assembly drawings are laid out following the principles of orthographic projection, which has been explained in detail in other sections of this book. Pictorial style drawings can also be used to help explain complex assemblies. These pictorials usually take the form of exploded isometric drawings. The parts are numbered in the assembly drawing and these numbers refer, where necessary, to a detailed drawing of that part.

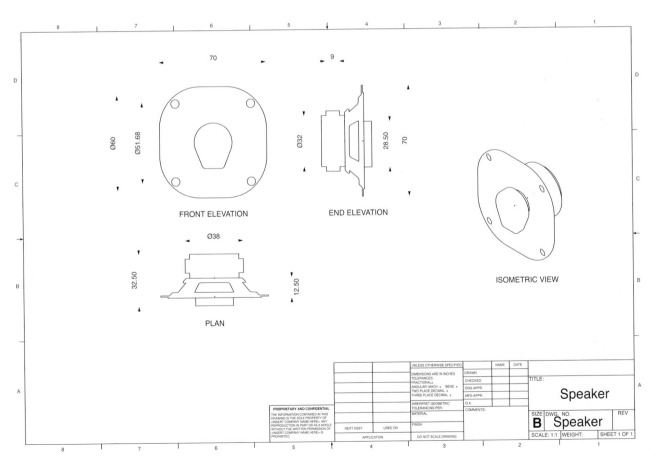

Fig. 12.25

Evaluating the Design

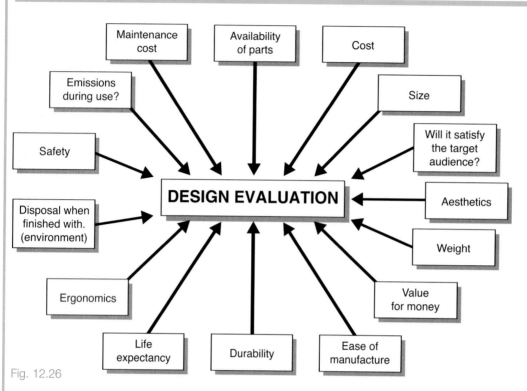

Maintenance cost

Availability of parts

Cost

Emissions during use?

Size

Safety

Will it satisfy the target audience?

DESIGN EVALUATION

Disposal when finished with. (environment)

Aesthetics

Weight

Ergonomics

Value for money

Life expectancy

Durability

Ease of manufacture

Fig. 12.26

HIGHER LEVEL

When evaluating a design it can be done with reference to a variety of criteria. These criteria, such as cost, aesthetics, size, weight, ergonomics, durability, safety, function etc. will vary in importance, depending on the use to which the design is to be put, the people who will use it, where it is to be used and so on. The evaluation process can be both difficult and time-consuming, but it is a vital stage in the design process and must be one thought through with great care. It is at this stage that critical feedback is produced which, if acted on, will produce a better design.

Before embarking on a design evaluation, it is important to clarify under which criteria the design should be assessed and the relative importance of each criteria. Some may be of little importance and may be almost ignored while others may be so important that getting them right will determine the success or failure of the design. Three criteria which are usually dominant are function, ergonomics and aesthetic qualities. We will look at these three in more detail.

Function

It is surprising to see how many designs are produced which do not fulfil their function. The product does not do what it was designed to do. This failure in function may be due to bad design, bad choice of materials, careless manufacturing or because the functional requirements of the design are less important than the aesthetic requirements. An example of this would be the brass/brassed companion sets for a fireplace, Fig. 12.27.

The brush is generally too small, the use of brass for the poker makes it very difficult to keep clean and the tongs are rarely of any use to pick up fuel or coals. Yet every house with an open fire will have one of these companion sets. Why, for instance, are the tongs always so poor? The reason may be a combination of several factors:

- poor workmanship,
- poor design,
- cost saving.

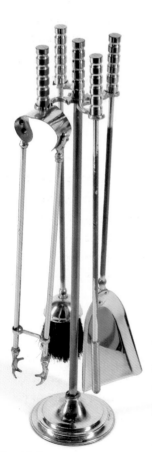

Fig. 12.27

The main reason, however, is that the companion set is designed more as an aesthetic addition to the hearth than as a working item. Aesthetics and a medium/low cost is what ensures this design's success.

A second example where function has been overridden by aesthetics was with the invention of a new tin opener, which in spite of looking very stylish, left the open tin in a dangerous condition. This tin opener opened tins by cutting horizontally under the seal rim at the top of the tin and thus removing the whole tin top. The tin, without the strengthening rim at the top now distorts very easily and if squeezed even slightly will cause the contents to overflow. Furthermore, the tin is now razor sharp and a potential hazard, Fig. 12.28. The traditional tin opener, although not stylish, avoids both of these problems by leaving the seal rim intact and cutting vertically round the top. Tin openers have largely been surpassed by a new design. What is this and why is it so successful?

Fig. 12.28

Ergonomics

Ergonomics, as explained earlier, is the tailoring of a design around the human user. Most designs are aimed at the mass market and therefore must be capable of being used, in relative comfort, by a wide spectrum of people of different shapes and sizes. Even for one-off designs, ergonomics are a key factor and form an important set of criteria against which the design is evaluated. If asked to design a set of bookshelves, most designers would opt for a tall, rectangular design, perhaps based on the proportions of the golden rectangle. This design may be ergonomically unsound if the top shelves are too tall for easy access. Surely bookshelves which are short and wide will have the same capacity and allow more easy access to all the books. The wooden T-square is a well-established, simple design and appears to suit the masses, yet I have never seen a wooden T-square designed specifically for a left-handed person. T-squares in their present form better suit right-handed people, from an ergonomic viewpoint.

When evaluating the design ergonomics it is important to establish the exact user population at which the design is to be aimed. The design must be evaluated from this user population's viewpoint, not from the designer's own viewpoint. Many products do not work well because the presence of the user is not strongly represented during design. This can happen because the designer is subject to many (often conflicting) pressures which require trade-offs to be made between users' needs and other factors. Another factor to consider is that many decisions on ergonomics are made after reference to anthropometric tables and data. The average values are used to hopefully give general ergonomic acceptance. Unfortunately it is very rare to find an individual that is average in more than just a few categories.

Aesthetic qualities

How often have you heard of an item being bought because it looked good only to find that when it is brought home it works badly, not at all, or has some other design fault. Aesthetics is very important for the sale of designs and can be the most important criteria to get right. The car industry is largely driven by aesthetics, particularly at the higher end of the market. It is taken for granted at this level that the car performance is good, the engine is reliable etc., but the styling is what can clinch the sale.

Obviously aesthetics is a very personal judgment and for this reason we have a variety of styles in our designs. It must be emphasised, therefore, that evaluation of the aesthetic quality of the design by the designer himself/herself is not a good idea. It is best to get a range of opinion from as large a group of potential users as possible and use these views to produce a less-biased, aesthetic qualities evaluation.

Generating Design Briefs

The formal starting point for the design of a new product is the design brief. This is a statement which aims to clarify what the new product is expected to be and to do. It should also give some background information on the need for the new design as well as some criteria which the final design must meet.

The design brief is not a statement of the design solution, but rather of the design problem. Furthermore, it is important that the design brief is clear and detailed yet not so detailed as to stifle the opportunity for creative work. The following guidelines may be useful:

- Make sure the design brief shows a clear purpose for the design.
- Do not make it so vague that the designer does not know where to start.
- Do not be too specific and define the design criteria so precisely that there is no room for innovation.
- Make sure that the key details are given.

Writing a design brief involves judgment in setting appropriate limits to the designer's freedom. What is most important is that the brief specifies the **desired attributes** and **required performance** but not a **particular solution**. The brief specifies what the product must do rather than what it must be – it specifies ends, not means.

Worked Examples

DESIGN BRIEF 1

Design a slug trap

As a design brief this is too vague and has no specific criteria for success. It does not give any background information nor does it give any key details.

The use of slug pellets is seen as an inhumane way of killing slugs and a danger to birds in the garden. Design a slug trap.

This is an improvement because it identifies the need for an alternative means of disposing of slugs from a garden.

The use of slug pellets is seen as an inhumane way of killing slugs and a danger to birds in the garden because they can eat the dead slugs and/or eat the pellets. Design a slug trap that traps slugs but does not kill them.

Identifies need and shows a clear purpose for the design.

The use of slug pellets is seen as an inhumane way of killing slugs and a danger to birds in the garden because they can eat the dead slugs and/or eat the pellets. Design a slug trap that traps slugs but does not kill them. The trap should be cheap to produce unobtrusive, lightweight and should have a long life expectancy.

This modification of the design brief appears to have all the requirements of a good design brief.

It must be remembered when writing design briefs not to have a preconceived image of the solution and to steer the designer toward this solution by placing restrictive clauses in the design statement.

DESIGN BRIEF 2

Design a bicycle rack for use on the back of a car.

Many people like to bring their bicycles with them when going on holidays. Design a bicycle rack which will safely carry three bicycles on the back of a car.

Identifies a need and a purpose.

Many people like to bring their bicycles with them when going on holidays. Design a bicycle rack which will safely carry three bicycles of varying sizes on the back of a car. The rack should be lightweight, easily assembled and disassembled, and adjustable to fit all makes of car. The rack must also be lockable to the car and must be totally weather-resistant.

Activities

DRAWING AND CAD

Q1. It has been said that design and communication graphics is a global language. Explain why you agree or disagree with this statement.

Q2. The advancement in the ability of computers to model new designs in 3-D means that the making of test designs, mock-ups and prototypes is no longer needed. Discuss.

Q3. No matter what the advancements in CAD, there will always be a place for the sketchpad, pencil, the board and the T-square. Discuss.

Q4. Traditionally there has been a large amount of drawing geometry learned in the classroom. Will this all be made obsolete by the introduction of CAD?

Q5. Skills with the drawing instruments (set-squares, compass, T-square) should be built up before CAD should be learned. Discuss.

Q6. Is it time to discard the drawing instruments from the classroom completely and do all our learning using CAD? Give reasons for your answer.

THE DESIGN PROCESS

Q7. There are three key factors in defining a problem at the start of the design process:
(i)   Identify and establish the need.
(ii)   Develop a problem statement.
(iii) Establish criteria for success.
        Explain what each of these mean.

Q8. The second stage of the design process involves investigation and research. In general terms what should the designer be looking for at this stage?

Q9. Design is best carried out in a group. Discuss.

Q10. Explain 'brainstorming' and 'sketchstorming'.

Q11. The fourth step in the design process involves analysis and selection of a solution. What are the important areas that must be looked at to complete this stage?

Q12. What is the link between ergonomics and anthropometrics?

Q13. What makes a design aesthetically pleasing in your opinion?

Q14. How do you design for safety?

Q15. Explain the term 'green design'.

Q16. To test a proposed solution it is often helpful to make a prototype or a model. What is the difference between a prototype and a model?

Q17. During the design process the drawings used vary from quick sketches, to detailed sketches, to CAD models, to exploded isometrics, to working drawings and assembly drawings. Plot the use of these drawings at the different stages in the design process.

DESIGNING

Q18. When working at a desk the working area can often get cluttered with pens, pencils, eraser, ruler, correction fluid, calculator, stapler etc. Design a desk tidy that will accommodate these and other useful stationery. The desk tidy must be stylish and compact and should allow easy access to all the items.
Generate three possible solutions.

Q19. There are many desks on the market built specifically to hold a home computer. These are not suitable for holding a games console and a small TV. Design a desk for a child's bedroom that will neatly accommodate a games console, a portable TV, a steering wheel, 2 control pads and 20 games cases. The desk must be neat and mobile and blend with the other furniture in the room.
Generate two possible solutions.

Q20. It can often be difficult to use a drawing board and T-square in the home because the board is not held at the correct angle. Design a stand that would be adjustable in height on which a drawing board could be rested when being used. The top of the stand must also be adjustable in order to incline the board between horizontal and 45° to the horizontal. The stand when not in use must be able to fold/collapse into a small space.
Use a sketchstorming session to produce ideas and develop these ideas to get one final solution.

Q21. Identify and list some improvements to your classroom. Record these ideas with sketches.

Q22. A firm that specialises in designing car accessories has identified a need for a car CD storage unit. The unit must be capable of holding up to 20 CDs and must blend in with the car interior. It should be lockable and removable. Produce diagrams of three possible solutions and analyse these to determine the best solution.

GOOD DESIGN

Q23. Explain the term 'proportion' and describe what is meant by the 'golden rectangle'.

Q24. When selecting materials for a design the following factors must be considered:
- materials' performance properties,
- materials' processing properties,
- materials' economic properties,
- materials' aesthetic properties,
- materials' environmental impact.
Write a brief note on each of these.

Q25. Describe how colour is used in design. Use everyday examples in your answer.

DESIGN EVALUATION

Q26. Evaluate the design of your drawing desk with respect to the following criteria:
- life expectancy,
- ergonomics,
- aesthetics,
- functionality,
- choice of materials,
- ease of production.

Q27. Evaluate the design of your school bag with respect to the following criteria:
- function,
- size,
- value for money,
- choice of materials,
- aesthetics,
- ergonomics,
- life expectancy,
- safety.

Q28. Evaluate the design of your compass with respect to the following criteria:
- function, • value for money, • aesthetics, • ergonomics, • choice of materials.

GENERATING DESIGN BRIEFS

Q29. Generate a design brief for the design of a holder/case to keep a student's drawing equipment safe from damage.

Q30. Generate a design brief for the design of a storage unit for dirty boots and shoes which is to remain outside the back door.

Q31. Generate a design brief for the design of a plant watering device that can be left to water a single plant over a period of time. The water volume delivered should be regulatable.

HIGHER LEVEL

13 Communication of Design

Once a design has been formulated, has passed through the rough sketches phase and is ready for production/manufacture, it is important that a full set of working drawings is produced. These drawings must convey the information necessary for the complete manufacture of all parts and for the assembly of these parts. Furthermore these drawings must be presented in a format that is readily understandable to anybody who is required to read them. In this chapter we will examine what is required to produce such working drawings.

Presentation

Paper Size

The size of the piece of paper used will obviously have an effect on the amount of information that can be placed on each sheet and on the selection of scale used for the drawings. Fig. 13.1 shows the relationship between the sheet sizes of the A series of drawing sheets. An A1 sheet is half the size of an A0 sheet, an A2 sheet is half the size of an A1 sheet and so on. Most of our drawings are done on A2 or A3 sized paper.

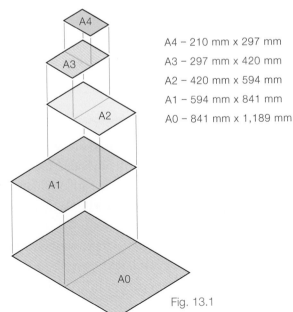

A4 – 210 mm x 297 mm
A3 – 297 mm x 420 mm
A2 – 420 mm x 594 mm
A1 – 594 mm x 841 mm
A0 – 841 mm x 1,189 mm

Fig. 13.1

Sheet Layout: Title Block

Regardless of what is to be drawn on the sheet and of what sheet size is to be used, it is important that the work is laid out neatly and that the sheet has a margin and a title block. The margin is usually 10 mm in from the edge of the page and the title block is placed in the lower right corner, Fig. 13.2. This title block can take many forms but it would usually have spaces to accommodate the following:

- The name of the part(s) being represented.
- The scale being used.
- The date the drawing was produced.
- The name of the draughtsman.
- The drawing number.
- A parts list.
- A revision list.

Not all sheets will require so many subcategories and the title block can be adapted to suit. The lettering must be clear and neat. The size of the lettering will vary. Items of greater importance are indicated by larger lettering and/or heavier lettering, Fig. 13.3.

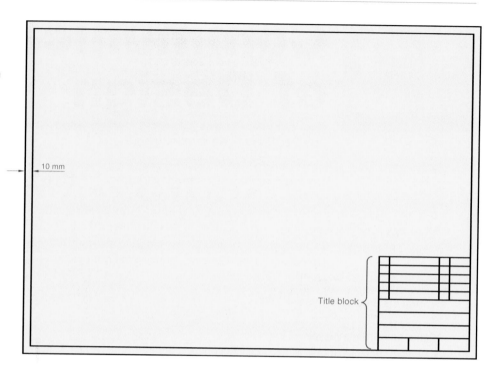

Fig. 13.2

4	Table	1	Steel
3	Clamp shoe	1	Steel
2	Housing	1	Steel
1	Table	1	Aluminium
No.	Name	Reqd	Material
Checked by:			
Drawn by: JOHN SMITH			
GRINDER VICE ASSEMBLY			
Scale 1:2	20-6-05	Sh. 2 of 3	

Fig. 13.3

Parts List

A parts list consists of an itemised list of the parts represented on the drawing. These are generally in order of size or importance with the larger/more important listed first. The number given to each part on the list will also be written down beside the drawing of that part. Additional information for each part, like the number required and the material to be used in manufacture, will also be placed in the parts list.

Standard parts such as bolts, screws, springs, pins, bearings, washers, keys etc., often will not be drawn in the detail drawings but will be listed in the parts list. No extra information is given by drawing these standard parts in a detail drawing but they do need to be listed so that they can be identified from the assembly drawing.

Lines and Linework

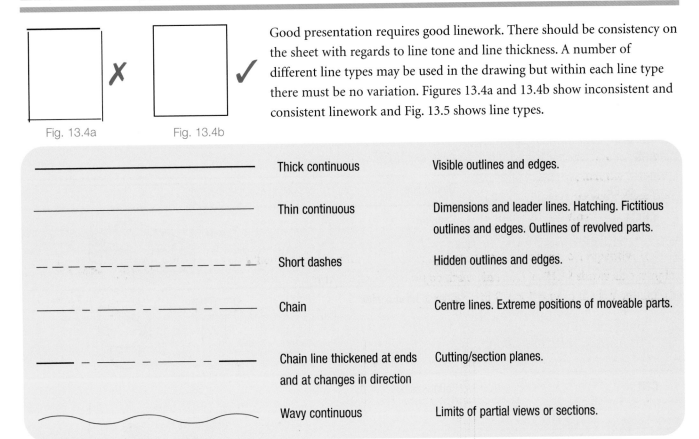

Fig. 13.4a

Fig. 13.4b

Good presentation requires good linework. There should be consistency on the sheet with regards to line tone and line thickness. A number of different line types may be used in the drawing but within each line type there must be no variation. Figures 13.4a and 13.4b show inconsistent and consistent linework and Fig. 13.5 shows line types.

Line	Name	Use
————	Thick continuous	Visible outlines and edges.
————	Thin continuous	Dimensions and leader lines. Hatching. Fictitious outlines and edges. Outlines of revolved parts.
– – – – –	Short dashes	Hidden outlines and edges.
— – — – —	Chain	Centre lines. Extreme positions of moveable parts.
— – — – —	Chain line thickened at ends and at changes in direction	Cutting/section planes.
∿∿∿	Wavy continuous	Limits of partial views or sections.

Fig. 13.5

Symbols

It is common practice to use a number of symbols in drawings both to save space on the drawing and to save time.

First- and Third-angle Projection Symbol

As previously mentioned, the more usual system of projection in Europe is first-angle projection. The projection symbol should be shown on all drawings, Figures 13.6a and 13.6b.

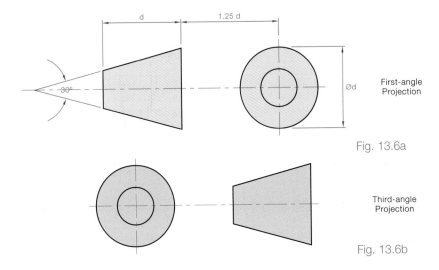

First-angle Projection

Fig. 13.6a

Third-angle Projection

Fig. 13.6b

Abbreviations

Abbreviation	Meaning	Sketch Explanation
A/C	Across corners	
A/F	Across flats	
HEX HD	Hexagon head	
ASSY	Assembly	
CRS	Centres	
₵ or CL	Centre line	
CHAM	Chamfer	
CH HD	Cheese head screw	
CSK	Countersunk	
C'BORE	Counterbore	
CYL	Cylinder or cylindrical	
DIA	Diameter – in a note	
Ø	Diameter – in a dimension	
R	Radius – in a dimension	
DRG	Drawing	
FIG	Figure	
LH	Left hand	
LG	Long	
MATL	Material	
NO.	Number	

Abbreviation	Meaning	Sketch Explanation
PCD	Pitch circle diameter	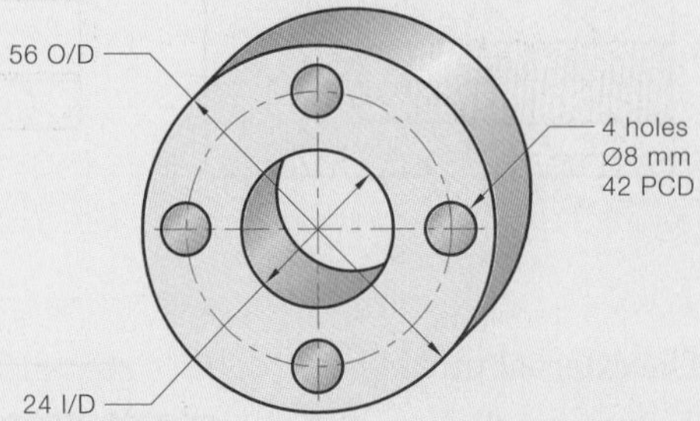 56 O/D, 4 holes Ø8 mm 42 PCD, 24 I/D
I/D	Inside diameter	
O/D	Outside diameter	
RH	Right hand	
RD HD	Round head	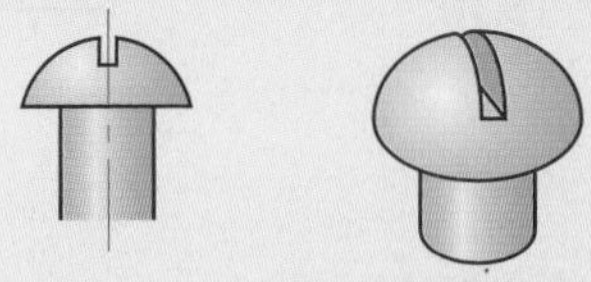
SPEC	Specification	
SQ ☐	Square – in a note Square – in a dimension	☐ 20
STD	Standard	
U'CUT	Undercut	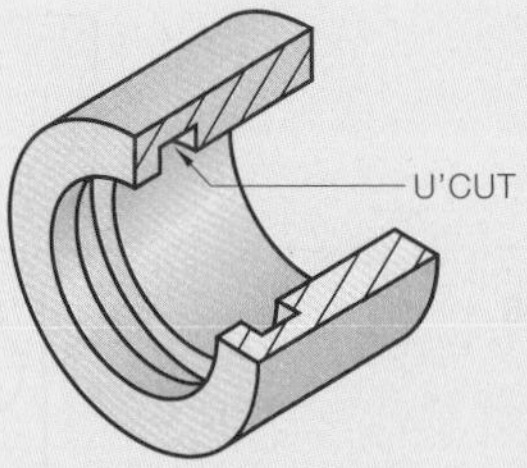 U'CUT
MM	Millimetres	
NTS	Not to scale	
RPM	Revolutions per minute	

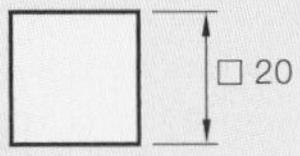

Fig. 13.7

Conventional Representation of Common Features

There are many components commonly used in designs such as bolts, bearings and springs which in themselves are complicated to draw in full. Many of these may be represented in a simplified form to save drawing time.

External thread

Fig. 13.8a

A line parallel to the side represents the screw thread. The distance between the two lines approximately equals the depth of thread. A broken circle in the end view represents the thread, Fig. 13.8.

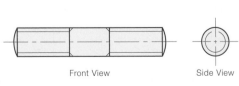

Front View · Side View

Fig. 13.8b

Internal thread

Fig. 13.9a

Front View

Side View

Fig. 13.9b

The sides of the hole drilled into the material are drawn with heavy lines. The section lines pass through the threads. A thin broken line, on the outside, in the side view represents the thread,

The external thread is drawn over the internal thread. Note the hatching, Fig. 13.10.

Stud in a tapped hole

Fig. 13.10a

Front View

Side View

Fig. 13.10b

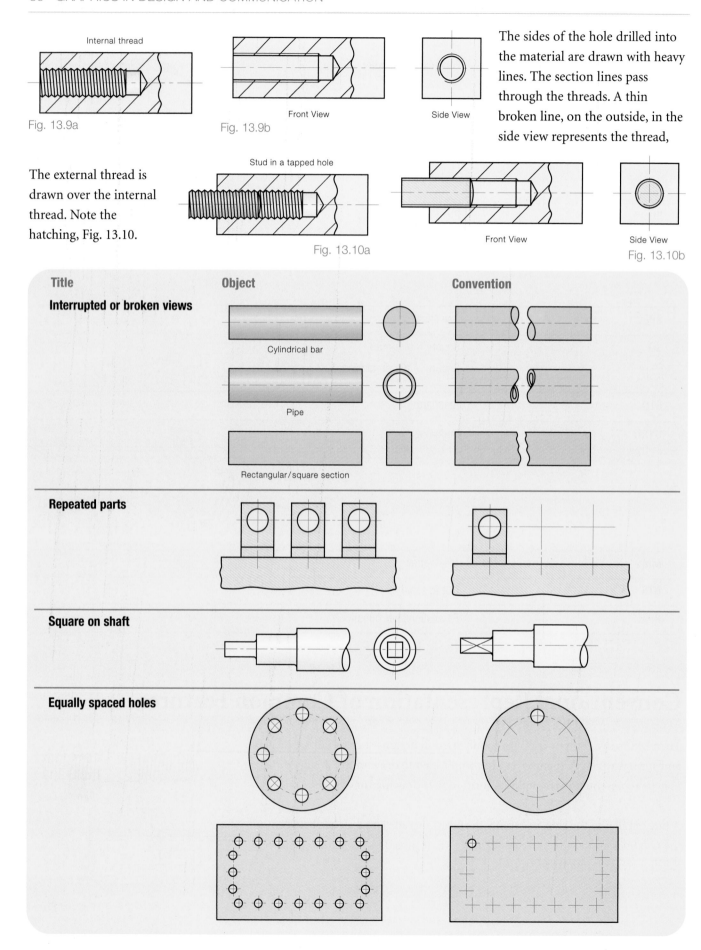

Title	Object	Convention
Interrupted or broken views	Cylindrical bar	
	Pipe	
	Rectangular / square section	
Repeated parts		
Square on shaft		
Equally spaced holes		

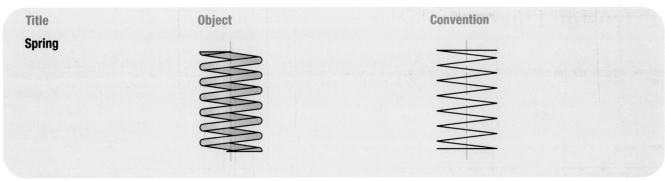

Title	Object	Convention
Spring		

Fig. 13.11

Materials

Wood that has been planed/machined		Rough wood	
Plywood		Particle board eg chipboard, MDF etc.	
Blockboard		Glass, clear perspex	
Concrete		Stone	
Sheet metal		Thick metal	

Fig. 13.12

Learning to Dimension

When applying dimensions to a drawing or a number of drawings on a sheet, it is important to follow certain rules. These rules help to keep the presentation both neat and regular in appearance. They also ensure that the drawing and the dimensions remain clear and legible. These rules will be outlined below.

Dimension Lines

A dimension line is a thin, dark, solid line which usually ends with arrowheads. The dimension line indicates the *direction* and *extent* of a measurement. It should be placed at least 10 mm from the object outline. The spacing of dimension lines should be uniform throughout the drawing.

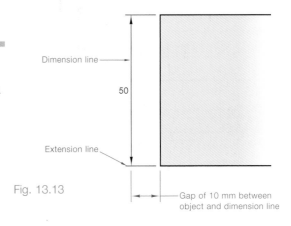

Dimension line

50

Extension line

Fig. 13.13

Gap of 10 mm between object and dimension line

Extension Lines

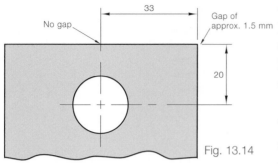

Fig. 13.14

An extension line is a thin, dark, solid line which 'extends' from the point on the object to which the dimension refers. A gap of approximately 1.5 mm should be left between the start of the extension line and this point. If a centre line is being used as an extension line there should be no gap left at the object outline, Fig. 13.14.

The arrowheads indicate the extent of dimensions. They are drawn freehand and should have a length to width ratio of 3:1. They must be uniform in size and style throughout the drawing. Long slender arrowheads look best, Fig. 13.15.

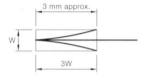

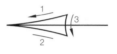

Fig. 13.15

Placement of Dimension Lines and Extension Lines

There are several basic rules that should be followed:

(1) Shorter dimensions are placed nearest to the object, Fig. 13.16.

(2) Dimension lines should not cross extension lines, Fig. 13.17.

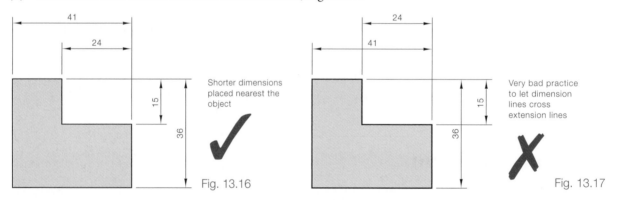

Shorter dimensions placed nearest the object

Fig. 13.16

Very bad practice to let dimension lines cross extension lines

Fig. 13.17

(3) Extension lines should not be shortened as shown in Fig. 13.18.

(4) Where possible, dimensions should be outside the object, should not cross and should not form a continuation of a line/outline of the drawing, Fig. 13.19.

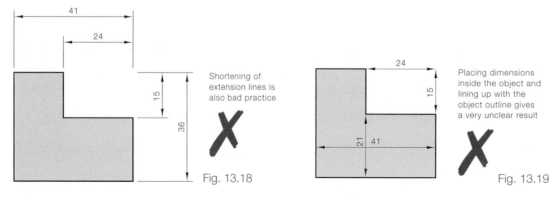

Shortening of extension lines is also bad practice

Fig. 13.18

Placing dimensions inside the object and lining up with the object outline gives a very unclear result

Fig. 13.19

(5) Where possible the dimensions should be grouped together at the same level, Fig. 13.20. They should not vary in height, Fig. 13.21.

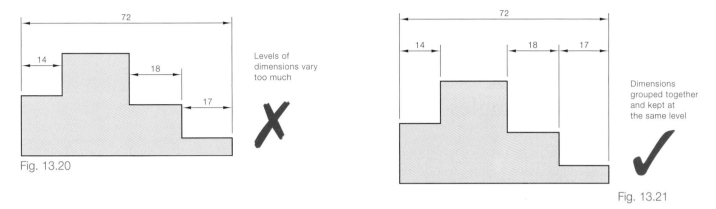

Levels of dimensions vary too much

Fig. 13.20

Dimensions grouped together and kept at the same level

Fig. 13.21

Dimensioning Arcs and Fillets

Arcs and circles are dimensioned in the view in which they are seen as true shapes. The centre of the arc/circle should be indicated with a small cross except where they are either very small or unimportant. The dimension should be radial and where practical should be placed inside the curve, Fig. 13.22.

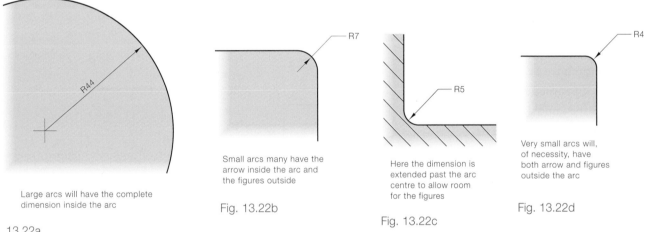

Large arcs will have the complete dimension inside the arc

Fig. 13.22a

Small arcs many have the arrow inside the arc and the figures outside

Fig. 13.22b

Here the dimension is extended past the arc centre to allow room for the figures

Fig. 13.22c

Very small arcs will, of necessity, have both arrow and figures outside the arc

Fig. 13.22d

For fillet radii, which may often be of similar size throughout a drawing, it is neater to print a note rather than dimension each fillet. A note such as: 'All fillet radii are 6 mm unless otherwise specified' is ideal.

Leaders

A leader is a thin, continuous line which starts from a note or dimension and ends with an arrow or a dot. If an arrow is used it should touch the part to which the note/dimension refers, e.g. the outline of the object or the side of a hole. If a dot is used it should be within the object.

The leader should be inclined and should extend from the beginning or end of a note. A leader referring to an arc or circle should be radial so that if extended it would pass through the centre, Fig. 13.23.

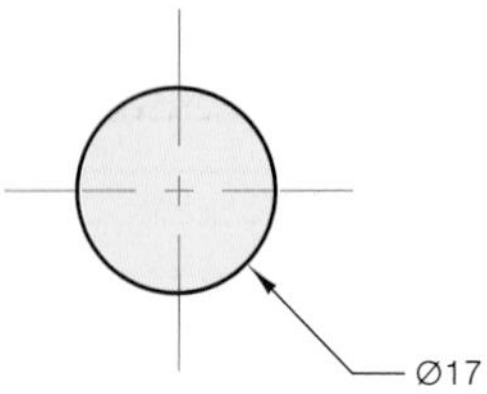

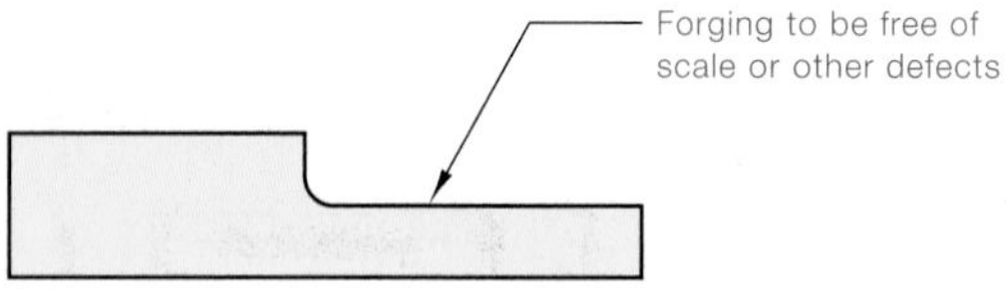

Forging to be free of
scale or other defects

Fig. 13.23b

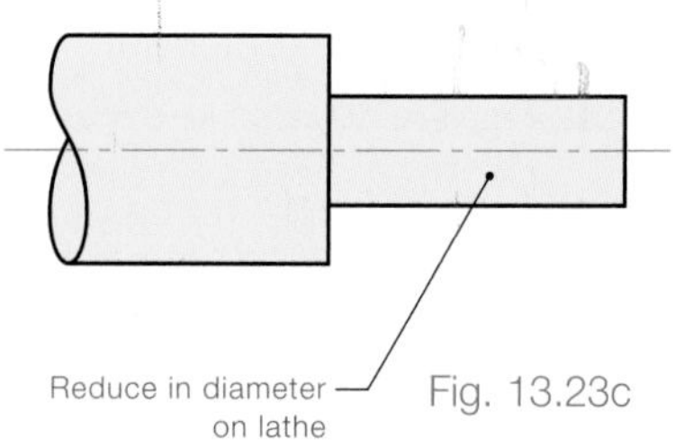

Ø17

Fig. 13.23a

Reduce in diameter
on lathe   Fig. 13.23c

Chamfers and Angles

Angles are dimensioned by means of coordinates, Fig. 13.24, or by degrees, Fig. 13.25, or with a combination of both, Fig. 13.26. Using coordinates is a more accurate method than using degrees.

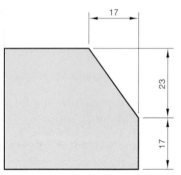

17

23

17

Fig. 13.24

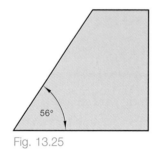

56°

Fig. 13.25

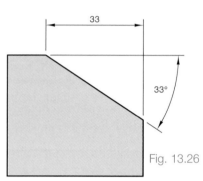

33

33°

Fig. 13.26

Chamfers can often be very small and difficult to dimension in the normal way. If they are all the same size a note will be sufficient, otherwise they can be dimensioned as shown below in Fig. 13.27.

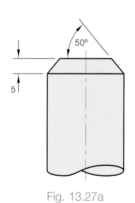

50°

5

Fig. 13.27a

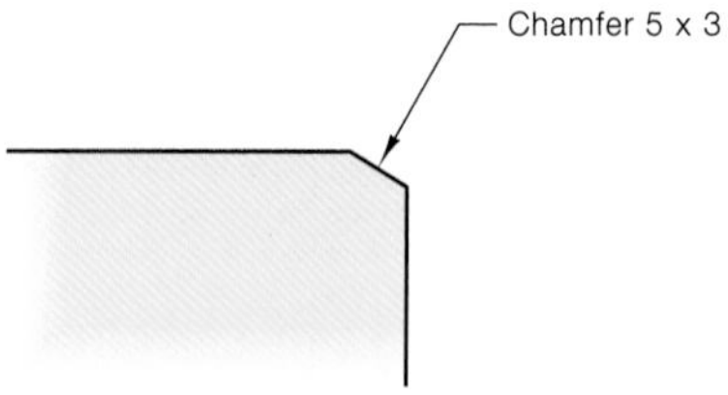

Chamfer 5 x 3

Fig. 13.27b

Working Drawings

Full working drawings may include assembly drawings, detailed drawings, isometric views, exploded views or whatever views are necessary to clearly communicate the project. The drawings should be neatly and clearly presented and use recognised drawing standards. We will look at the preparation of a set of working drawings for a simple object like an adjustable set-square.

Detailed Drawings

Note the use of **detail extraction** to allow the clear dimensioning of the holes for a quite complicated area. The detail is drawn at three times full scale and is removed out of the way so that it does not interfere with the other dimensioning.

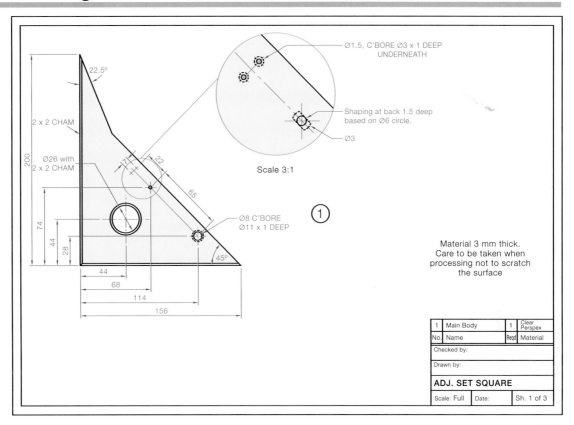

Fig. 13.28

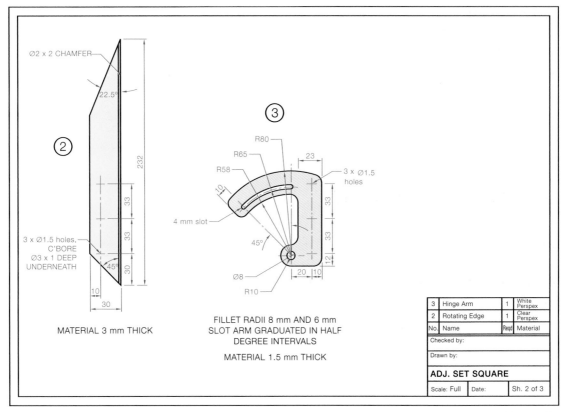

Fig. 13.29

Note: In sheet 3 the components are drawn using an enlarging scale to give clear information on small parts.

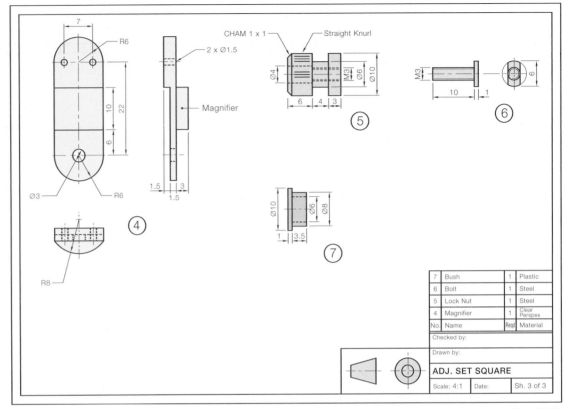

Fig. 13.30

Assembly Drawing

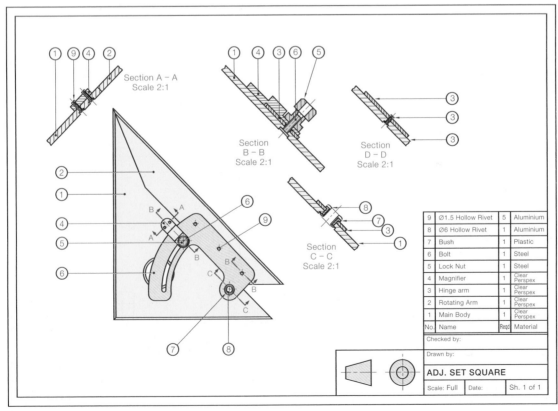

Fig. 13.31

The assembly drawing shows all the parts shown in the detail drawings put together in the correct order. Standard parts used in the assembly usually are not drawn and are listed in the parts list. In this example the hollow rivets have not been shown in the detail drawings but are shown in the assembly drawing. The parts in the assembly are **balloon-referenced**. These numbers refer to the parts list on the sheet or to corresponding numbers on the detail drawings. There is no necessity to dimension the parts in the assembly drawing as the sizes of each individual piece are given in detail in the detail drawings. Overall heights, widths and thicknesses of the assembled object are sometimes given.

The use of a sectional view often clarifies an assembly detail. In this example they are drawn to twice full size. When balloon-referencing, care should be taken to place the circles in line and not to draw the leaders crossing each other.

Exploded Pictorial Views

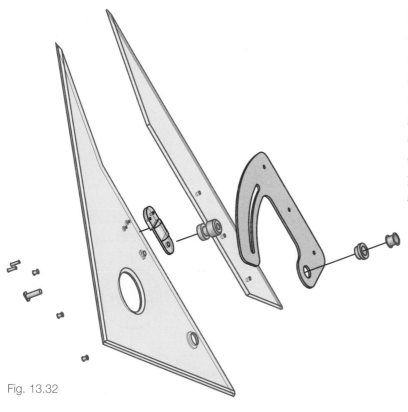

Fig. 13.32

Exploded pictorial views are often used in design presentations, catalogues, sales literature, machine manuals etc. They may be drawn using any of the pictorial methods but the most usual is isometric projection. Exploded views are a great way of showing all the parts of an assembly and how they fit together. The drawings themselves may be very slow to produce depending on the complexity of the assembly.

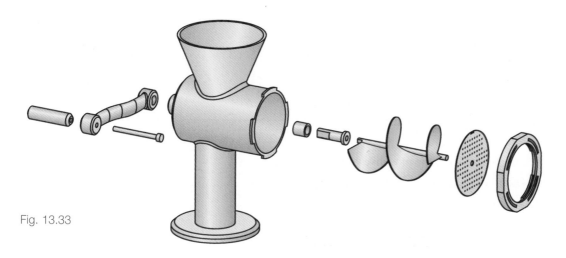

Fig. 13.33

Computer Modelling

Producing a 3-D computer model of a design is another great presentation method. The 3-D model can be viewed from any angle and individual parts can be rendered, by the computer, to match the properties of the production materials. Information on material volumes and weights can also be easily calculated by the computer.

Schematic Diagrams

Schema: a Greek word, meaning plan or diagram. The original *schema* were drawings of the heavens and they were used to show the position of the stars and their relationships to each other.

Diagramma: A Latin word, meaning a line drawing used to explain a concept or a plan.

Schematic diagrams are simple, line diagrams used to explain or describe a process. The process will involve a flow of some sort, e.g. a flow of electricity, of fluid, of ideas or of actions.

A schematic diagram should be clear, unambiguous and should be both easy to read and easy to understand. If these simple rules are followed, then the result will be a representation that is far superior to a linguistic description. The results of the interacting of components in the diagram can be instantly obvious. This action-reaction interplay can be difficult to describe in words but can quickly be understood from a diagram.

The schematic diagram shown in Fig. 13.34 shows the possible flow of thought as a design is brought from design brief stage to working drawing stage. The process begins with the design brief. From this comes a clarification or elaboration of the required task leading to an outline specification for the proposed product.

The next stage is that of conceptual design. Broad solutions are proposed, rough sketches are produced. Several alternative ideas should be generated and examined. Often the designer will have to refer back to the design brief and the problem clarification at this stage to sharpen his/her focus on the problem in hand.

The conceptual design solutions are rated and the most likely successes are selected and developed in more detail in the design embodiment stage. Perhaps only one candidate will emerge after this stage into the selected design. There may well be a need to cycle back to an earlier stage if a good design solution does not evolve.

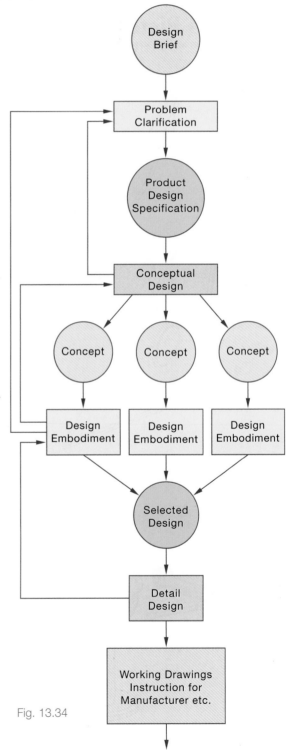

Fig. 13.34

The final stage looked at is that of detailed design. A very large number of detailed points need to be decided and the work of detailed drawings, calculations and testing is carried out at this stage. Again, there may be cycling back to earlier stages as problems are encountered.

Fig. 13.35 shows a less detailed representation of the same thought process.

Both schematic diagrams show the flow of thought and ideas in a clear, easily followed way. A written explanation of the same process is long-winded and convoluted.

Fig. 13.36 shows the flow of information and money in a market-driven manufacturing plant.

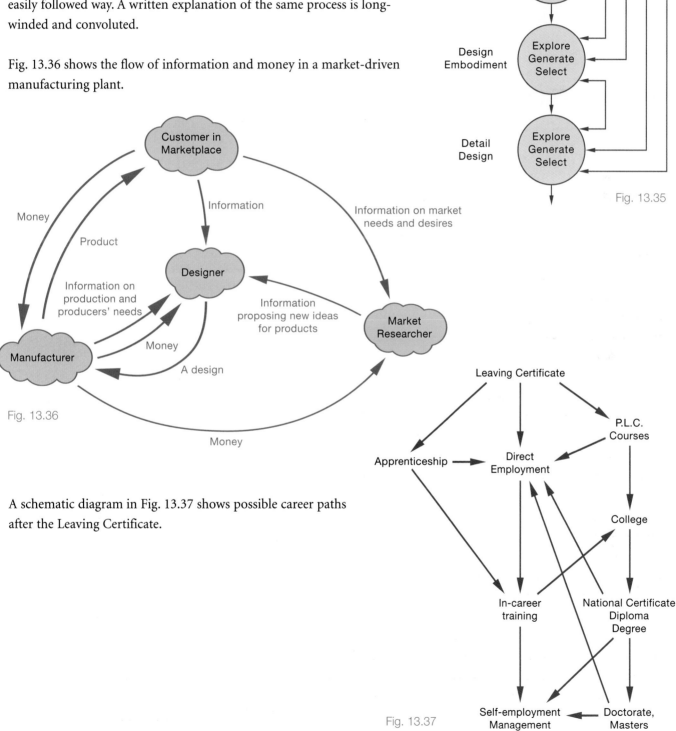

Fig. 13.35

Fig. 13.36

A schematic diagram in Fig. 13.37 shows possible career paths after the Leaving Certificate.

Fig. 13.37

Activities

Q1. Using notes and/or diagrams explain the following abbreviations:

- CSK
- O/D
- U'CUT
- RPM

- CYL
- A/C
- CRS
- SQ

- RD HD
- SPEC
- C'BORE
- MATL

Q2. Using notes and/or diagrams explain the following abbreviations:

- CYL
- CH HD
- A/F
- PCD

- STD
- NTS
- Ø
- CHAM

- DRG
- I/D
- RH
- HEX HD

Q3. Draw in conventional form, having M15 screw thread.
(i) A double-ended stud with a 20 mm non-threaded area in the centre.
(ii) A blind hole.
(iii) A stud in a tapped hole.

Q4. Make neat diagrams showing the following drawing conventions:
(i)
- a break in a circular pipe,
- a break in a solid cylindrical bar,
- a break in a solid rectangular bar.
(ii) A square end on a cylindrical shaft.
(iii) A coil spring.

Q5. Using examples, describe how time can be saved when drawing by using conventions. Make particular reference to the drawing of repetitive elements of a drawing.

Q6. Using diagrams, show the standard symbols for the following materials:
- metal (thick),
- rough wood,
- concrete,
- glass,
- planed wood,
- plywood.

Q7. Reproduce the following figures and dimension them fully.

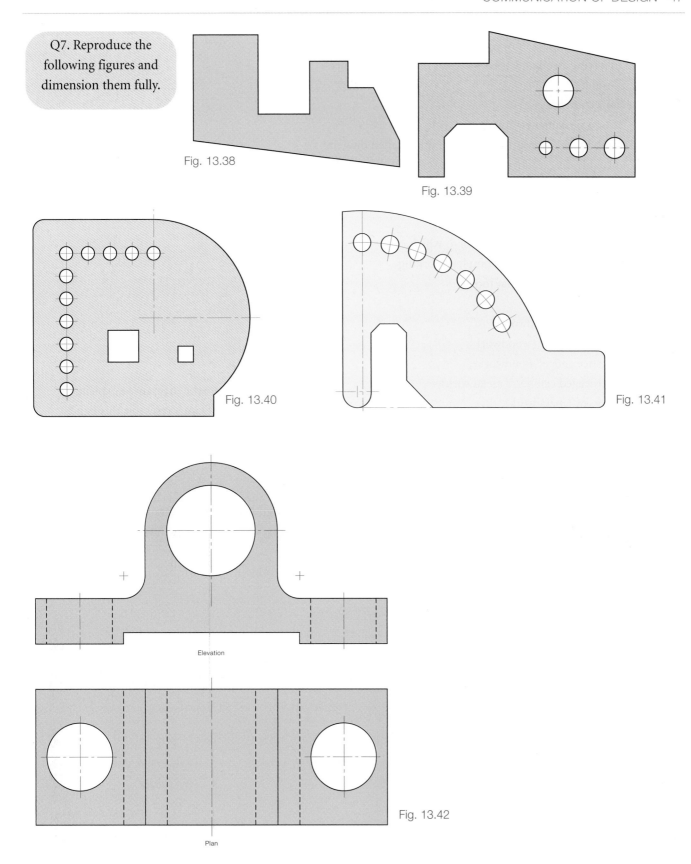

Fig. 13.38

Fig. 13.39

Fig. 13.40

Fig. 13.41

Elevation

Plan

Fig. 13.42

Q8. Produce working drawings for the manufacture of one of the following frequently used pieces of drawing equipment:

(i)   T-square.

(ii)   Your compass.

(iii) Your adjustable set-square.

Remember to use appropriate scaling in the detailed drawing(s) to enable easy reading and dimensioning of the parts.

Q9. Select a simple workshop tool to which you have access and produce complete working drawings of that tool.

Suggested tools:

- try square (woodwork),
- marking gauge (woodwork),
- mortice gauge (woodwork),
- odd-legged callipers (metalwork),
- hacksaw (metalwork),
- snips (metalwork).

Q10. Produce a schematic diagram to explain the movement of water from a reservoir through to domestic use and back to the reservoir.

Q11. Produce a schematic diagram to explain the process of acquiring a part-time job.

Q12. Design a schematic diagram to illustrate the process of producing a school magazine.

14 Freehand Drawing

SYLLABUS OUTLINE
Areas to be studied (in an applied context):
- Materials for freehand drawing. • Observation techniques. • Representing shape, form, texture and material.
  • Light and shade. • Design sketching. • Freehand detailing. • The use of colour.

Learning outcomes
Students should be able to:

Higher and Ordinary levels
- Use freehand sketching as a tool to explain an idea.
- Produce freehand drawings.
- Select the most suitable medium for producing and rendering sketches and drawings.
- Identify the surfaces of an object relative to each other in three-dimensional space.
- Use various methods of rendering and colouring to enhance a drawing.

Higher level only
- *Analyse critically the texture and colour of a surface and choose suitable rendering media by which the surface can be accurately represented.*
- *Represent graphically the effects light and shade have on surface.*

Freehand sketching is the process of representing an object, a scene, or an idea by making lines on a surface. This drawing is generally linear in nature but it may include other elements such as dots and brush strokes. Whatever form a drawing takes, it is the principle means by which we organise and express our visual thoughts and perceptions. It can be regarded as a form of artistic expression but also as a practical tool for formulating and working through design problems or graphics problems as presented in a subject like this one.

In design, the role of sketching expands to include recording what exists, working out ideas, as well as speculating and planning for the future. Throughout the design process we use drawing to guide the development of an idea from concept, to proposal, to constructed reality.

Materials for Freehand Drawing

Two of the most versatile media for sketching available to students are pencil and ink. Of the two, the pencil provides the best solution for quick sketches, sketching used to develop ideas, sketches of a non-permanent nature and sketches used to rough-out an idea.

Fig. 14.1

Fig. 14.2

The use of ink can produce permanent and almost microscopically detailed drawings which can then be further improved using water colours, colouring pencils etc. Ink as a medium, therefore, is usually reserved for the final presentation drawing.

There are many other drawing media which can be used for sketching purposes or to enhance sketches already produced in pencil or ink. These include felt-tipped markers, pastels, wax crayons, colouring pencils, charcoal etc. Throughout this chapter we will focus on building up skills with a pencil with the understanding that the skills learned are transferable to these other media.

Pencil Types

There are many different types of pencil to allow the drawing of lines of various weights and thicknesses. A pencil's grade is denoted by using the letters **H** and **B**, which refer to the pencil lead. H stands for hardness while B stands for blackness. In general it is the softer pencils that are used for freehand sketching but of course any pencil may be used.

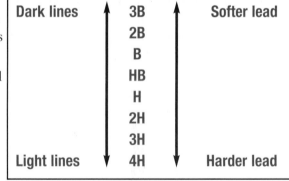

Dark lines		3B		Softer lead
		2B		
		B		
		HB		
		H		
		2H		
		3H		
Light lines		4H		Harder lead

Fig.14.3

Fine-line pencils and/or clutch pencils may also be useful. Because fine-line pencils hold leads of specific thickness, e.g. 0.3 mm, 0.5 mm, they do not need sharpening. The constant line thickness can, however, be restrictive, particularly when shading or applying tone and texture. Clutch pencils hold lengths of pencil lead which are available in a range of grades and as such can be sharpened and used in the same way as a pencil.

Pencil Sharpening/Pencil Points

The tapered point produced by a pencil sharpener is perfectly satisfactory for most work. The lead point can be touched up using a sandpaper pad or a sheet of medium/smooth sandpaper. Another useful point type is the chisel point. Here the wood is usually whittled away with a sharp knife, taking care not to break the lead or reduce its size by too much, Fig. 14.4.

Then, holding the pencil in a normal drawing position, rub the point on some sandpaper until it is quite blunt. This point can now be used to make either a broad or a fine stroke, depending on how the pencil is held, Fig. 14.5.

Fig. 14.4

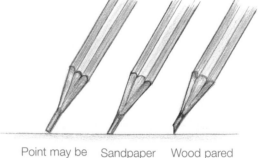

Fig. 14.5

Point may be used to give broad lines or fine lines.   Sandpaper to give chisel point.   Wood pared away.

Holding the Pencil

How you position your hand depends on the drawing being done – whether it requires bold, sweeping strokes or more carefully executed lines. Most typically, the pencil is held as if for writing with the hand resting lightly on the table. For short lines and lines demanding considerable pressure you need little arm movement. Swing the hand at the wrist, or let the fingers alone perform the necessary motion, Fig. 14.6. For longer

Fig. 14.6

Fig. 14.7

strokes the pencil is held back from the point. The entire forearm and hand are swung freely from the elbow and there is minimal wrist and finger movement, Fig. 14.7.

For particularly unrestrained sketching hold the pencil at its unsharpened end. The pencil should be full length. Swinging the hand will produce rapid, bold lines, Fig. 14.8.

Fig. 14.8

Sketching Practice

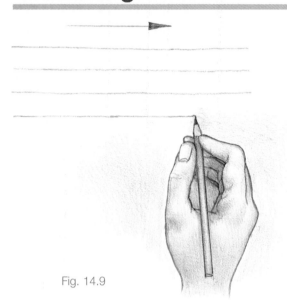

Fig. 14.9

Horizontal Lines

Lock your wrist and fingers and use an arm movement to move the pencil. Your hand slides across the paper as you are sketching the lines.

Vertical Lines

Again an arm movement is used rather than a wrist or finger movement. It may prove easier to rotate the sheet by 90° and draw the lines as if they are horizontal.

Sketching with Short Overlapping Strokes

Rather than trying to draw long lines using one continuous stroke it may often be better to build up the line with short overlapping lines. Sketch a short line return to the middle of the first line and make a similar, second short line. Repeat this overlapping process until the line is as long as is needed.

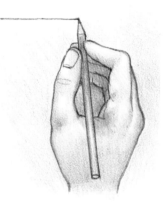

Fig. 14.10

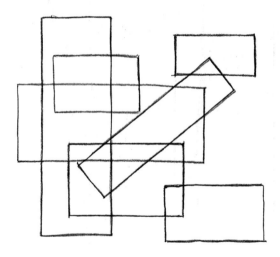

Fig. 14.11

Squares and Rectangles

Continue to practise drawing horizontal, vertical and inclined lines and use these lines to build up squares and rectangles. These two-dimensional shapes will form the building blocks for many diagrams.

Circles

Before drawing a circle it is advisable to draw the square into which the circle is to fit. Divide the square into quarters. This gives the circle centre and four points on the circumference. When drawing the circle draw in one quarter at a time. Use the overlapping stroke technique and sketch lightly. Use your wrist as a pivot to help draw the curves. You will draw more naturally if your hand is inside the curve. When you are happy with the circle it can be darkened. The sheet can, of course, be rotated to any position to help the drawing of the curve.

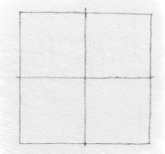

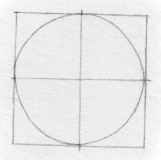

Fig. 14.12

For larger circles:

(1) Draw the square into which the circle is to fit.
(2) Sketch in the diagonals and lines to divide the square into quarters.
(3) If each half-diagonal is now divided into three equal parts (Fig. 14.13) then more points can be found on the circumference.
(4) Draw in the curve as before.

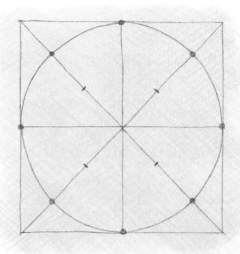

Fig. 14.13

Ellipses

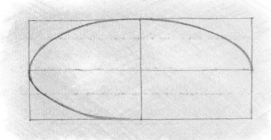

Fig. 14.14

All ellipses will fit into rectangles just as circles fit into squares.

(1) Draw the rectangle into which the ellipse is to fit.
(2) Draw in the centre lines which form the major and minor axis of the ellipse.
(3) Sketch in the ellipse.

Large ellipses may be constructed using any of the methods discussed earlier in the book. The rectangle method is probably the most suitable as it is constructed solely using straight lines.

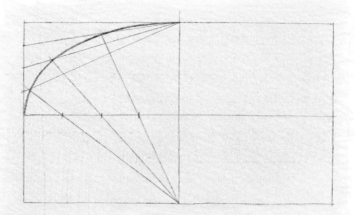

Fig. 14.15

Sketching Pictorials

There are many different types of pictorial views. One of the quickest to sketch and the easiest to visualise is an isometric view. The sketches are built up using **crating** in a similar way as when producing isometrics using instruments. The idea behind crating is to break down an object into its component geometric parts, i.e. rectangular prisms, cylinders, cones etc. Each component part is then crated in, on the sketch, and completed individually. Fig. 14.16 shows an example of this technique.

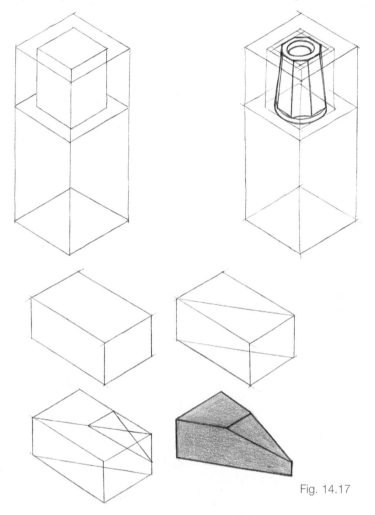

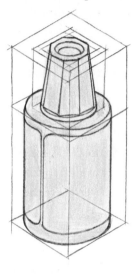

Fig. 14.16

This procedure remains the same whether the object is simple or complex. What should be remembered, however, is that the larger masses should be outlined/ghosted in first, with more detail coming later. In this way it is easier to keep the sketch in proper proportion.

Fig. 14.17

Circles in Pictorials

For smaller circles we start by drawing an isometric square into which the circle will fit. Then divide it into quarters. This gives the centre and four points on the circumference. The circle, which appears as an ellipse, is sketched in one quarter at a time.

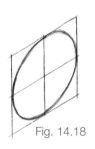

Fig. 14.18

For larger circles start by drawing, in isometric, the square into which the circle will fit. Sketch in the diagonals and lines parallel to the sides through the square's centre. Each half-diagonal is divided into roughly three equal parts in the same way as when drawing a circle. This provides eight points on the isometric circle's circumference. Sketch in the pictorial circle.

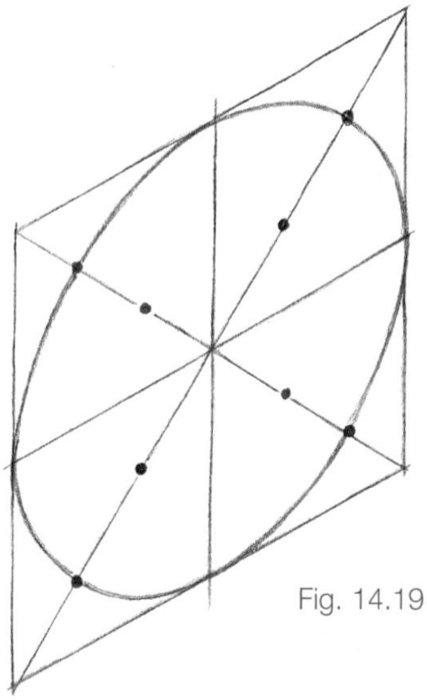

Fig. 14.19

Worked Examples

Given the orthographic views of an object in Fig. 14.20. Produce a neat pictorial sketch of the solid. Choose a viewing orientation that gives a good view of the object's details.

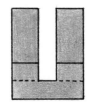
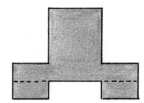
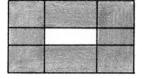

(1) Decide on the best angle to view the object.
(2) Sketch out the cage frame to the overall length, width and height.
(3) Rough in the object's features on the cage faces.
(4) Complete the shape and darken all visible lines, Fig. 14.21.

Fig. 14.20

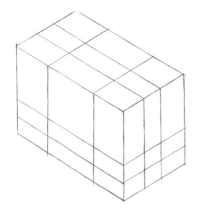
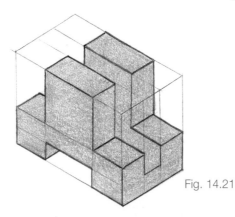

Fig. 14.21

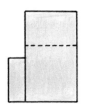
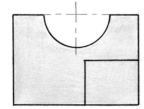

Given the plan, front elevation and end view of an object in Fig. 14.22. Make a neat, freehand, pictorial sketch of the object.

(1) Some objects are best divided into parts with a separate cage framework for each part.
(2) Locate the semicircle centre and complete the half square into which it will fit.
(3) Draw in the diagonals and centre lines.
(4) Draw in the curve.
(5) Darken all visible lines, Fig. 14.23.

Fig. 14.22

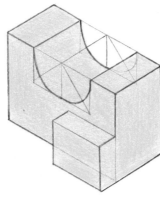

Fig. 14.23

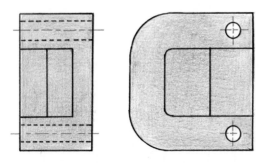

Fig. 14.24

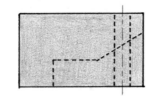

Given the orthographic views of an object in Fig. 14.24. Produce a neat pictorial sketch of the solid. Choose a viewing orientation that gives a good view of the object's details.

(1) Decide on the best orientation for the sketch.
(2) Box out the overall dimensions.
(3) Locate the main features and planes.
(4) Locate the centres of all circular features. Draw their centre lines and box out the general shape.
(5) Darken the visible shape, Fig. 14.25.

Note: The main outline may be thickened slightly to improve the visual impact of the drawing.

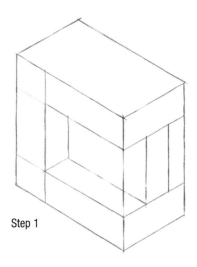

Step 1

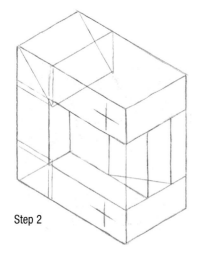

Step 2

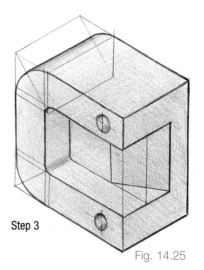

Step 3

Fig. 14.25

Given the plan and elevation of an object in Fig. 14.26.
Produce a neat isometric sketch of the object choosing
the most descriptive orientation.

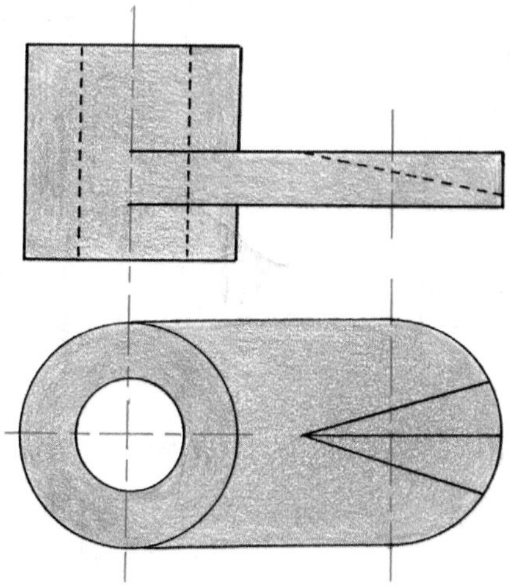

Fig. 14.26

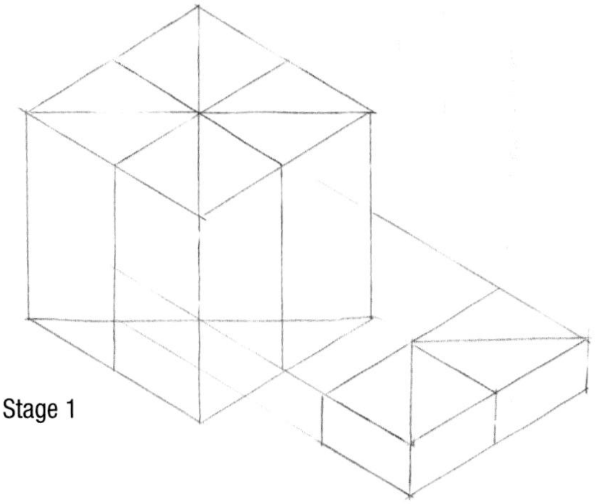

Stage 1

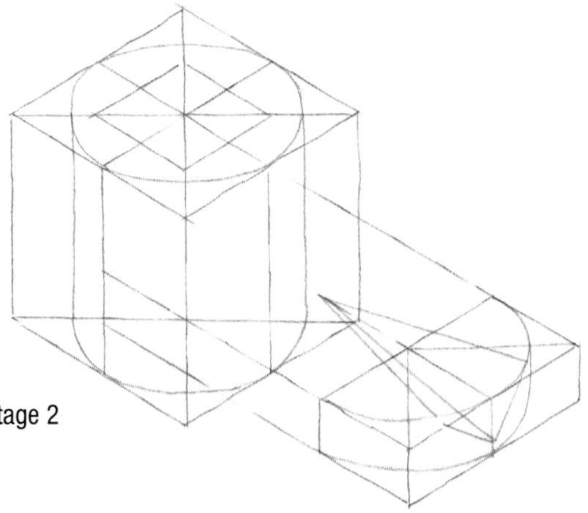

Stage 2

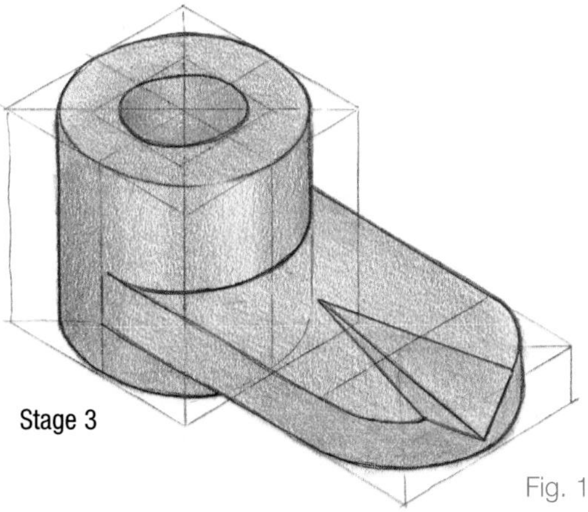

Stage 3

Fig. 14.27

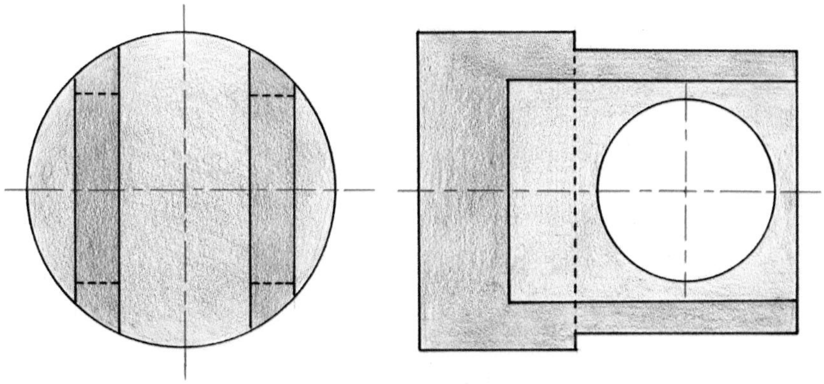

Given the front elevation and end
elevation of an object in Fig.
14.28. Complete an isometric
sketch of the object choosing the
most descriptive orientation for
your pictorial.

Fig. 14.28

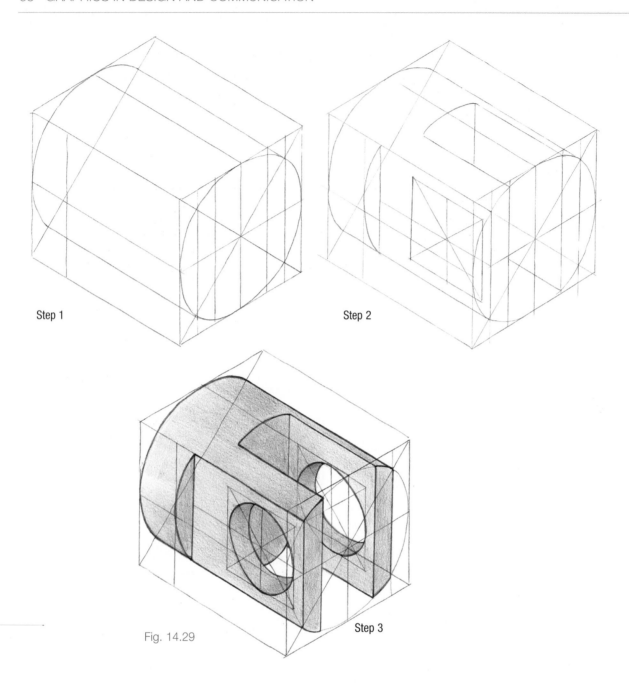

Step 1

Step 2

Step 3

Fig. 14.29

Sketching in Orthographic

As we have seen elsewhere throughout this book, the fundamentals of orthographic projection are widely applied to most areas of technical drawing. Moreover, these fundamental principles are universally accepted and understood in most countries around the world. Sketching in orthographic can provide a quick method of conveying ideas and also provide more information than a pictorial sketch. Furthermore, orthographic sketches lend themselves better to dimensioning than do pictorials and it is with measurements and proportions that design ideas move from the drawing board into production.

All the practices observed when drawing orthographic views using instruments should be followed when sketching in orthographic. Position of views, projection lines, xy lines etc. are all equally important in the sketch as in the drawing produced using instruments. An orthographic sketch which is technically inaccurate is of little value as it does not communicate the idea(s) properly.

Worked Examples

> **Given a pictorial view of an object. Make neat, freehand, orthographic views of this object showing all hidden detail.**

(1) Start by drawing in an xy line and boxing in the space for the front elevation and the plan directly beneath it.
(2) 'Project' these boxes around in the usual way to give the position and size of the end view.
(3) The circle and semicircle are sketched in by first drawing squares and fitting the circles into these squares.
(4) Thicken and darken all outlines and visible details, Fig. 14.31.

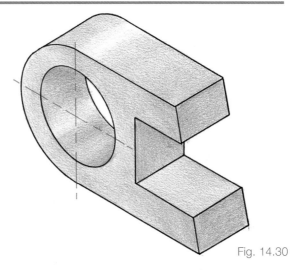

Fig. 14.30

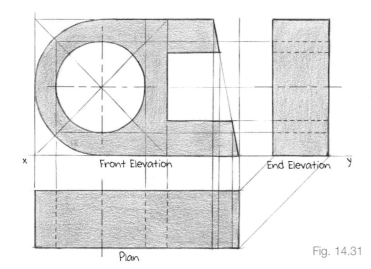

Front Elevation   End Elevation   y

x

Plan

Fig. 14.31

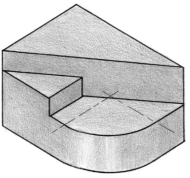

Fig. 14.32

> **Given the pictorial of an object in Fig. 14.32. Make a neat, three-view orthographic sketch of the object.**

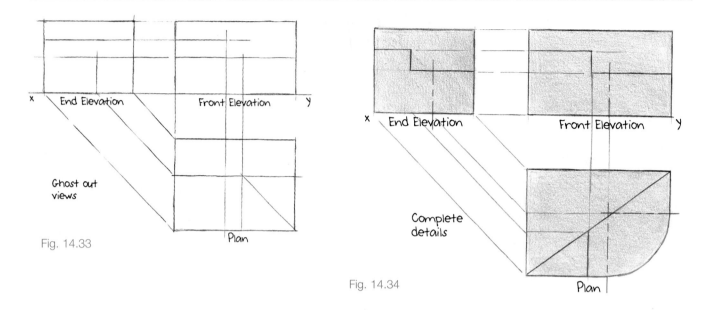

Fig. 14.33

Fig. 14.34

Given an isometric of a shaped solid in Fig. 14.35. Make a neat, freehand sketch showing a front elevation, end elevation and plan of this object.

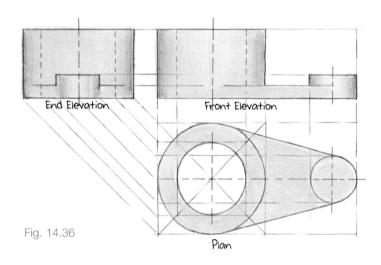

Fig. 14.36

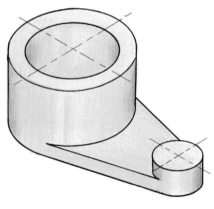

Fig. 14.35

Perspective Sketching

One of the most popular types of pictorial sketches are perspective sketches. Many illustrators, designers and architects use it almost exclusively because it presents a drawing most like the image the camera records or the eye sees. The perspective drawing is a pictorial projection that can take several forms depending on the vanishing points. Unlike orthographic or isometric projections which assume parallel lines of sight from the observer to the object, the perspective uses lines of sight that converge at one, two, three or more points. Fig. 14.37 shows an upside-down cardboard box drawn using one-point, two-point and three-point perspective.

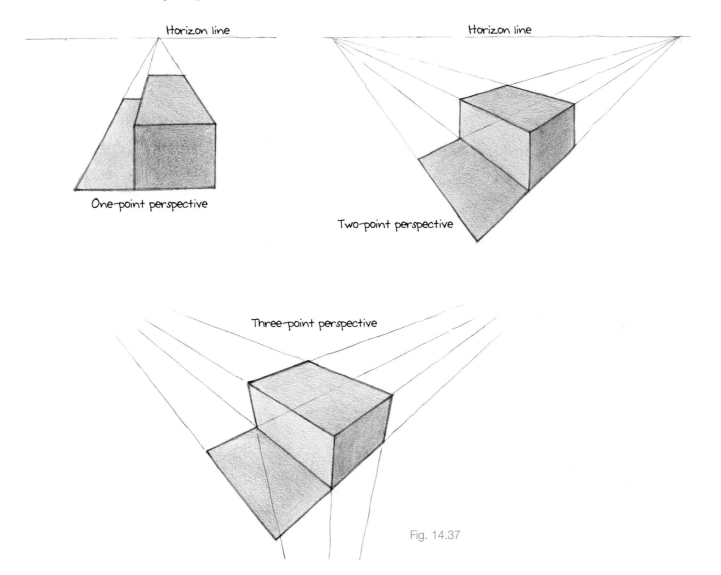

Fig. 14.37

The rules followed when drawing perspective views with instruments should also be followed when producing a perspective sketch.

- Horizontal lines vanish to vanishing points on the horizon.
- Parallel lines vanish to the same vanishing point.
- Lines and edges behind the picture plane appear shorter than their true length while lines/edges in front of the picture plane appear longer than their true length.

As with the isometric pictorial sketch, your first step is to establish the major points and lines by boxing in the object. The object is then broken into parts with the larger areas/planes being found first and then working toward the finer details.

It is vital before setting up a perspective sketch to understand the relationships of the various elements: the picture plane spectator, ground line, horizon line, vanishing points. A variation in any of these produces a different perspective view, Fig. 14.38.

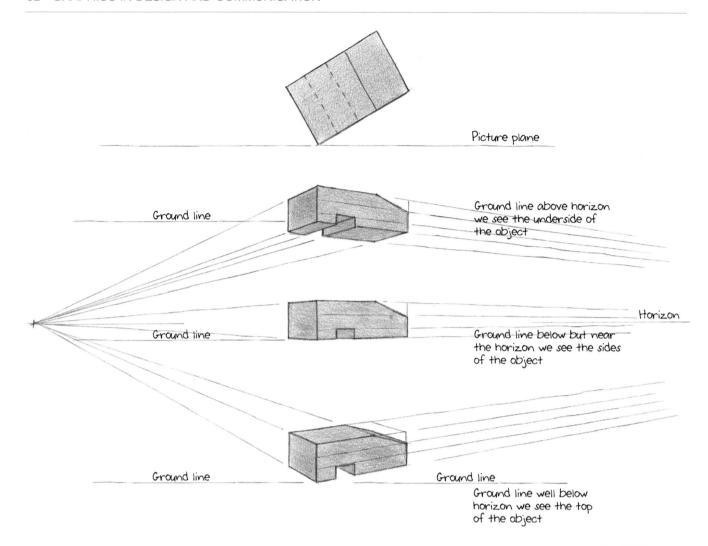

Fig. 14.38

When setting up a sketch it is important to bear in mind that vanishing points placed too close together result in a distorted perspective. They should usually be placed as far apart as is practical. Sometimes the vanishing points may even have to be assumed to lie off the paper.

The following series of diagrams show the way that a change in one variable can affect the final perspective view. These should be sketched out by the student.

By moving the picture plane the perspective view changes only in size. When the picture plane is close to the spectator the perspective produced is small (Perspective 1 in Fig. 14.39). Having the picture plane placed behind the object will enlarge the perspective (Perspective 2 in Fig. 14.39).

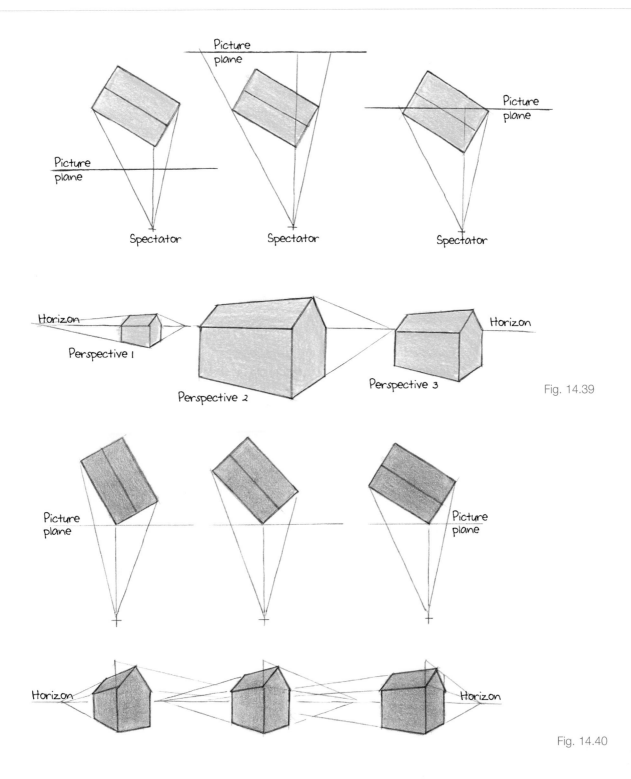

Fig. 14.39

Fig. 14.40

The angle the object makes with the picture plane determines which faces are visible and the degree to which they are foreshortened. The more oblique the angle a face makes with a picture plane the more the face will appear foreshortened. Faces that are parallel to the picture plane are not distorted.

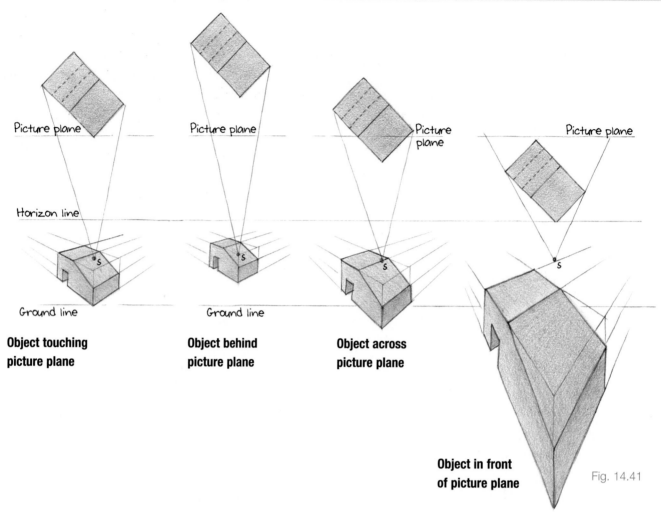

**Object touching
picture plane**

**Object behind
picture plane**

**Object across
picture plane**

**Object in front
of picture plane**

Fig. 14.41

Moving the object relative to the picture plane affects the perspectives.

Worked Examples

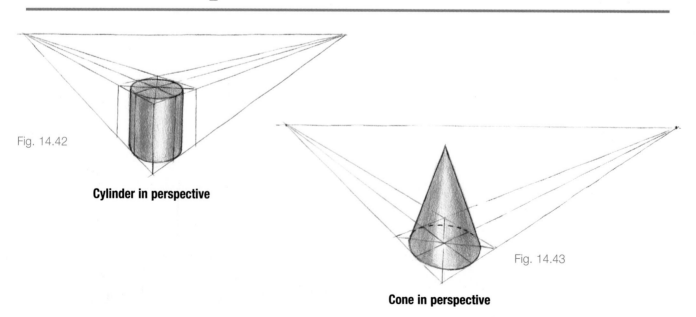

Fig. 14.42

Cylinder in perspective

Fig. 14.43

Cone in perspective

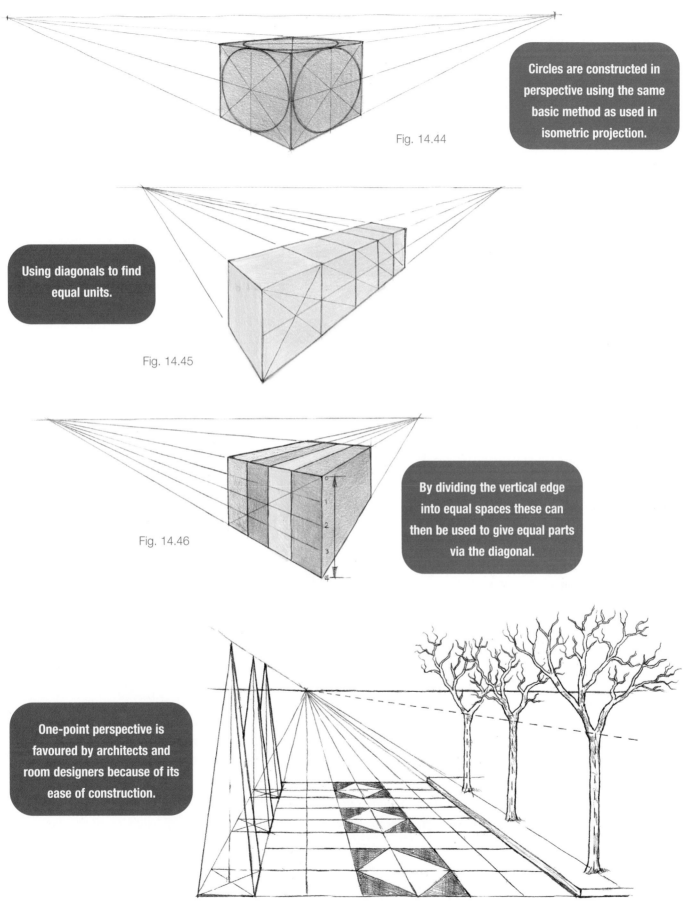

Fig. 14.44

Circles are constructed in perspective using the same basic method as used in isometric projection.

Using diagonals to find equal units.

Fig. 14.45

Fig. 14.46

By dividing the vertical edge into equal spaces these can then be used to give equal parts via the diagonal.

One-point perspective is favoured by architects and room designers because of its ease of construction.

Fig. 14.47

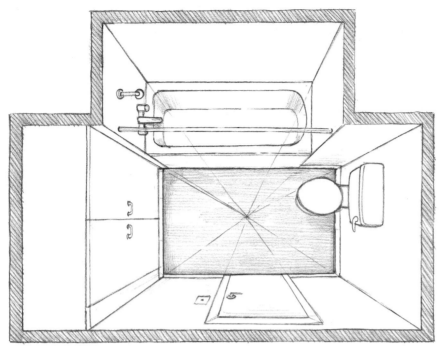

Fig. 14.48

Tone

Lines are obviously essential to outline shape, areas and contours. However, certain visual qualities of a surface cannot be fully described by lines alone. In order to improve our representation of such surfaces we must become skilful in the rendering of tonal values. Through the use of such rendering a good sense of light, mass and space are produced. Sketches can change from being flat and two-dimensional to being vibrant and three-dimensional.

Seeing patterns of light and dark is essential to our perception of objects. In a drawing it is tonal values that depict the lightness or darkness of an object, that describes the play of light on their forms and clarifies their arrangement in space. Tonal value can also be used to depict colour. Fig.

Apple
Dark green

Pear
Light green
or yellow

Plum
Dark purple

Fig. 14.49

14.49 shows an example of this. Tone is used both to indicate light and shade and also to show colour. It can be seen here that the drawing is completely drawn with pencil yet we can easily visualise the green apple, the light green or yellow pear, and the rich dark purple plum.

Techniques Used to Create Tonal Value

Using the traditional medium of pencil, there are several techniques for creating tonal values. These are:
- hatching,
- crosshatching,
- scribbling,
- stippling.

We will look at each of these separately.

Hatching

Hatching in sketching consists of a series of more or less parallel lines. These lines, drawn freehand, may be either long or short. Variation in tonal value is achieved in two ways:
- by varying the grade of lead used or increasing/decreasing the pressure with which we draw,
- by varying the spacing and density of the hatching.

The most flexible freehand technique for hatching uses relatively short, rapid, diagonal strokes. Start at the edges and work inwards. Strokes may overlap slightly. Apply a second or even a third layer of strokes at a slightly different angle to the first to build up the density and tonal value of an area. Hatching on a curved surface should curve to depict the contours of the surface.

Fig. 14.50

Fig. 14.51

By varying the spacing of the hatching we can vary the tone.

Fig. 14.52

Work inwards from the edges to produce crisp, clear, precise, edges.

Fig. 14.53

By applying additional layers of strokes at a slightly different angle we can also vary the tone.

Fig. 14.54

In this diagram the variation in tone is obtained by varying the spacing of the lines and by varying the line darkness.

Crosshatching

Crosshatching uses two or more sets of parallel lines to create tonal effects. The simplest type consists of two perpendicular sets of parallel lines which gives a simple weave pattern. By adding more sets of lines, darker tonal values can be achieved.

In practice, hatching and crosshatching are combined into a single technique. Simple hatching is used to provide the lighter tones and crosshatching is used to render the darker values, Fig. 14.55.

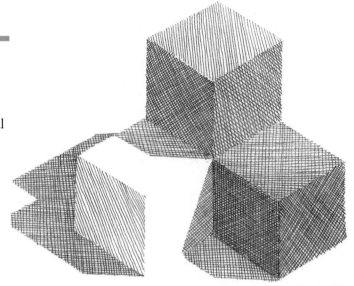

Fig. 14.55

Fig. 14.56

A simple crosshatch weave is very effective. The orientation of the weave will also give a different effect.

Fig. 14.57

A tight weave mesh produces a strong tonal value.

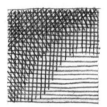

Fig. 14.58

Variation in tone across a surface is achieved by varying the degree of hatching.

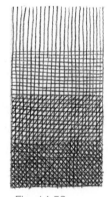

Fig. 14.59

In this diagram it can be seen that the building up of the four layers of hatching increases the tonal value.

Scribbling

Scribbling is the fastest of the shading techniques and offers great flexibility during sketching. It involves the use of multi-directional lines with the pencil being lifted from the paper only occasionally to change direction. It is a less rigid and less formal method of shading than the previous two methods we have looked at. The lines are varied to suit the style required. They may be continuous, straight, curved, jagged, wavy. The scribbling may be single-layered or many-layered. By drawing the lines close together a dense, dark tonal value may be achieved.

The surface texture may also be conveyed using this technique, as can pattern and the surface quality.

Fig. 14.60

Fig. 14.61

Scribbling as a shading technique is fast and effective.

Fig. 14.62

Different scribbling methods gives both tone and texture.

Fig. 14.63

This scribbling technique relies on a completely freeform pattern.

Stippling

Stippling uses fine dots as a means of defining different tonal values. It is the slowest of the methods mentioned and requires good patience. Stippling relies on the density of the dots to determine the tone; closely packed dots will produce a dark tone while well-spaced dots will produce a light tone. The size of the dots used on an area will affect the apparent texture of that surface. By using small dots a fine texture is portrayed, while by using larger dots a coarse texture appears. If, however, the dots are drawn too large the stippling loses its effectiveness.

The shapes are first drawn very lightly. Dots are used over these lines to define the objects' edges. Areas to be shaded are then covered with an even distribution of dots. This will produce a light tonal value. By adding more layers of stippling darker tones are attained.

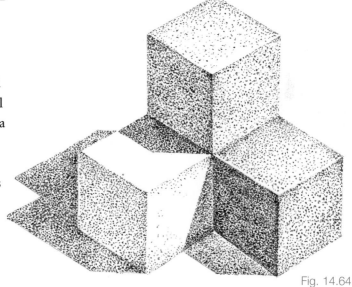

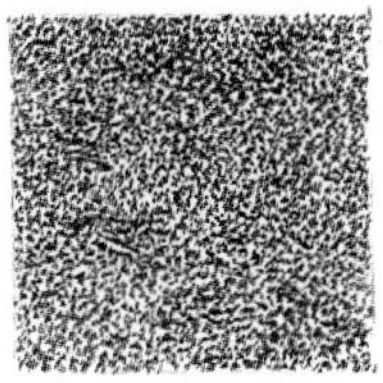

Fig. 14.64

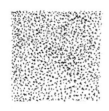

Fig. 14.65

A dark tone with a fine texture is achieved by using small dots closely spaced.

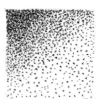

Fig. 14.66

A medium tone with a coarse texture is achieved by using larger dots with medium spacing.

Fig. 14.67

Variation in tone across an area can be achieved by varying the dot spacing.

Modelling Form

Modelling is the technique of making a two-dimensional drawing of an object or objects appear to have depth, volume and a relative position to each other in space. The two-dimensional drawing appears to gain three-dimensional status. This process is achieved by using shading and tonal values to transform a drawing of contours into **forms** in space.

The modelling of surfaces using light and shade can help us understand whether the surface is flat or curved or whether it is smooth or rough. Light patterns on curved surfaces such as cylinders, cones and spheres move gradually from light to dark. On planar solids such as cubes, prisms and pyramids there is a more abrupt change in shade/tonal value from plane to plane.

Fig. 14.68

Gradual change from light to dark on the curved surface of the cylinder in comparison to an abrupt change from plane to plane on the pyramid.

Fig. 14.69

Fig. 14.70

As the faces of an object turn away from the light their tonal value increases.

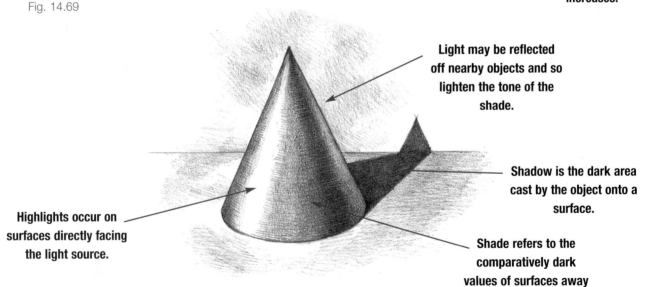

Light may be reflected off nearby objects and so lighten the tone of the shade.

Shadow is the dark area cast by the object onto a surface.

Highlights occur on surfaces directly facing the light source.

Shade refers to the comparatively dark values of surfaces away from the light.

Fig. 14.71

Colour

The use of colours when sketching can be a very effective tool. Colours can improve presentation, can identify materials being used, can highlight contrasts between two different parts of an object and/or can be used to draw attention to a particular part of a diagram. A note of caution here, the use of too much colour can confuse the viewer and can make a sketch fussy and distracting. The main function of sketches and diagrams in technical drawing is to convey an idea or to help solve a problem, they are not visual art in the same way as an artist's sketch or painting is.

Primary Colours

Red, yellow and blue are known as the primary colours and are shown on a colour wheel in Fig. 14.72.

All other colours can be achieved by mixing these primary colours. By mixing red and yellow, for example, orange is produced; yellow and blue mixed gives green; and blue and red mixed gives violet. Colours obtained by mixing two primary colours are called **secondary colours**. An even greater range of colours is found by mixing a primary colour with a secondary colour. These colours are termed **tertiary colours**.

Black and white are neutral colours and when mixed with other colours affect the tone of the colour.

The colour blue in Fig. 14.74 decreases in tone from left to right. This is achieved by allowing more of the white background to emerge through the colour.

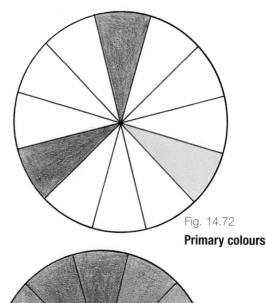

Fig. 14.72

Primary colours

Fig. 14.74

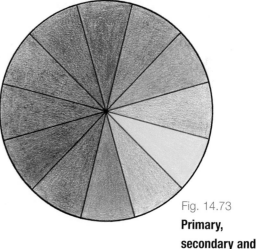

Fig. 14.73

Primary, secondary and tertiary colours

Application of Colour

Colour may be applied to sketches using many different mediums:
- watercolour,
- felt-tipped pens,
- colouring pencils,
- coloured pens/biros etc.

Each of these has its own characteristics.

Watercolour

Watercolours are used for shading of large blocks or areas. They are usually used as a wash over a finished drawing rather than as a means of building up the drawing itself. They can cover a large area quickly but do not lend themselves to intricate detail with many colour changes.

Fig. 14.75

Felt-tipped Pens

Felt-tipped pens are useful for block shading or where a coarse application of colour is adequate. They cannot be removed once applied which may cause problems. The colours produced are very vibrant. Variations in tone are difficult to produce, Fig. 14.75.

Coloured Pens/Biros

These can be used very effectively using the methods described earlier for pencil sketching. Obviously it must be always remembered that

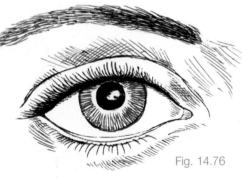

Fig. 14.76

the ink will not be erased in the same way as a pencil. However, a biro/pen can give a more permanent feel to a sketch and will not be smudged when handled. By tracing over light pencil lines we can combine the advantages of sketching in pencil with the advantages of having sketches finished with ink, Fig. 14.76.

The thickness of the lines produced cannot be varied when using biro but the line quality is very good. The range of colours available is also limited and they do not lend themselves to the mixing of colours, Fig. 14.77.

Fig. 14.77

Colouring Pencils

Colouring pencils provide one of the best means of applying colour to a sketch or diagram. They come in a wide range of colours and also can be mixed by applying one layer over another. They can be sharpened in many ways to give different line widths and can be erased. Sketches may be drawn from start to finish using colouring pencils or they can be used to enhance a pencil or ink sketch.

Fig. 14.78 **Pencil sketch with colouring pencil applied afterwards**

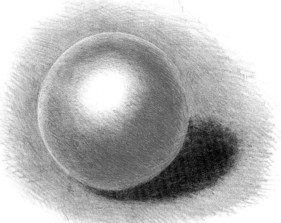

Fig. 14.79 **Sketch done solely with colouring pencils**

Tone and Texture

When we use hatching, stippling or scribbling to create a tonal value we are simultaneously creating texture. Furthermore, as we try to describe a material's texture with lines we are also creating tone. There is a constant relationship between tone and texture. We should therefore always be aware of this when attempting to produce either.

The texture of an object may be smooth or rough, high sheen or dull, hard or soft. When rendering tone on a sketch it is often possible to convey this texture quality through the use of different shading techniques. Large-scale strokes will produce a rough texture while small-scale strokes produce a fine-grained effect. Polished surfaces depend on the reflection of light to convey their texture. They reflect light brilliantly and appear sharply in focus. Matt surfaces absorb and diffuse light and therefore appear less sharp. Coarse surfaces cast shadow patterns on themselves thus revealing their textural quality.

Fig. 14.80

Fig. 14.81a

Short strokes

H I G H E R   L E V E L

Fig. 14.81b

Smooth, blended strokes

Fig. 14.81c

Rough, large strokes

Fig. 14.81d

Irregular scribble

Representation of Some Common Materials

By critical analysis of the texture and colour of various materials we should be able to accurately represent these materials in our sketching.

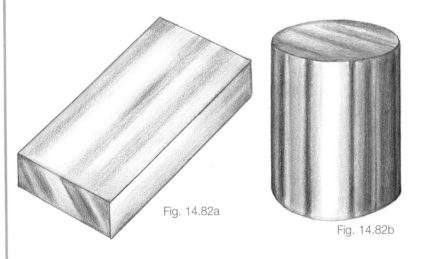

Fig. 14.82a

Fig. 14.82b

Metal

Metals have a smooth surface and are highly reflective of light. Shading on the surfaces is unidirectional and uses straight lines. Shading on the end is inclined. The shading is laid down in bands as shown in Figures 14.82a and 14.82b. For highly polished surfaces it is important to catch the light high points and the reflections of other objects in the surface, Fig. 14.83. Blue/grey is best to represent steel while an orange/yellow best represents brass or gold.

Fig. 14.83

HIGHER LEVEL

Wood

Wood can have many variations both in colour and texture and also has the added interest of grain pattern. The faces of a rectangular block of wood will show quite different grain patterns but it should be remembered that the grain patterns are all interlinked. If a grain feature reaches an edge of a face it will continue in some form on the adjoining face. Some woods show very little grain pattern while for others the grain pattern dominates each face.

Fig. 14.84a

Fig. 14.84b

The colours used are generally light brown or orange as a base colour, with a darker brown or orange to show the grain.

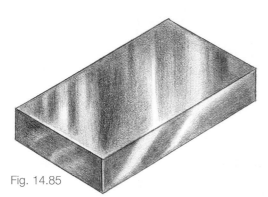

Fig. 14.85

Plastic (opaque)

Opaque plastic is smooth and generally shiny with often strong colouring. Attention should be paid to the light high points and colour depth.

Clear plastic and glass

It can be difficult to depict a transparent or semi-transparent material. The standard way of representing colour materials is to draw groups of parallel lines using a ruler. These lines are angled across the surface as shown in Fig. 14.86.

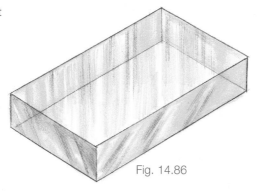

Fig. 14.86

Because of the reflective nature of these materials when they are grouped together they will reflect light onto each other. Shade and shadow will not be uniform in value as a result of this bouncing light. Curved glass or plastic will also distort the image of an object seen through it, Fig. 14.87.

Fig. 14.87

Shade and Shadow

Many sketches need no shading yet all sketches may be shaded. The amount of effort put into shading depends on the purpose of the sketch, the subject being drawn, the type of drawing and the need for clarity. Most sketches are more pleasing to the eye if surfaces are emphasised and contrasts are indicated. By using shading and shadow to differentiate between vertical, horizontal and inclined surfaces the drawing becomes easier to read. Pictorial sketches are regularly shaded but orthographic or working drawings are usually left unshaded.

There is one guiding principle in shading or rendering a drawing. The rendering must always make the drawing either clearer or more attractive. If it fails in these it is better to omit it. Rendering should not be used to hide inaccuracy or mistakes. It can only be successful if the basic drawing is correct.

Terminology

We must first define what we mean by shade and shadow because they are not two words for the same thing.

Shadow

A shadow is a relatively dark figure, cast by an opaque object or part of an opaque object, onto a surface. It is caused by the object intercepting or blocking the light rays from a source.

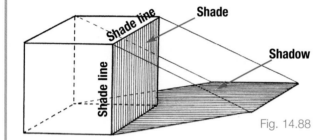

Fig. 14.88

Shade

Shade refers to the varying amount of light that is reflected to an observer by the surfaces of an object. Shade will be at its darkest on areas turned away from the light and will vary in brightness as a surface turns toward the light, Fig. 14.88.

Shade line

A line on an object that separates an illuminated surface from one in shade. Also called the casting line.

Shadow line

The edge of the shadow cast on a receiving body.

> **Surfaces are shaded and shadows are cast.**

Shadow of a line

(1) When a vertical line casts a shadow onto a horizontal surface the shadow will be in the direction of the shining light rays.

(2) If the line intersects the surface then the shadow starts where the line and surface meet.

(3) A straight line will cast a straight shadow onto a plane surface.

(4) A straight line will produce a shadow plane, Fig. 14.89. This is a plane produced by the shadows of adjacent points on the line. The intersection of the shadow plane with another surface produces a shadow.

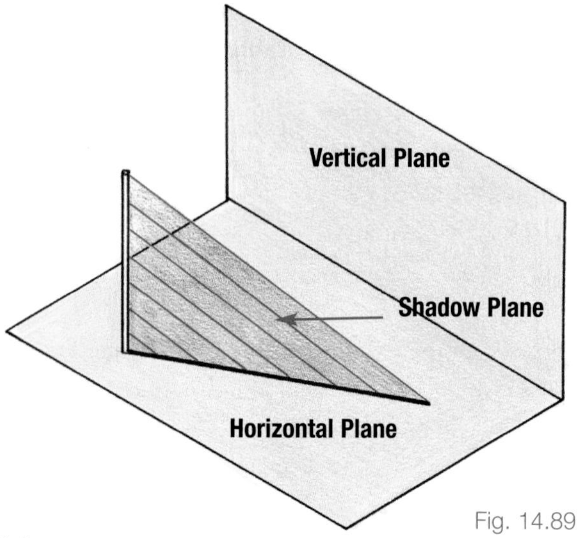

Vertical Plane

Shadow Plane

Horizontal Plane

Fig. 14.89

The hypotenuse of this shadow plane establishes the direction of the light rays.

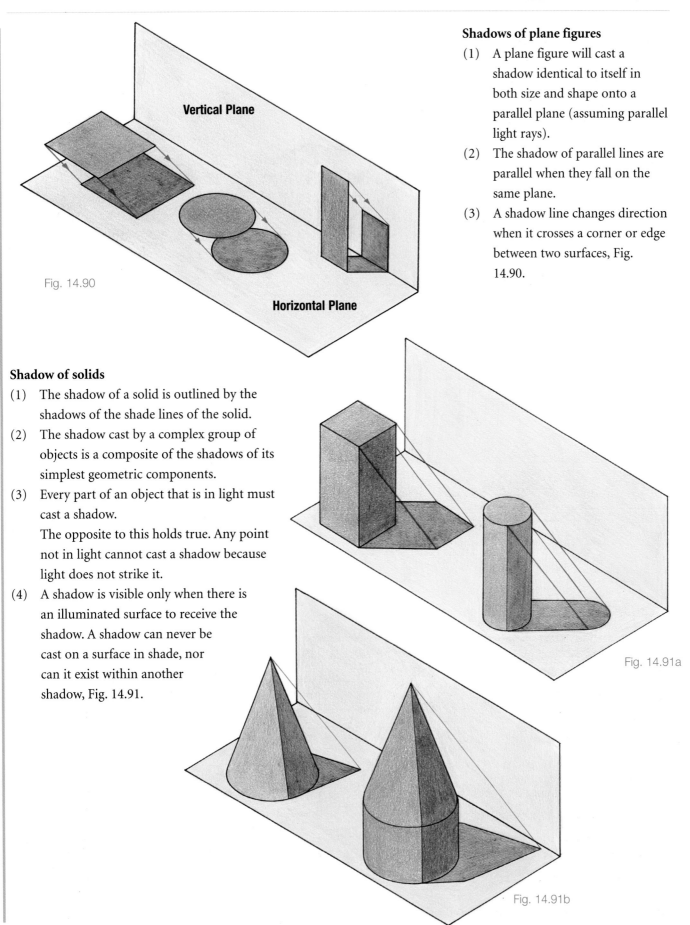

HIGHER LEVEL

Shadows of plane figures

(1)   A plane figure will cast a shadow identical to itself in both size and shape onto a parallel plane (assuming parallel light rays).

(2)   The shadow of parallel lines are parallel when they fall on the same plane.

(3)   A shadow line changes direction when it crosses a corner or edge between two surfaces, Fig. 14.90.

Vertical Plane

Horizontal Plane

Fig. 14.90

Shadow of solids

(1)   The shadow of a solid is outlined by the shadows of the shade lines of the solid.

(2)   The shadow cast by a complex group of objects is a composite of the shadows of its simplest geometric components.

(3)   Every part of an object that is in light must cast a shadow.
The opposite to this holds true. Any point not in light cannot cast a shadow because light does not strike it.

(4)   A shadow is visible only when there is an illuminated surface to receive the shadow. A shadow can never be cast on a surface in shade, nor can it exist within another shadow, Fig. 14.91.

Fig. 14.91a

Fig. 14.91b

Light Source

As has been mentioned earlier, for most sketching we assume that the light rays shining on the object are parallel, i.e. the source of light is very far away, e.g. the sun. This makes the working out of the shadow simpler than if the rays are non-parallel. The light source can be anywhere, behind, above, in front, to the left, below etc. The position of the light source will effect the shade and the shadow, see Fig. 14.92.

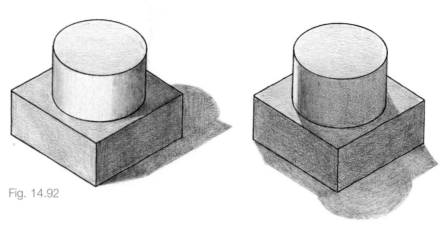

Fig. 14.92

Worked Examples

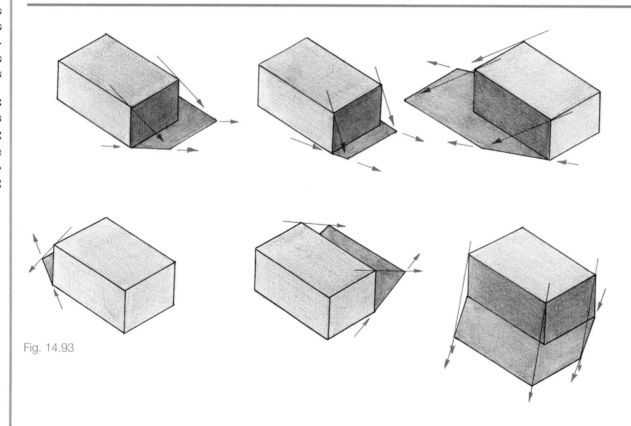

Fig. 14.93

More Worked Examples

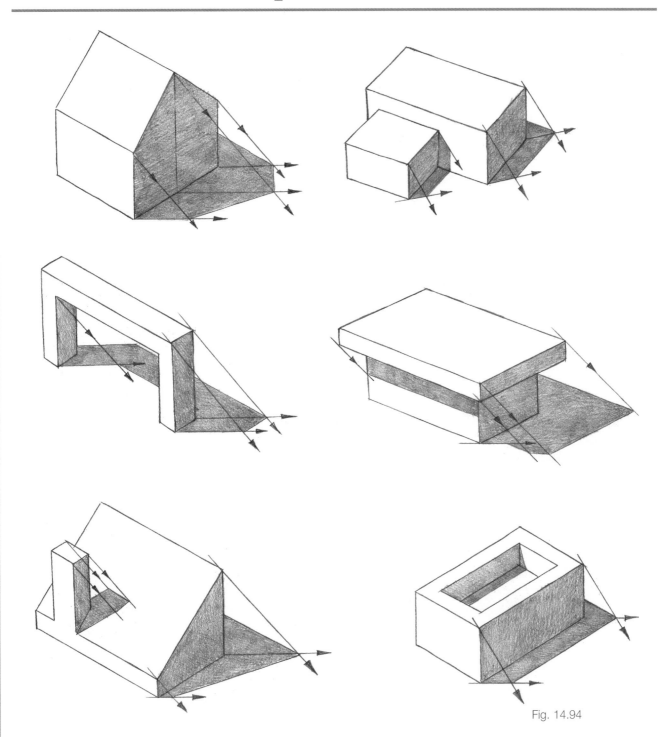

Fig. 14.94

Activities

Q1. Make neat freehand sketches of the plane figures shown in Figures 14.95, 14.96 and 14.97.

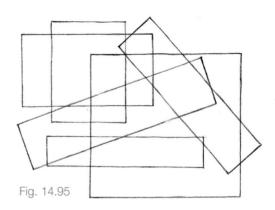

Fig. 14.95

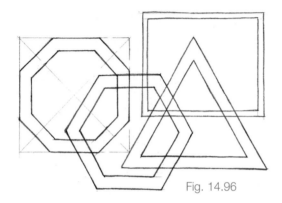

Fig. 14.96

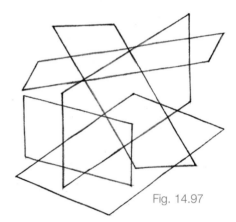

Fig. 14.97

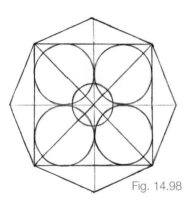

Fig. 14.98

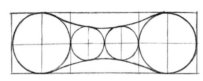

Fig. 14.99

Q2. Sketch the diagrams shown in Figures 14.98, 14.99 and 14.100 which are based on circles.

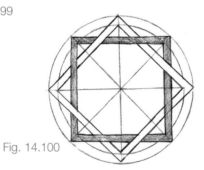

Fig. 14.100

Q3. Make neat diagrams of the objects shown in Figures 14.101 and 14.102 which are based on ellipses.

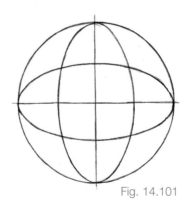

Fig. 14.101

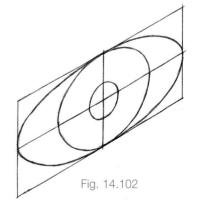

Fig. 14.102

Q4. Given the front elevation, end elevation and plan of an object in Figures 14.103, 14.104, 14.105 and 14.106. In each case make a neat, freehand, pictorial sketch of the object.

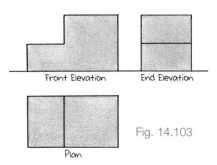

Fig. 14.103

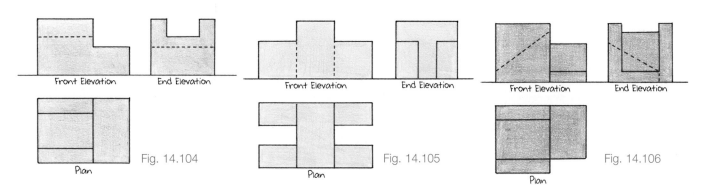

Fig. 14.104

Fig. 14.105

Fig. 14.106

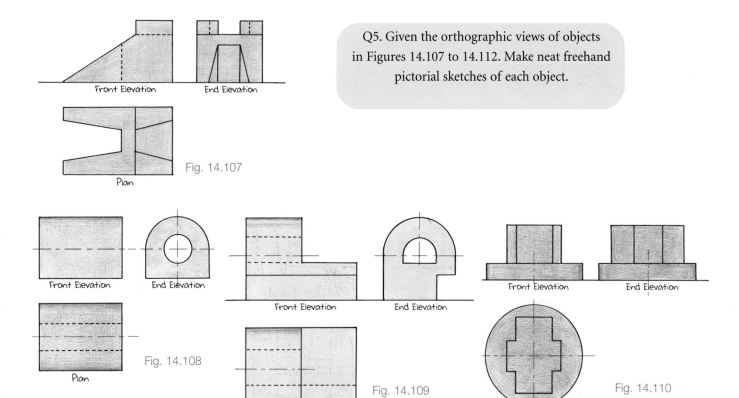

Fig. 14.107

Q5. Given the orthographic views of objects in Figures 14.107 to 14.112. Make neat freehand pictorial sketches of each object.

Fig. 14.108

Fig. 14.109

Fig. 14.110

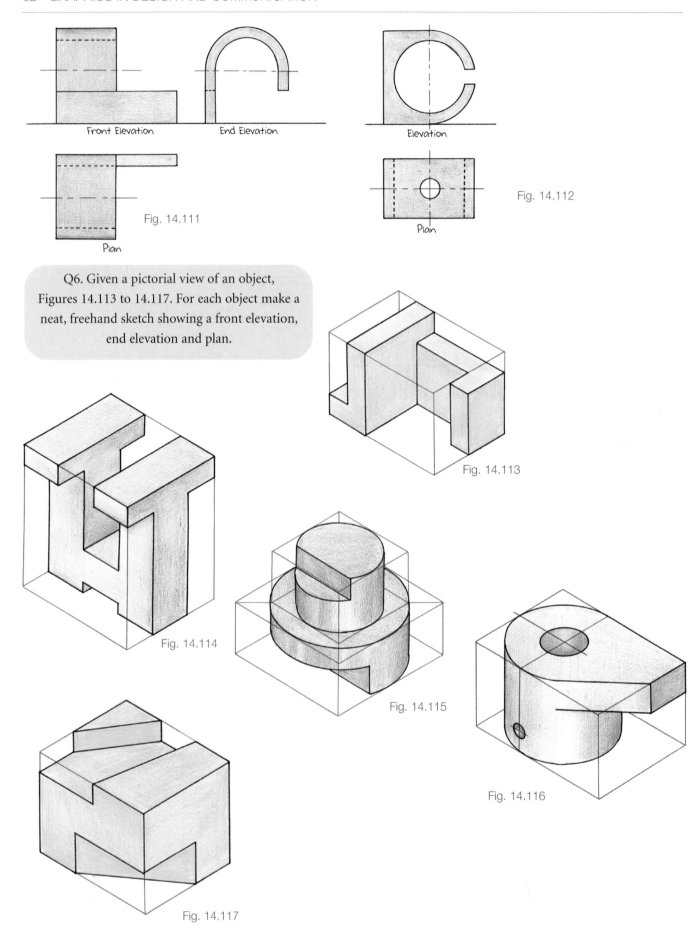

Front Elevation

End Elevation

Elevation

Fig. 14.111

Fig. 14.112

Plan

Plan

Q6. Given a pictorial view of an object, Figures 14.113 to 14.117. For each object make a neat, freehand sketch showing a front elevation, end elevation and plan.

Fig. 14.113

Fig. 14.114

Fig. 14.115

Fig. 14.116

Fig. 14.117

Q7. Sketch one-point perspective views of the objects shown in Figures 14.118 to 14.121.

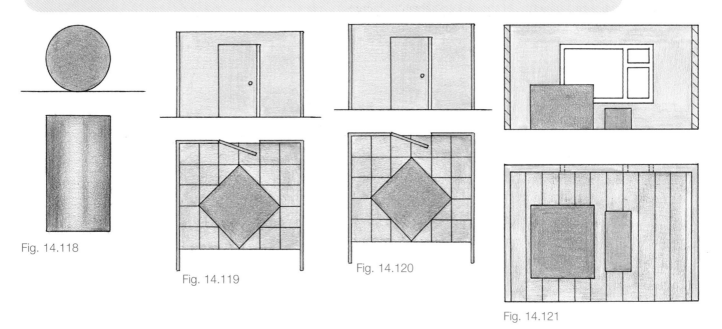

Fig. 14.118

Fig. 14.119

Fig. 14.120

Fig. 14.121

Q8. Make neat two-point perspective sketches of the objects shown in Figures 14.122 to 14.126. Vary the height and position of the spectator to give different views.

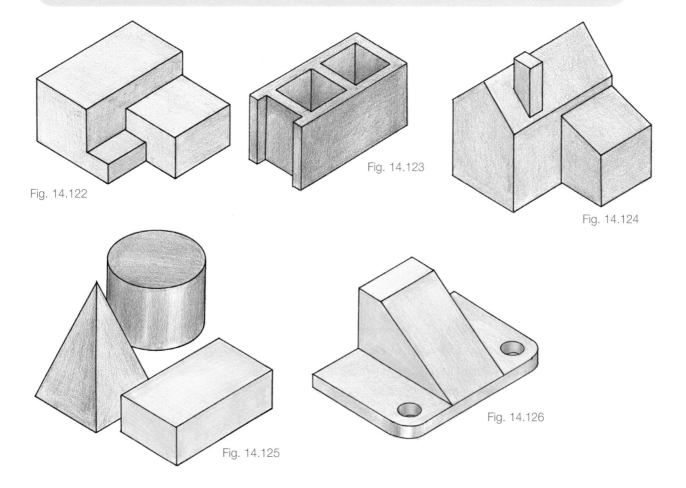

Fig. 14.122

Fig. 14.123

Fig. 14.124

Fig. 14.125

Fig. 14.126

Q9. Using the hatching technique to produce tonal value, enhance the diagrams of the objects shown in Figures 14.127 to 14.130. Vary the imagined light source.

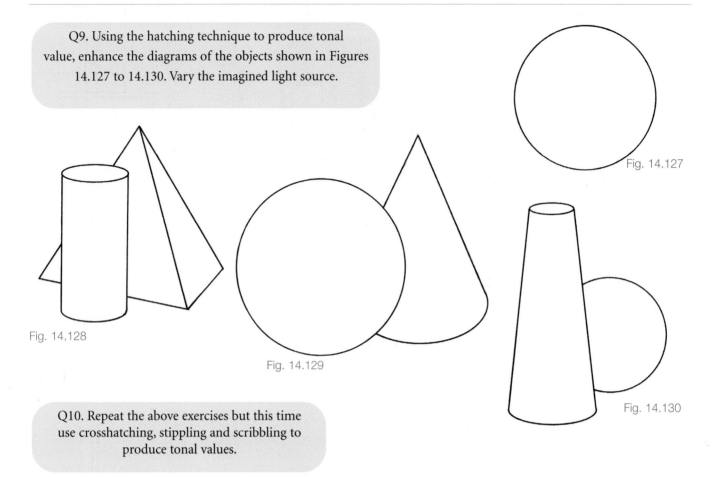

Fig. 14.127

Fig. 14.128

Fig. 14.129

Fig. 14.130

Q10. Repeat the above exercises but this time use crosshatching, stippling and scribbling to produce tonal values.

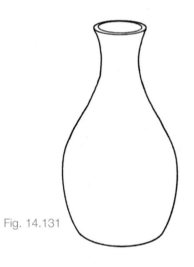

Fig. 14.131

Q11. Make a diagram of a vase. Repeat this diagram several times. By using varied shading techniques convey differing textures for each vase, Fig. 14.131.

Q12. Make a neat diagram of a block like that shown in Fig. 14.132. Repeat this diagram to produce four similar blocks. By using colour and the techniques outlined in this chapter, make the first block represent wood, the second represent opaque plastic, the third represent glass or clear plastic, and the fourth represent metal.

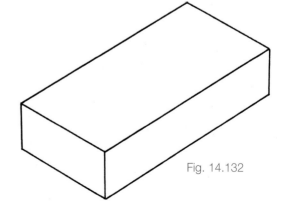

Fig. 14.132

HIGHER LEVEL

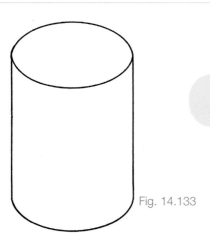

Fig. 14.133

Q13. Repeat the above question using Fig. 14.133 as your base shape.

Q14. Reproduce the diagram shown in Fig. 14.134. Using colour and shading techniques show the four objects as being from:

(1) glass,
(2) wood,
(3) opaque plastic,
(4) metal,
(5) a combination of the above.

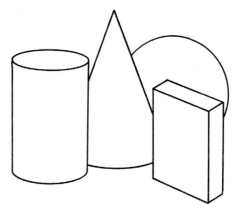

Fig. 14.134

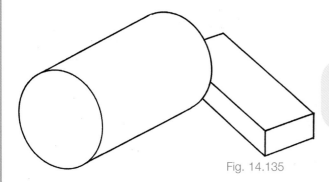

Fig. 14.135

Q15. Reproduce the following diagrams and enhance them using shade and shadow. Assume a light source to the left and slightly behind the objects.

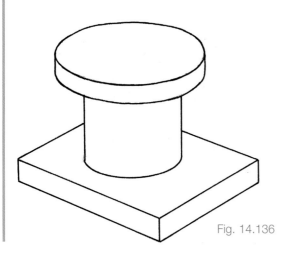

Fig. 14.136

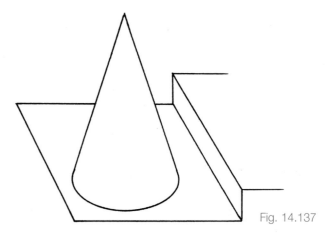

Fig. 14.137

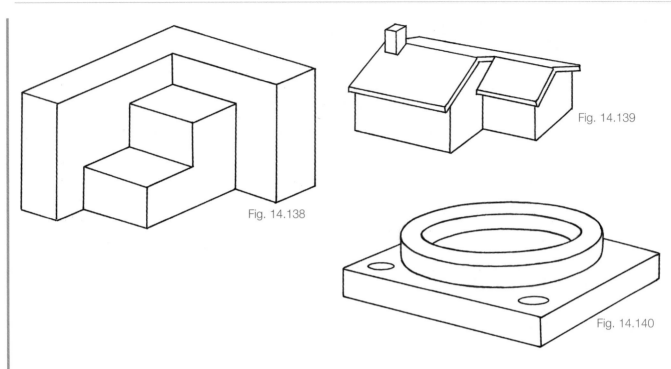

Fig. 14.138

Fig. 14.139

Fig. 14.140

Q16. Repeat as for Q15. This time assume a light source to the right and slightly behind the objects.

15 CAD Using SolidWorks

SYLLABUS OUTLINE

Areas to be studied (in an applied context):

• File management. • Graphics and CAD terminology. • Graphics and CAD software. • Generate working drawings from part and assembly models. • CAD sketching principles. • Creating 3-D assemblies. • Generation of presentation drawings from parametric models. • Generation of exploded views and animated sequences from parametric models. • Modelling and editing. • Use of templates and libraries. • Data exchange between applications. • Graphic output.

Learning outcomes

Students should be able to:

Higher and Ordinary levels
- Appreciate the power of contemporary hardware and software as they apply to design and communication of design.
- Use the various computer input and output devices as they relate to CAD.
- Use CAD drawings to produce three-dimensional CAD models.
- Understand the impact of design intent in CAD modelling.
- Generate multi-view drawings from 3-D models.
- Produce presentation drawings from CAD models.
- Effectively use the editing features of CAD software.
- Exchange data between applications.
- Efficiently use the standard tools and manipulation features of CAD software.
- Produce exploded and assembled presentation drawings.
- Animate sequences.

Higher level only
- *Realise the design intent in the CAD model.*
- *Use CAD modelling to explore geometric concepts and principles.*
- *Import and export files.*

Both computers and computer-aided design technology are rapidly evolving, so much so that as soon as you become accustomed to one software package there is a new even better package released. These are exciting times for the drawing and designing industries and it is vital that we all appreciate the great potential that CAD holds for workers in these areas. The best way to do this is through hands-on experience. By using a CAD package and by following graded exercises both confidence and a firm knowledge base are built up. This chapter will attempt to outline the basics of 2-D and 3-D modelling common to all CAD software. It must be stressed at this stage, however, that detailed descriptions of the various methods would fill many chapters and is beyond the scope of this book.

One of the keys to understanding any new subject is to master its jargon, an essential aspect of the subject. We must become familiar with this jargon and the basic operating processes used in graphics generation. This chapter will concentrate on transmitting a simple, yet accurate description of these processes.

Page Setup

Grid

Having a grid of squares or dots displayed on the screen can be of great benefit when drawing two-dimensional shapes. If the spacing or size of this grid is set at the outset to a size that matches the drawing in hand, it can be even more effective. The grid can be turned on or off at will and is a visual reference for the user.

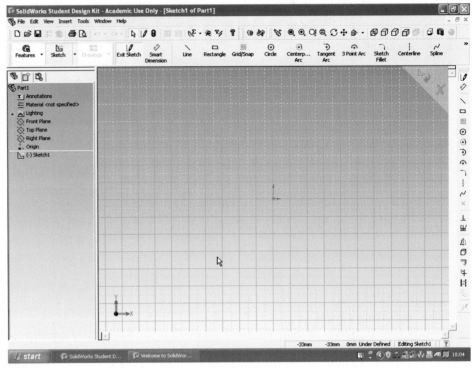

Fig. 15.1

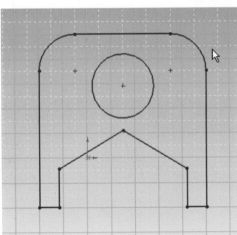

Fig. 15.2

If, for example, the grid setting was set to 10 mm squares and the snap setting was set to half of this at 5 mm, then the pointing device will jump to the grid points and to points exactly halfway between these grid points. If the required drawing is constructed with lines, circles and/or curves having dimensions of multiples of 5 mm, then the snap and grid will be very useful. When the snap is turned on, the pointing device will not rest between snap points.

Snap

The Snap command forces the pointing device to jump to the nearest point of an invisible grid. The size of this invisible grid can be set by the user.

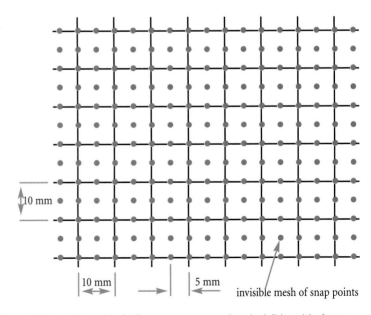

10 mm

10 mm   5 mm

invisible mesh of snap points

Fig. 15.3 A visible grid of 10 mm squares and an invisible grid of snap points set at spacings of 5 mm.

Paper Size

When producing drawings using traditional methods we select a sheet size that will accommodate the required views with ease and allow space for dimensioning and printing. When drawing using a CAD package a virtual sheet of paper is being used. The size of this virtual sheet is selected in the same way.

When producing solid 3-D models using CAD it is not a virtual sheet of paper that is being used but a virtual 3-D space. When the model is completed and working drawings are being constructed from the 3-D model, then virtual sheets of the correct size must again be selected.

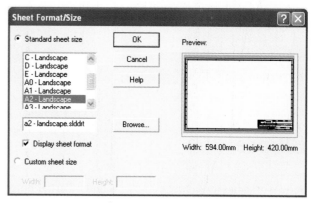

Fig. 15.4 Sheet and size orientation being selected.

Drawing Commands

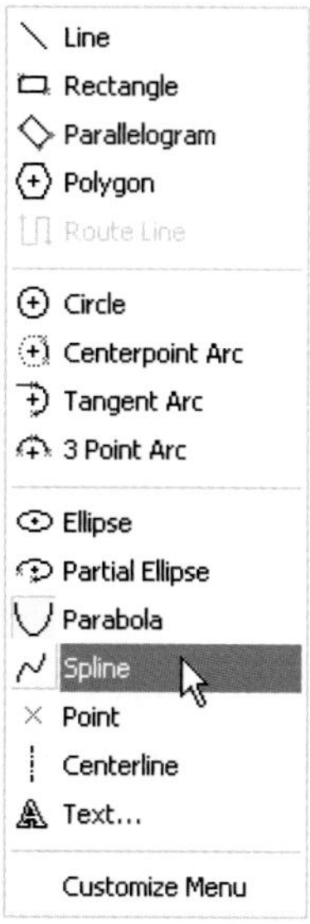

Whether producing a 2-D drawing or a 3-D model, use will be made of the drawing commands and a brief explanation of the more frequently used of these will now be given.

Fig. 15.5 Some of the drawing commands.

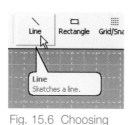

Fig. 15.6 Choosing the Line command.

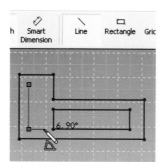

Fig. 15.7 Selecting the Line start and end points on the graphics window.

Line

A line is produced by selecting the Line command, Fig. 15.6, and then choosing the line's start and end points on the graphics window. The grid and snap are of great benefit when drawing rectilinear shapes using the Line command.

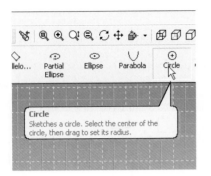

Fig. 15.8 Selecting the Circle command.

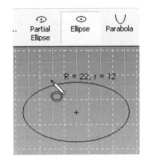

Fig. 15.9 The circle is drawn by selecting a centre and a point on the circumference.

Circle

The Circle command allows the construction of a circle by selecting the circle centre and a point on the circumference.

Ellipse

SolidWorks has an Ellipse command and a Partial Ellipse command. Fig. 15.10 shows an ellipse being drawn.

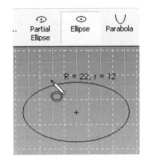

Fig. 15.10 SolidWorks has a specific Ellipse command. Select the centre, end of the major axis and point on the curve.

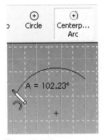

Fig. 15.11 Centerpoint Arc command. Select the arc centre, then a point on the circumference and finally the end point.

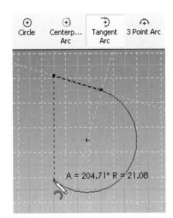

Fig. 15.12 Tangent Arc command. The end point of a line is selected. The arc will be drawn tangential to this line.

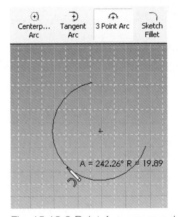

Fig. 15.13 3 Point Arc command. Select the arc start point, its end point and a third point on the arc circumference.

Arc

3 Point Arc enables you to construct an arc by specifying the end points on the arc. Tangent Arc enables the construction of an arc tangential to a selected line or arc. Centerpoint Arc enables construction of an arc by first specifying the curve centre and then the end points.

Rectangle

The Rectangle command enables the construction of a rectangle by specifying the diagonal end points. The rectangle will be orientated in a horizontal/vertical direction.

The Parallelogram command constructs a rectangle using three insert points. The first two points specify the ends of one of the rectangle sides. The third point chosen defines the length of the rectangle in the other direction, Fig. 15.15. This command is useful for drawing rectangles which are not horizontally/vertically orientated.

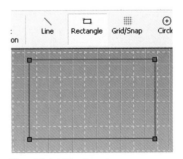

Fig. 15.14 Rectangle command.
Select two points which form the endpoints of a diagonal of a horizontally/vertically orientated rectangle.

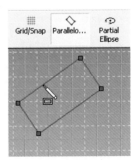

Fig. 15.15 Parallelogram command.
Select the two end points of one of the sides. The third point selected defines the width of the rectangle.

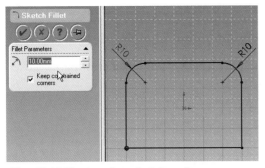

Fig. 15.16 The two lines that form the corners are selected. The fillet radius must also be given.

Fillet and Chamfer

The Fillet command constructs a rounded corner at the intersection of two lines, Fig. 15.16. The radius of the fillet curve to be used is defined and then the two lines forming the corner are selected.

The Chamfer command works in a similar way to the Fillet command. The chamfer can be placed in any of three ways as shown in Figures 15.17, 15.18 and 15.19.

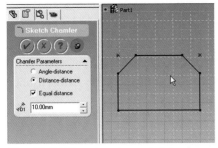

Fig. 15.17 Chamfer of equal distance on each edge.

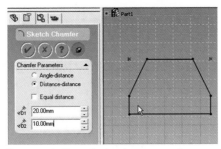

Fig. 15.18 Chamfer having unequal distances on each edge.

Parabola

The Parabola command will draw a parabola when a focal point is selected and a vertex point.

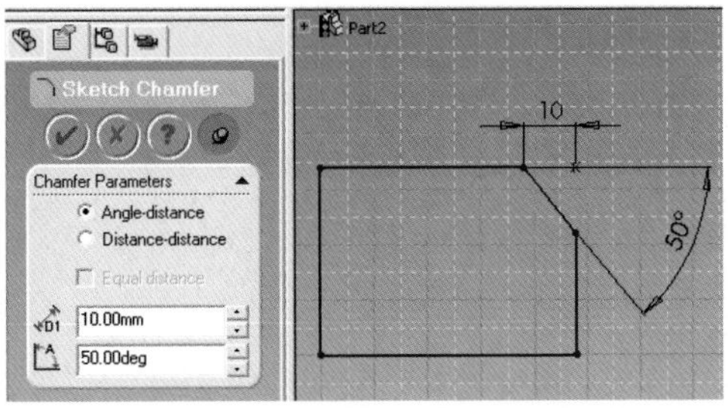

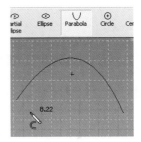

Fig. 15.19 Chamfer drawn by using a distance and an angle.

Fig. 15.20 Parabola command. Select the parabola focal point and its vertex.

Polygon

The Polygon command places a polygon by selecting a centre point and the location of a vertex, i.e. a polygon inscribed in a circle. The number of sides required on the polygon is selected from a menu box.

The polygons shown in Fig. 15.22 have inscribed circles. Fig. 15.21 shows polygons with circumscribed circles. The size of the polygon can be altered by changing the radius of these circles in the menu box.

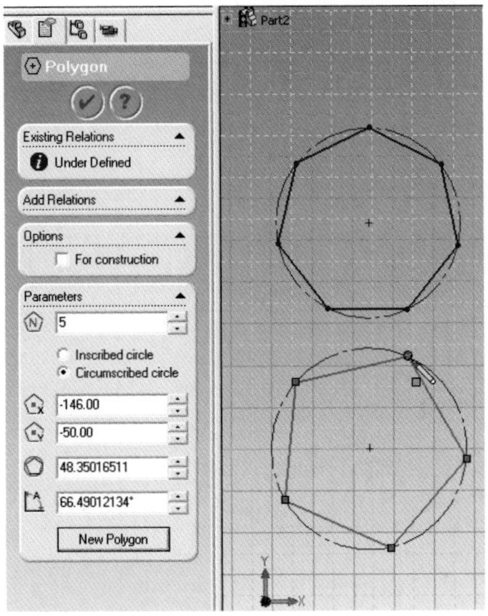

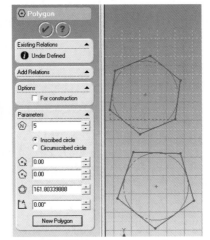

Fig. 15.21 Polygon command. These polygons have circumscribed circles. The size of these circles can be specified in the menu box which then defines the polygons' sizes.

Fig. 15.22 Polygon command. Select the polygon centre and the location of one vortex. The required number of sides must be specified.

Manipulating Your Drawing

There are several commands which speed up the drawing process by adapting/duplicating an existing drawing.

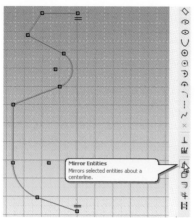

Fig. 15.23 Half of a symmetrical shape is drawn. The axis of symmetry must be drawn by using the Centerline command.

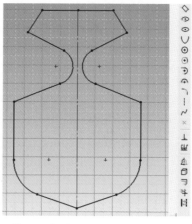

Fig. 15.24 The completed, mirrored sketch.

Mirror

The Mirror command reflects and duplicates a feature. The centre line command must be used to draw the axis. The Mirror command is very useful when drawing symmetrical objects as only half the object needs to be constructed, the other half is found by reflection.

Array: Rectangular Pattern, Linear Step and Repeat

The Rectangular Pattern command allows the copying and placing of a rectangular pattern of objects or features. The object is first selected and then the number of rows and columns needed are specified. The result is a rectangular array of the copied object.

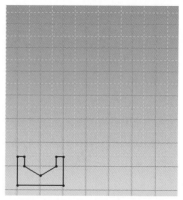

Fig. 15.25 The original object to be copied as an array.

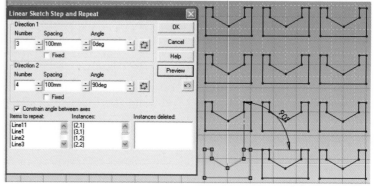

Fig. 15.26 The object is copied in a rectangular pattern using the Linear Step and Repeat command. In this example, there are three columns and four rows.

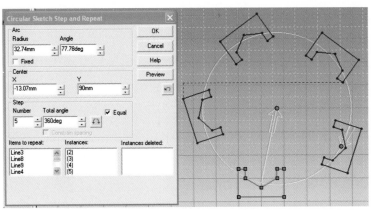

Fig. 15.27 The object to be copied is selected. The total angle of rotation, number of copies and rotation centre are specified. The rotation centre can be dragged around the screen.

Array: Circular Pattern, Circular Step and Repeat

This command copies an object or feature and places the copies in a circular pattern about a given point. The number of copies are specified by the user and the total angle to be used may also be specified. For example, a circular pattern of 360° would place the copies in a complete circle while an angle of 90° would only place the copies in a quarter-circle.

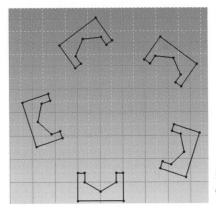

Fig. 15.28 The object is copied and rotated.

Offset

Offset makes a copy of an entity parallel to, and a chosen distance from, the original entity. When the original geometry is selected (Fig. 15.29), the Offset command can place a new geometry inside the original, Fig. 15.30, or outside the original, Fig. 15.31.

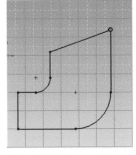

Fig. 15.29 The original geometry is drawn and selected.

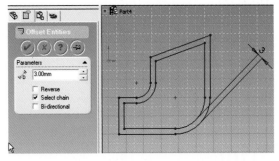

Fig. 15.30 The offset geometry can be drawn inside the original sketch.

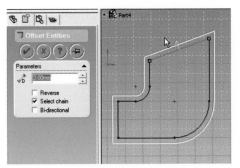

Fig. 15.31 The offset geometry can be drawn outside the original sketch.

Move

The Move command moves an object or feature by using a translation. The object's size is not altered in any way, nor is its orientation.

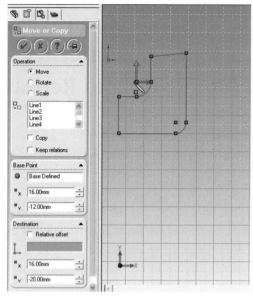

Fig. 15.32 The object to be moved is selected and a base point is selected.

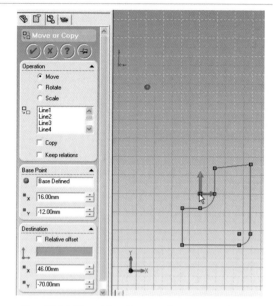

Fig. 15.33 The object is moved – a translation. It has not been rotated or altered in size in any way.

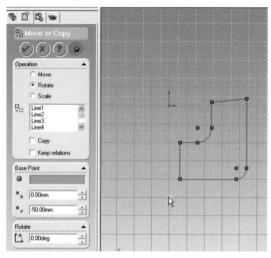

Fig. 15.34 The object to be rotated is selected and the point about which it is to be rotated is selected.

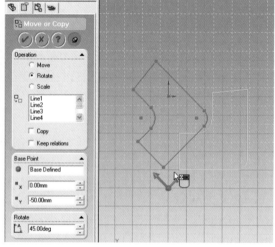

Fig. 15.35 The object has been rotated by 45° in an anti-clockwise direction.

Rotate

The Rotate command allows an object to be rotated through a specified number of degrees about a centre point. The centre point can be inside or outside the object and the rotation can be clockwise or anti-clockwise.

Trim

This allows the cutting away of unwanted portions of lines, circles or arcs. The trimmed-off portions are deleted. Figures 15.36, 15.37 and 15.38a show a series of steps in trimming away an unwanted portion of a sketch.

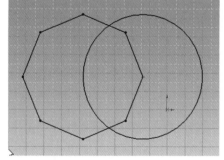

Fig. 15.36 The original sketch.

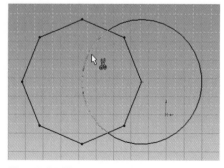

Fig. 15.37 The unwanted portion of the sketch is selected to be trimmed away.

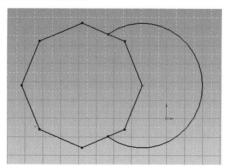

Fig. 15.38a The finished sketch with the unwanted arc trimmed off.

Making Sketches Using CAD

We have already explained in detail how important the sketching process is when designing. Sketches are produced freehand and are quickly put down on paper. It is through the visualisation of the product and the sketching process that the design is refined, altered and improved. Generally the sketches are not measured or completely in proportion but are good enough to convey the essence of the design. Measurements and dimensions come later.

This sketching phase can be emulated using CAD software. The computer is used as an electronic sketch pad to record design ideas. The designer concentrates on forms and shapes rather than dimensions. In the absence of exact dimensions a rough 'freehand' sketch is constructed. After constructing the sketch the geometry can be refined using **geometric constraints** and the sizes modified by using **parametric dimensions**. After sketching, a solid feature can be modelled from the sketch or sketches.

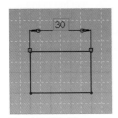

Fig. 15.38b The length of the side of the rectangle is 30 mm.

Fig. 15.38c The value of the parametric dimension is changed to 40 mm.

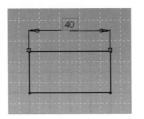

Fig. 15.38d The rectangle lengthens to match the dimension value.

Parametric Dimensions

To define any sketch, dimensions must be added. By adding parametric dimensions they can refine the design as well as define the design. A parametric dimension differs from a conventional dimension in that it not only reports the size of the object on which it is placed but it also can be used to drive the size of that object. For example, a line is drawn that is 20 units long. A parametric dimension is placed on the line and it displays the exact length of 20 units. This dimension length can be accepted or it can be changed. If a new length of 25 units is entered the length of the line is changed to 25 units in length. The length of the line is driven by the dimension. Parametric dimensions can be modified at any time during the design process which allows great freedom in altering the design's geometry and scale without having to redraw from the start.

Geometric Relations

After you are satisfied with the general form and shape of a sketch you refine it by specifying the geometric relationships between the various elements of the sketch. For example, you might want to set an edge to be perpendicular to another edge or to set an arc to be concentric with a circle. To specify these geometric relationships, they must be assigned to the sketch. There are many kinds of geometric constraints. Table 15.1 gives a brief description of each constraint type. For any selected sketch entity, only those constraints that are relevant to that entity are available and displayed.

Fig. 15.39 shows some of the more common relations that are added to a sketch.

You can choose whether these more common geometric relations are automatically created as you produce the sketch. As you sketch the pointer changes shape to show which relation can be added.

Fig. 15.39 Some of the more common geometric relations.

Relation	Entries to Select	Resulting Relations
Horizontal or Vertical	One or more lines or two or more points.	The lines become horizontal or vertical (as defined by the current sketch space). Points are aligned horizontally or vertically.
Collinear	Two or more lines.	The items lie on the same infinite line.
Cordial	Two or more arcs.	The items share the same centre point and radius.
Perpendicular	Two lines.	The two items are perpendicular to each other.
Parallel	Two or more lines.	The items are parallel to each other.
	A line and a plane (or a planar face) in a 3-D sketch.	The line is parallel to the selected plane.
ParallelYZ	A line and a plane (or a planar face) in a 3-D sketch.	The line is parallel to the YZ plane with respect to the selected plane.
ParallelZX	A line and a plane (or a planar face) in a 3-D sketch.	The line is parallel to the ZX plane with respect to the selected plane.
AlongZ	A line and a plane (or a planar face) in a 3-D sketch.	The line is normal to the face of the selected plane.
Tangent	An arc, ellipse, or spline, or a line or arc.	The two items remain tangent.
Concentric	Two or more arcs, or a point and an arc.	The arcs share the same centre point.
Midpoint	A point and a line.	The point remains at the midpoint of the line.
Intersection	Two lines and one point.	The point remains at the intersection of the line.
Coincident	A point and a line, arc, or ellipse.	The point lies on the line, arc, or ellipse.
Equal	Two or more lines, or two or more arcs.	The line lengths or radii remain equal.
Symmetric	A centre line and two points, lines, arcs, or ellipses.	The items remain equidistant from the centre line, on a line perpendicular to the centre line.
Fix	Any entity.	The entity's size and location are fixed. However, the end points of a fixed line are free to move along the infinite line that underlies it. Also, the end points of an arc or elliptical segment are free to move along the underlying full circle or ellipse.
Pierce	A sketch point and an axis, edge, line or spline.	The sketch point is coincident to where the axis, edge or curve pierces the sketch plane. The pierce relation is used in Sweeps with Guide Curves.
Merge Points	Two sketch points or end points.	The two points are merged into a single point.

Table 15.1

Fig. 15.40 shows the automatic relations and how the pointer changes.

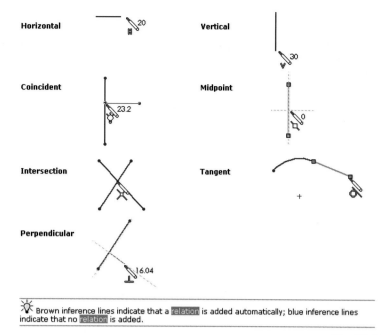

Fig. 15.40

Solid Modelling

A complex solid model can be broken down into simpler solid features. These are then combined to form the complex object. There are six kinds of sketched solid feature:

● Extrude, ● Revolve, ● Loft, ● Sweep, ● Coil, ● Split.

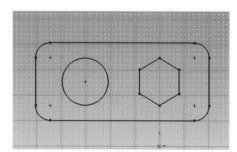

Fig. 15.41a The profile to be extruded is sketched.

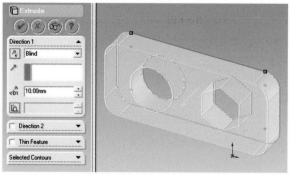

Fig. 15.41b The distance that the profile is to be extruded is specified. In this case it is 10 mm.

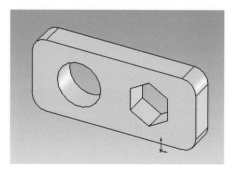

Fig. 15.41c The extruded solid is produced.

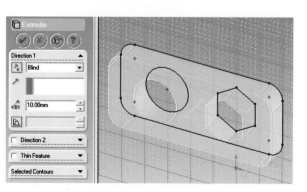

Fig. 15.41d The extruded solid may be extruded forwards.

Extruded Feature

To make an extruded solid, a sketch is first made. This sketch is then extruded in a direction perpendicular to the plane of the sketch (Figures 15.41a to 15.41f). The sketch is extruded in either direction or from mid-plane.

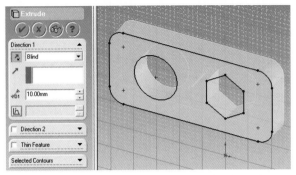

Fig. 15.41e The profile may be extruded backwards.

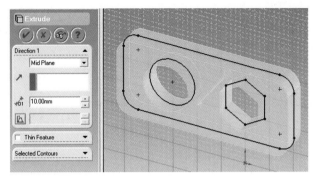

Fig. 15.41f The profile may be extruded equidistantly on both sides of the sketch.

Revolved Feature

To make a revolved solid a sketch is made again. This sketch is then revolved about an axis to produce the solid feature, Figures 15.42a to 15.42d. The axis may be an edge of the sketch or may be away from the sketch, Figures 15.43a and 15.43b.

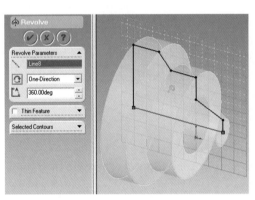

Fig. 15.42a The profile is rotated about one of its sides to produce a revolved solid.

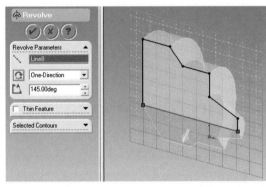

Fig. 15.42b The profile may be revolved through a set number of degrees and in either direction.

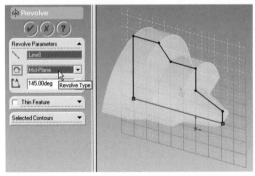

Fig. 15.42c The profile may be rotated by equal amounts about the sketch.

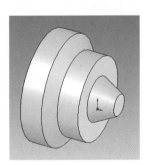

Fig. 15.42d The rotated sketch as a solid.

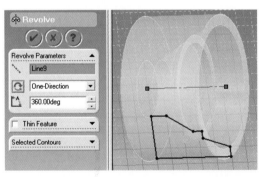

Fig. 15.43a If the axis is chosen away from the sketch profile a different solid will be produced.

Fig. 15.43b The revolved solid.

Loft Feature

To make a loft solid, you construct two or more sketches on a number of sketch planes and transit along the sketches.

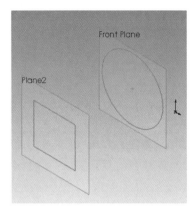

Fig. 15.44a The circle has been drawn on the front plane and a square on a parallel plane (Plane 2).

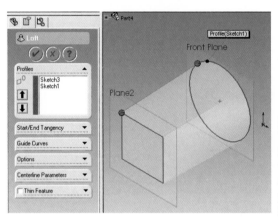

Fig. 15.44b The loft feature is selected and the two sketched profiles are highlighted.

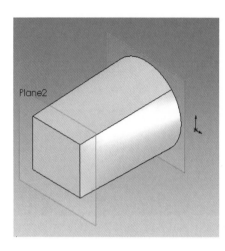

Fig. 15.44c A lofted solid is generated. It is a transition piece between the circle and square.

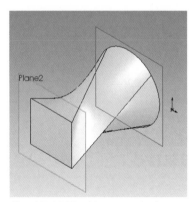

Fig. 15.44d In this example the lofted feature is twisted as it forms.

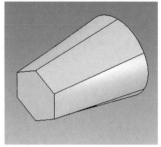

Fig. 15.44e A loft feature between a circle and a hexagon.

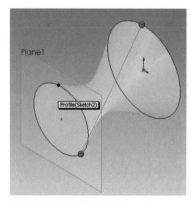

Fig. 15.44f A hyperboloid of revolution generated by using the loft feature.

Sweep Feature

To make a sweep solid, two sketches are constructed. One sketch is used as the cross-section and the other sketch as the path. The cross-section is swept along the path producing the solid.

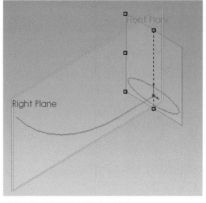

Fig. 15.45a The cross-section (ellipse) is drawn on one plane and the path that it is to be swept along is drawn on another plane.

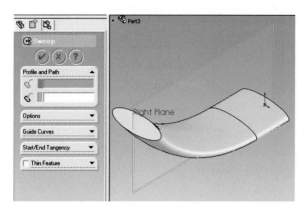

Fig. 15.45b The swept solid.

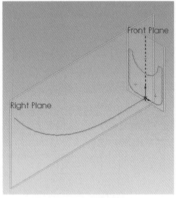

Fig. 15.45c Another example showing the cross-section drawn on one plane and the path it is to be swept along on another plane.

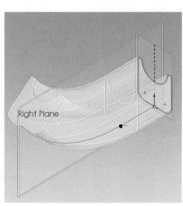

Fig. 15.45d The solid is ghosted in by the computer.

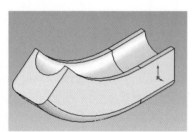

Fig. 15.45e The solid is modelled.

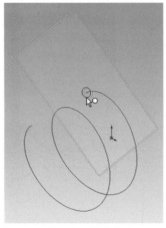

Fig. 15.46a The circle is to be swept along a helical path.

Fig. 15.46b The result is a coiled spring.

Coil Feature

A coil solid is a special type of sweep solid. The solid's cross-section is swept along a helical path.

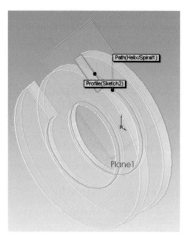

Fig. 15.46c Any shaped profile can be swept along a helical path. In this example a rectangle is used.

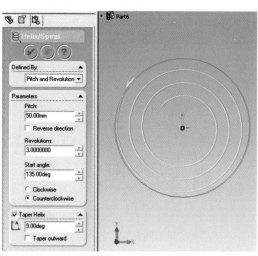

Fig. 15.46d The helix is constructed first. This helix, shown in plan view, has three revolutions, rotates clockwise, has a pitch of 50 mm and tapers by 9° as it goes up.

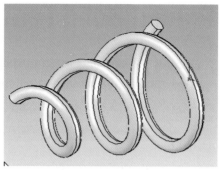

Fig. 15.46e A tapered spring.

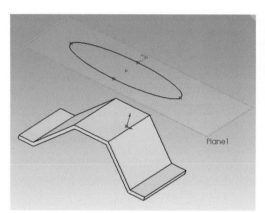

Fig. 15.47a An ellipse is drawn on a plane above a 3-D model.

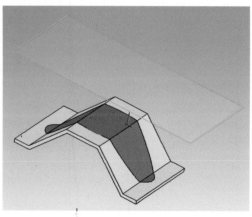

Fig. 15.47b The ellipse is projected onto the faces of the solid, splitting them into pieces.

Split Feature

The split feature is a means of splitting a face of a solid into two faces. A sketch drawn on one plane is projected onto the surface(s) of a solid feature, splitting the faces of the solid into pieces.

Fig. 15.47c An ellipse is drawn on a plane above the curved surface of the egg shape.

Fig. 15.47d The ellipse has been projected onto the curved surface, splitting it into parts.

Placed Solid Features

A placed solid feature is a pre-constructed feature which is commonly found in engineering. The type of feature is selected, the feature's parameters are specified and it is placed onto an existing solid model. The placed solid features are:
• Hole, • Shell, • Fillet, • Chamfer, • Rib, • Rectangular pattern, • Circular pattern, • Mirror, • Face draft.

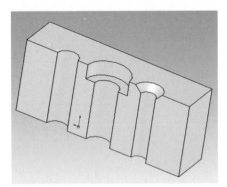

Fig. 15.48a A vertical section through a solid block showing:
• A through-bored hole.
• A through-bored hole with a counterbored top.
• A through-bored hole with a countersunk top.

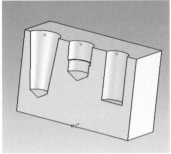

Fig. 15.48b A vertical section through a solid block showing:
• A taper-drilled, blind hole.
• A pipe tap hole.
• A blind hole with a flat bottom.

Hole Feature

A hole can be placed in a solid feature by specifying its size and location. The hole may be a blind one or may pass through the solid. The finish at the bottom of a blind hole may also be specified. The hole can be a tapped one to receive a threaded screw/bolt. It is also possible to have the top of the hole countersunk or counter-bored. Figures 15.48a, 15.48b and 15.48c show some of the options available when selecting this feature.

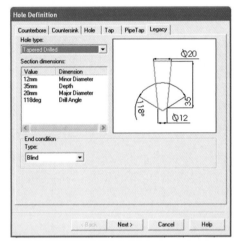

Fig. 15.48c The hole definition dialog box.

Shell Feature

As the name suggests, this feature makes a solid object hollow, thus converting it into a shell. The thickness of the shell can be specified. Figures 15.49a to 15.49d show some examples.

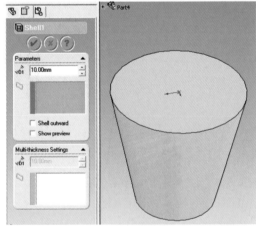

Fig. 15.49a The complete solid ready to be shelled out.

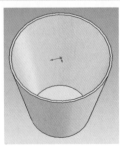

Fig. 15.49b The solid has been changed to a shell.

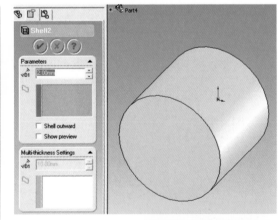

Fig. 15.49c A cylindrical solid is to be changed to a shell having a wall thickness of 2 mm.

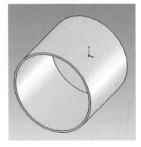

Fig. 15.49d The completed solid.

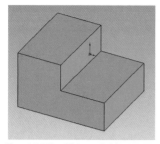

Fig. 15.50a This solid is to have three edges filleted.

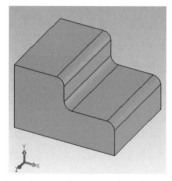

Fig. 15.50c The completed solid after applying a 6 mm fillet to the three edges.

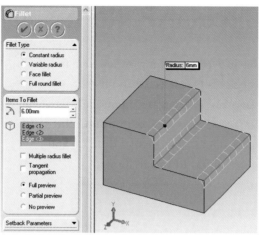

Fig. 15.50b A 6 mm fillet is selected and a preview shown.

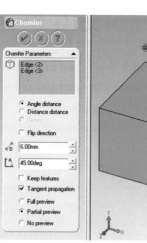

Fig. 15.51a The same solid as before but having 6 mm × 6 mm chamfers applied.

Fillet and Chamfer Features

Both these features are used in a similar way in 3-D work as they were when sketching in 2-D. Figures 15.50a to 15.50c show how fillets are applied. Figures 15.51a and 15.51b shows how chamfers are applied.

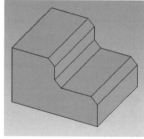

Fig. 15.51b The completed solid.

Rib Feature

A rib is a common feature on many engineering parts. This feature allows the easy placing of a rib with minimal work from the designer, most of the work being done by the software. The plane on which the rib lies must first be created and then a simple sketch drawn on this plane is used to generate the rib. Figures 15.52a to 15.52d show an example.

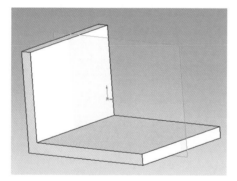

Fig. 15.52a The plane on which the rib will lie is first generated.

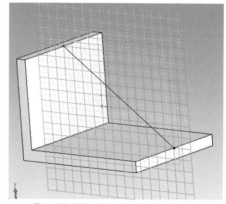

Fig. 15.52b A single line is drawn on this plane and is used to generate the rib. Its length is irrelevant but it must define the height of the rib.

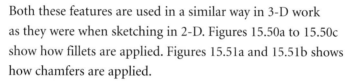

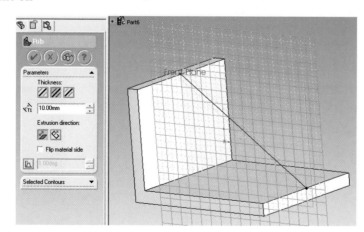

Fig. 15.52c The rib is created to straddle the plane.

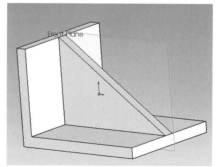

Fig. 15.52d The completed rib feature.

Linear Pattern and Circular Pattern

These two commands are used in a similar way in 3-D modelling as they were in 2-D sketching. A solid feature such as a hole or slot is first selected and then copied to form a rectangular array or a circular array. When using a Linear Pattern command the direction, distances and the number of rows and columns must be specified. The Circular Pattern command requires an axis, an angular distance and the number of repetitions to be specified. Figures 15.53a to 15.53c show an example of a linear pattern being created and Figures 15.54a to 15.54c show an example of a circular pattern being created.

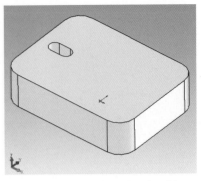

Fig. 15.53a A modelled block with a slot that needs to be copied in a linear pattern.

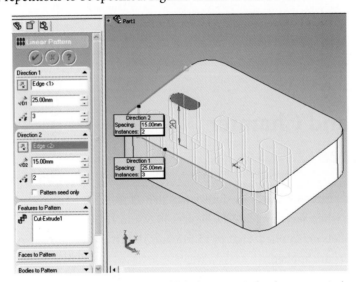

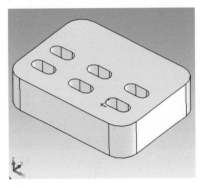

Fig. 15.53c The linear pattern of features is produced.

Fig. 15.53b The directions in which the rows and columns are to be placed are selected. The number of copies of the feature in each direction must also be specified. Finally, the spacing between the features must be entered.

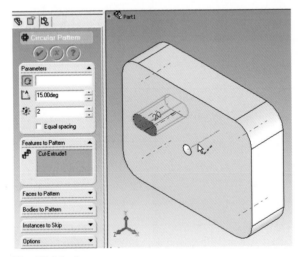

Fig. 15.54a A circular pattern of a feature must be rotated about an axis or edge. In this diagram the slot is to be copied about the axis of the central hole.

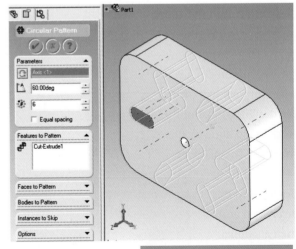

Fig. 15.54b The number of copies and the degree of rotation between each is specified.

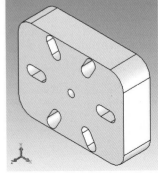

Fig. 15.54c The feature has been copied in a circular pattern.

Mirror Feature

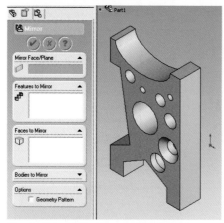

Fig. 15.55a Half of a symmetrical model is drawn, ready to be mirrored.

The mirror feature is very useful when producing models that have symmetrical features. A selection is made, a mirror plane is specified and the feature is mirrored through the plane, Figures 15.55a to 15.55c. The new feature is a child of the parent feature. Any changes to the parent feature will be reflected in the mirrored feature upon redraw. The mirror feature can reduce the time required to model, change or add features to symmetrical parts.

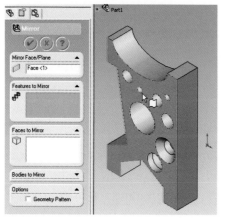

Fig. 15.55b The mirror face/plane is selected. The features to be mirrored are then selected.

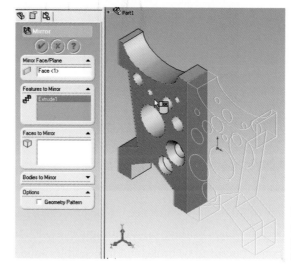

Fig. 15.55c The mirrored feature is previewed before selection.

Face Draft

Face draft is used to create a taper/slope to a model face. A neutral plane is first specified and then the draft angle and face to be drafted is selected. Figures 15.56a to 15.56d show this process in stages. SolidWorks can also draft a solid while extruding it as shown in Figures 15.56e and 15.56f.

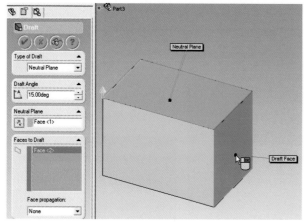

Fig. 15.56a The face draft feature is used to slope a model face. The end face is to be sloped outwards at 15° to its original position.

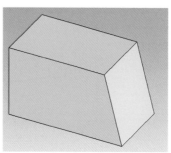

Fig. 15.56b The resulting face draft.

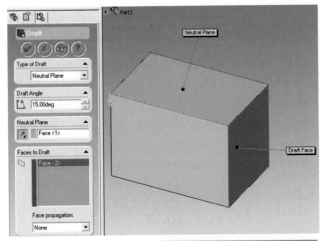

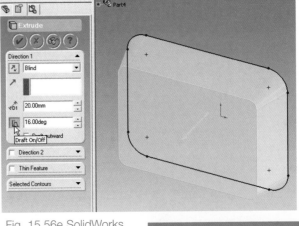

Fig. 15.56c The same block as in Fig. 15.56a, but this time the draft is to go inwards at 15°.

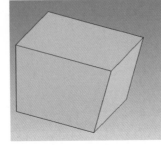

Fig. 15.56d The resulting face draft.

Fig. 15.56e SolidWorks can produce a draft while extruding a sketch. A draft angle of 16° has been used in this example.

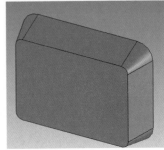

Fig. 15.56f The completed, extruded drafted solid.

3-D Models

There are a huge variety of 3-D shapes which need to be modelled. Each has its own individual shape, which will present a unique task to the person who is working on the computer model. In general terms, however, what needs to be done is that the complex 3-D object needs to be broken up into simpler solid features. These simpler features are easier to construct and represent on the computer and are combined to produce the whole.

The first sketched solid feature constructed is the base solid feature. When subsequent sketched solid features are constructed they must be combined with the base feature and/or each other. The features are combined using one of two methods:
• Join, • Cut.

Join

Join, joins two solids together making a single component. If the solids are intersecting, the computer calculates the line of intersection. Figures 15.57a to 15.57d show a joined solid being constructed. The first example is constructed

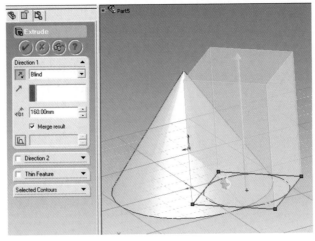

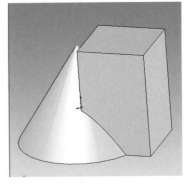

Fig. 15.57b The two solids are joined to form one solid.

Fig. 15.57a The cone and the square-based prism will be joined together. The software calculates the join line.

using the Extrude command and the second example is constructed using the Revolve command.

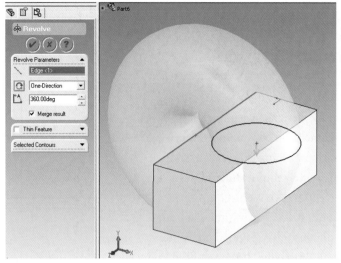

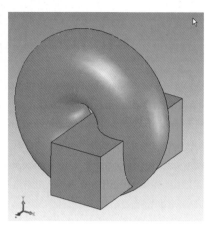

Fig. 15.57d The joined solids.

Fig. 15.57c The square prism and the torus are to be joined using the Revolve command. Again, the two solids become one solid.

Cut

Used to construct a combined solid which has the volume of one solid cut from another. Essentially the shape of one solid is being subtracted from another. SolidWorks has two commands for this purpose, Cut Extrude and Cut Revolve. Figures 15.58a to 15.58d shows examples of these two commands.

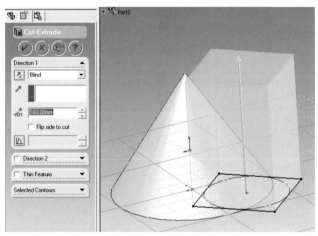

Fig. 15.58a Using the same two solids as in Fig. 15.57a, this time the Cut Extrude command is used.

Fig. 15.58b The square-based prism cuts through the cone.

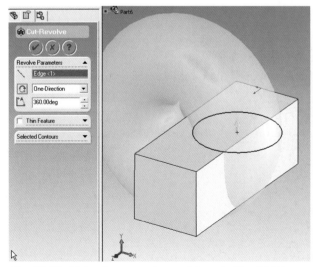

Fig. 15.58c Using the same two solids as in Fig. 15.57c, this time the Cut Revolve feature is used.

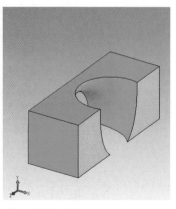

Fig. 15.58d The torus cuts a piece out of the prism.

Parametric Dimensions: Putting Sizes on Your Designs

Most modern day 3-D modelling software uses a system called parametric dimensioning to put size on the designs. A parametric dimension differs from a conventional dimension because it not only reports the size of the object that it describes, it can also be used to drive the size of that object. This concept is extremely important and deserves a little more attention. When using conventional drawing equipment, drawing board and T-square, we constantly strive to draw lines, arcs and curves as accurately as possible. When dimensions are added, the value of the dimension should reflect the length of the line. If the required line is to be 100 mm in length and it is originally drawn 95 mm long, then the line should be lengthened carefully by 5 mm. The dimension can then be placed and will truly reflect the line length. When parametric

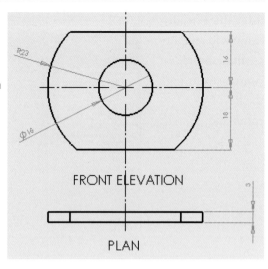

Fig. 15.59 The plan and elevation of a simple machine part which needs to be modelled in 3-D on the computer.

dimensioning is available the approach can be different. First the line is sketched. The term 'sketched' is used because it implies that you do not need to be one hundred per cent accurate, which is true. A parametric dimension is placed on the line which will show the line's length automatically. As the line was sketched it will probably be too long or too short.

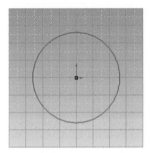

Fig. 15.60a Step 1. A circle of unspecified size is constructed. A parametric dimension will be added later which will drive the circle to the correct size.

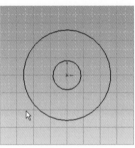

Fig. 15.60b Step 2. A second, smaller circle is added using the same centre point.

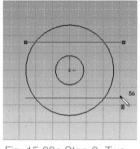

Fig. 15.60c Step 3. Two horizontal lines are added, one on each side of the small circle.

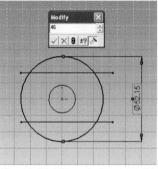

Fig. 15.60d Step 4. A parametric dimension is placed on the large circle. Its actual diameter is 52.15 mm. By editing this figure in the edit dimension dialog box to the required size of 46 mm, the dimension drives the circle to that size.

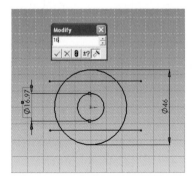

Fig. 15.60e Step 5. A parametric dimension is placed on the small circle. Its actual size is edited to 16 mm which drives the circle to the correct size.

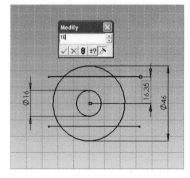

Fig. 15.60f Step 6. The upper line is driven to 16 mm above the circle centre.

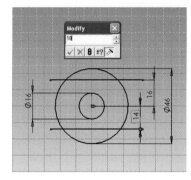

Fig. 15.60g Step 7. The lower line is driven to 18 mm below the circle centre.

By typing the required value of 100 mm into the dimension, the dimension drives the geometry. The line lengthens until it is exactly 100 mm long. Parametric dimensions are placed on 2-D sketch geometry so that the geometry can be shaped and driven with these dimensions. The value of these dimensions can be edited and the software will update the geometry. Figures 15.60a to 15.60i demonstrate how the use of parametric dimensions can speed up the drawing process and drive the sketch to exact requirements, Fig. 15.59 shows the machine part which we need to model.

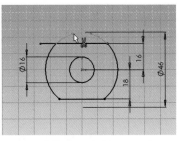

Fig. 15.60h Step 8. Unwanted parts of the drawing are trimmed away. The sketch is finished and has been altered by the parametric dimensions to the correct size.

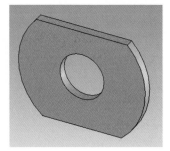

Fig. 15.60i Step 9. The sketch is extruded to a thickness of 3 mm to complete the 3-D model.

Creating 3-D Assemblies

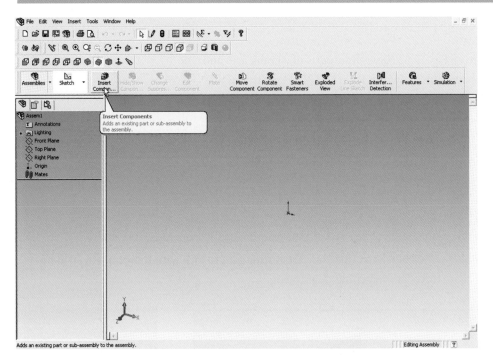

Fig. 15.61 The assembly window ready for the placing of 3-D components.

An assembly is a collection of component parts, put together properly, to form a more complex device. To construct an assembly using the computer an assembly file is needed. The individual parts are first modelled and then the assembly file is used to link these modelled component parts together. Furthermore, the assembly file keeps the information regarding how the component parts are put together. For complex devices that have many component parts, it is common practice to organise the component parts into a number of smaller subassemblies such that each subassembly has fewer parts.

When you design parts for an assembly, the relative sizes and position of holes, of slots, of screw holes etc. will have an impact of how the assembly fits together. You will need to determine if there is any interference between mating parts and if there is, the design will need to be altered to remedy the problem. To shorten the design lead time, you construct virtual assemblies in the computer to validate the integrity of a set of component parts.

In an assembly file, the components making up the assembly are placed into the assembly area, Fig. 15.61, using parts constructed earlier. Alternatively, parts can be constructed from within the assembly file. Using either approach, or a combination of both approaches, the parts are placed/constructed and are ready to be assembled together. In the beginning the parts are free to translate in three linear directions and three rotational directions. They are moved and rotated into

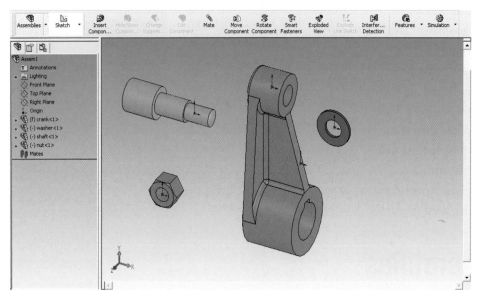

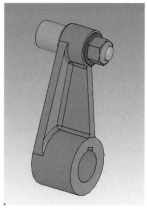

Fig. 15.63 The assembled parts after being manipulated into position and constrained

Fig. 15.62 The four pre-modelled parts of the assembly, the crank arm, shaft, nut and washer are placed into the assembly window.

position just like manipulating real objects. Fig. 15.62 shows four parts of a crank arm and are moved and constrained to form the assembly shown in Fig. 15.63. The constraints are set to ensure that faces are flush with each other, that axes line up together etc.

Fig. 15.64 These standard mate types are the main tools used to assemble parts.

The drop-down menu shown in Fig. 15.64 shows the standard mate types available in an assembly drawing. Usually a number of mate types must be set to achieve the required result.

Example 1, Figures 15.65a to 15.65g

In this example it is required to assemble the two blocks so that they are resting face to face with their top edges in line with each other and the midpoints of these top edges matching, Fig. 15.65g.

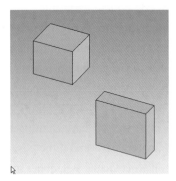

Fig. 15.65a The two objects are placed into the assembly window.

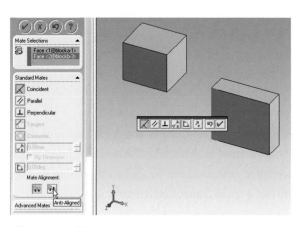

Fig. 15.65b The two faces that are to make contact with each other are selected.

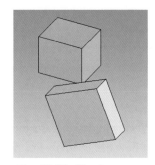

Fig. 15.65c The two faces make contact, but not yet as we want them.

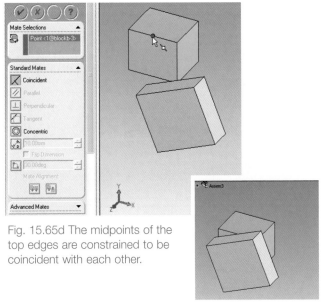

Fig. 15.65d The midpoints of the top edges are constrained to be coincident with each other.

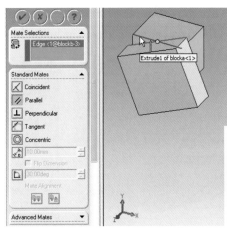

Fig. 15.65f The top edges are selected and constrained to be parallel with each other.

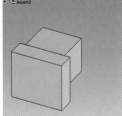

Fig. 15.65g The blocks move into their final positions.

Fig. 15.65e The blocks move into place but are still not aligned to our liking.

Example 2, Figures 15.66a to 15.66d

In this example it is required that a cylinder is constrained to rest on the surface of a block such that the curved surface is tangential to the block's top surface. Furthermore, the side of the block and the circular top of the cylinder are to lie flush.

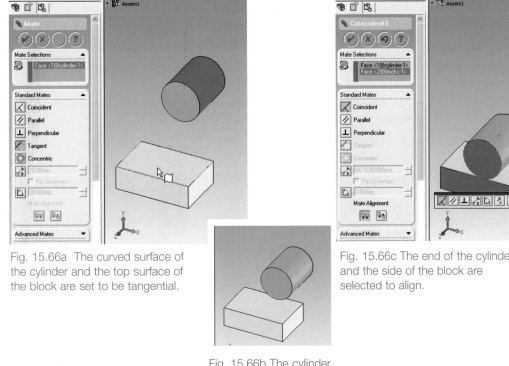

Fig. 15.66a The curved surface of the cylinder and the top surface of the block are set to be tangential.

Fig. 15.66b The cylinder moves into position.

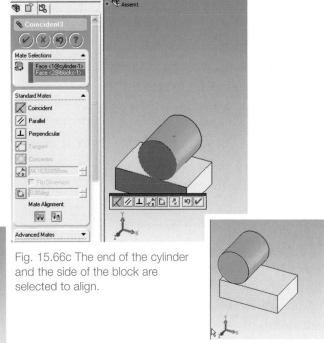

Fig. 15.66c The end of the cylinder and the side of the block are selected to align.

Fig. 15.66d The cylinder is constrained but can still move along the top of the block.

Example 3, Figures 15.67a to 15.67c

It is required to insert the rivet completely into the hole.

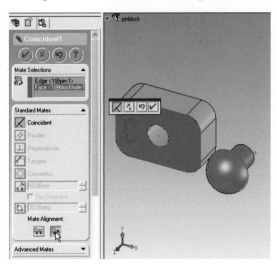

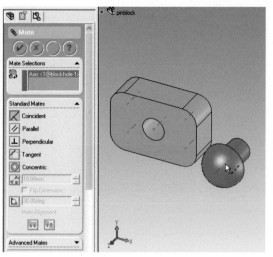

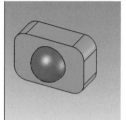

Fig. 15.67a The top surface of the block and the circular bottom of the rivet head are selected to align.

Fig. 15.67b The hole's central axis and the rivet's central axis are set to be coincident.

Fig. 15.67c The rivet is constrained into position.

Generating Multi-view Drawings from 3-D Models

Once you have constructed, within the computer, a 3-D solid or an assembly of 3-D solids, it is very simple to construct an engineering drawing of that part, or of that assembly.

The first step is to open a new drawing file. This opens a default sheet which is blank except for a margin and a title block. If you find the sheet layout appropriate you can start placing engineering drawing views on the sheet straight away. The sheet layout, i.e. margin and title block, can of course be altered if you wish.

The first drawing, the base view, is placed by selecting the 3-D part file or the 3-D assembly file and deciding from which direction this model should be viewed. Fig. 15.68 shows the crank and pin assembly being placed into the sheet. The drawing can be presented as a line drawing with hidden detail shown, as a solid object with no hidden detail or as a fully textured, full-colour drawing as shown in Fig. 15.68.

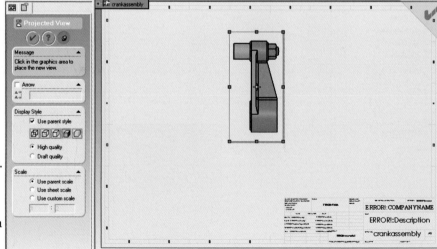

Fig. 15.68 The base view of the crank and pin assembly is placed into the assembly drawing. The assembly has been viewed from the front in high quality textured format.

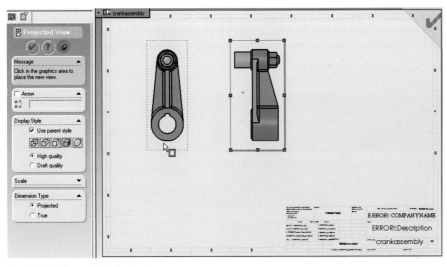

An end view is easily produced by using projected view. The computer will derive the view from a view already constructed. By selecting the base view and moving the cursor to the left of this front elevation, the computer will generate an end view. If the cursor was moved below the base view, a plan would be generated. Fig. 15.69 shows an end view of the crank and pin being constructed.

Fig. 15.69 A projected view is constructed to the left of the original view. The computer calculates the appearance of this end elevation.

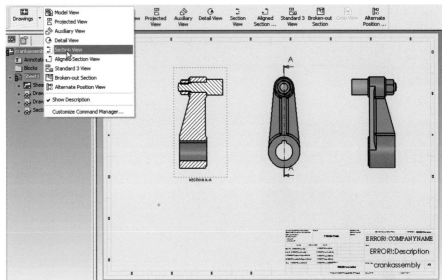

A sectional view is constructed by selecting the section plane and the direction of projection. Once the exact location for the section view is selected, the computer calculates the details and hatches the cut parts. Fig. 15.70 shows a sectional view being constructed. In order to have space for this view the two previous views were moved to the right. These two drawings are linked and therefore remain in line.

Fig. 15.70 A sectional view (A–A) is now constructed through the central axis of the assembly. It is hatched automatically.

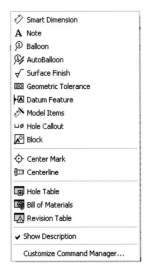

Fig. 15.71 The drawing annotation drop-down menu.

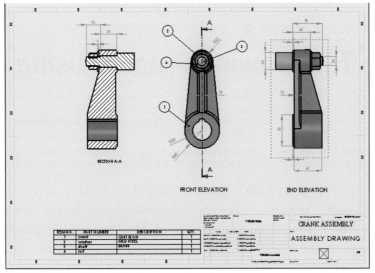

Fig. 15.72 The drawing has been dimensioned, the parts balloon referenced and a parts list added.

Once the drawing views have been produced, they need to be dimensioned, balloon referenced, text needs to be inserted etc. The drawing annotation menu, Fig. 15.71, makes this a simple operation. Fig. 15.72 shows the finished engineering drawing.

Producing Presentation Drawings and Animations

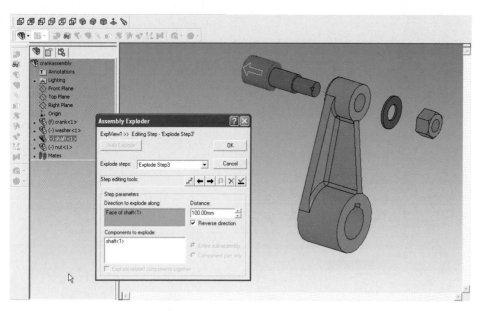

To illustrate how component parts of an assembly fit together, it is useful to have an exploded isometric view or views of the assembly and/or subassemblies. This is called a presentation drawing. To construct presentation views a new presentation file must be opened. The assembly to be exploded is selected and the parts are tweaked apart manually or automatically. Fig. 15.73 shows an exploded isometric of our crank and pin assembly. The direction in which each part is to be moved is specified and also the distance of travel. Trail lines can be added to help explain the lines of assembly.

Fig. 15.73 Presentation view. An exploded view of the crank and pin assembly.

Fig. 15.74 By adding a trail line the path of assembly is often made clearer.

Speeding Up The Drawing Process Using Templates and Libraries

Templates

It is important when producing working drawings for parts or assembly drawings to have a neat, clear and well-laid-out title block giving details of the parts, the materials, drawing number, date, scale etc. The format of this title block will be the same from sheet to sheet even though the information inserted into it may vary. By spending time to produce a sheet which is laid out exactly to your liking, with a margin and title block, and saving this sheet as a **template**, a lot of time can be saved. The template sheet can be called up again and again as a starting point for any new drawing.

Many CAD software packages will come with ready prepared sheet and title block templates. These can be used as they are, can be altered and used or a drawing template can be produced from scratch. Whatever method is used the use of a drawing template can be very helpful for commonly drawn elements. Fig. 15.75 shows a sheet title block being saved as a template.

SolidWorks has another useful template for producing a standard, front elevation; end elevation and plan of any 3-D modelled part; or of any assembly of 3-D modelled parts. The part or assembly is simply selected and the standard three views are produced. Fig. 15.76 shows an example of this type of drawing template being used.

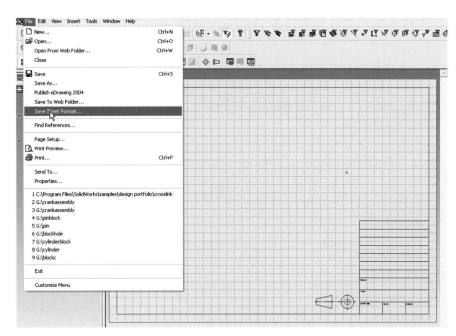

Fig. 15.75 A custom-made sheet layout is being saved as a template for future reuse.

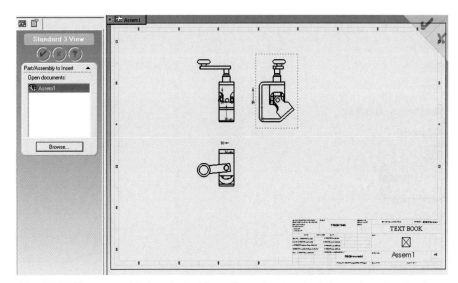

Fig. 15.76 The assembly is selected from file and a standard three-view drawing is produced automatically.

Libraries

There are many 3-D model parts which are used again and again in designs. Nuts and bolts, set screws, washers, springs etc. Each of these parts need only be drawn once and then saved in a parts library. These parts can be 'borrowed' from the library and copied into new drawings, thus saving time. It is most useful to build up your library of standard parts.

Exchanging Data between Applications

Parts, assemblies and drawings created using one type of modelling software can often be used in another, different type of modelling software. The trick is to save the part in the correct format. SolidWorks supports many file formats for the importing of files from other software and for the exporting of files to other software. Table 15.2 shows a table of the accepted file formats.

Application	Parts		Assemblies		Drawings	
	Import	Export	Import	Export	Import	Export
ACIS	X	X	X	X		
Autodesk Inventor	X					
CADKEY	X		X			
CATIA Graphics	X	X	X	X		
DXF/DWG	X				X	X
DXF 3-D	X		X			
eDrawings		X		X		X
Highly Compressed Graphics		X		X		
HOOPS		X		X		
IGES	X	X	X	X		
JPEG		X		X		X
Mechanical Desktop	X		X			
Parasolid	X	X	X	X		
PDF		X		X		X
Pro/Engineer	X	X	X	X		
Solid Edge	X		X			
STEP	X	X	X	X		
STL	X	X	X	X		
TIFF	X	X	X	X		X
Unigraphics	X		X			
VDAFS	X	X				
Viewpoint		X		X		
VRML	X	X	X	X		
ZGL		X		X		

Note: X = this option is available. A blank box = this option is not available.

Table 15.2

A brief descriptions of some of these file formats is given below:

ACIS	This file type has an SAT extension and is AutoCad's native solid format.
IGES	Initial Graphics Exchange Specification (IGES) is an American standard established by the American National Standards Institute. It is a format that only translates wire-frame lines and surfaces and therefore all volume data is lost.
DXF	AutoCAD Data eXchange Format file type.
DWG	AutoCAD drawing file type.
STEP	STandard for the Exchange of Product model data. This is a data-exchange standard that was developed by the International Organisation for Standardisation. It is used for translating lines, surfaces and solids. It has overcome many of the limitations of previous data conversion standards.
STL	STereo Lithography is a standard file format for use in most rapid prototyping machines. The entire model is reduced into multiple, flat, facets that approximate its shape.
ZGL	This is a compressed XGL format. This format captures all the 3-D information that can be rendered by the OpenGL rendering library.

Opening Files from Another Application

Re-using existing solid parts from other computer applications can speed up your design work tremendously. SolidWorks supports the file formats shown in Table 15.2. Once the file is imported it becomes a base solid. You can construct additional sketched features, work features and placed features as if you are working on an original SolidWorks file.

Activities

In the case of each of the following, sketch the 2-D profiles and insert the dimensions.

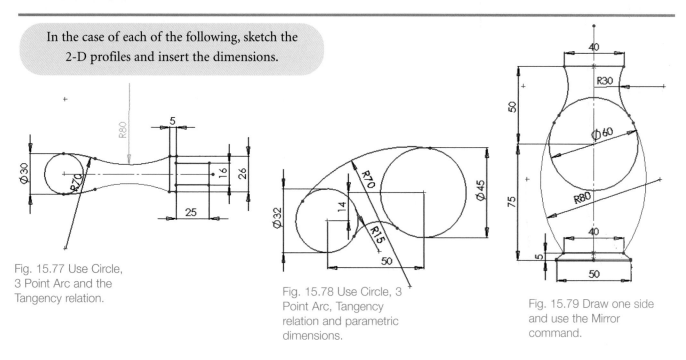

Fig. 15.77 Use Circle, 3 Point Arc and the Tangency relation.

Fig. 15.78 Use Circle, 3 Point Arc, Tangency relation and parametric dimensions.

Fig. 15.79 Draw one side and use the Mirror command.

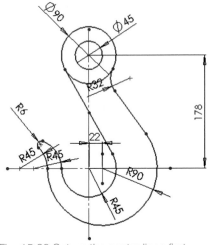

Fig. 15.80 Set up the centre lines first. Use the 3 Point Arc, Circle, Line and Trim commands.

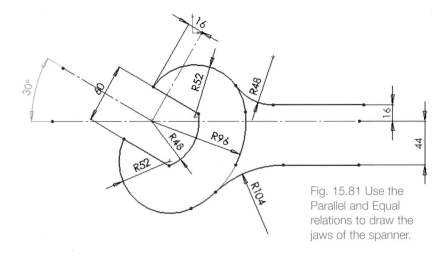

Fig. 15.81 Use the Parallel and Equal relations to draw the jaws of the spanner.

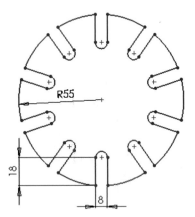

Fig. 15.82 Use the Circular pattern to copy the slot feature around the disc.

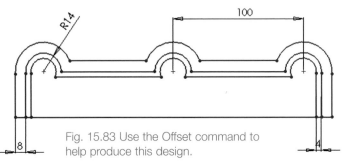

Fig. 15.83 Use the Offset command to help produce this design.

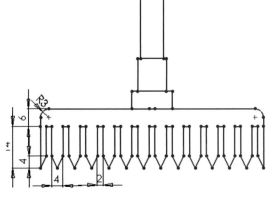

Fig. 15.84 Use the Rectangular Pattern command to copy the rake teeth.

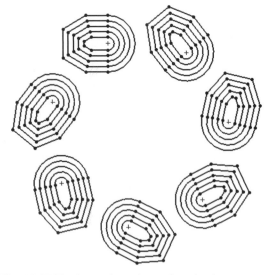

Fig. 15.85 The base shape is produced using a rectangle, semicircle and hexagon. Offset the design and use Circular pattern to copy the shape.

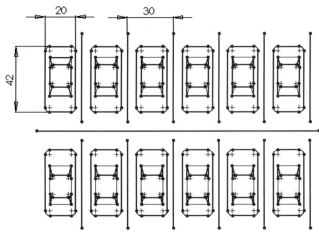

Fig. 15.86 Draw one car and use Rectangular pattern and Mirror to produce the copies.

EXTRUDE FEATURE

Construct Figures 15.87 to 15.92 using the
Extrude command to construct the base shapes.

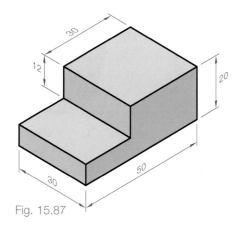

Fig. 15.87

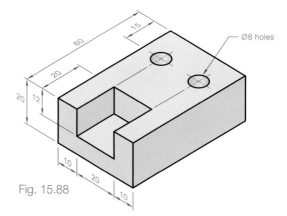

Fig. 15.88

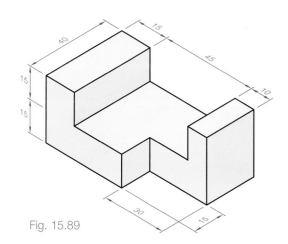

Fig. 15.89

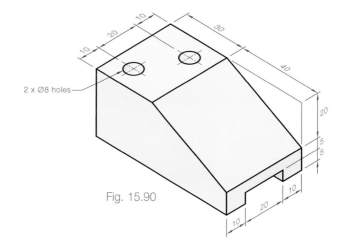

Fig. 15.90

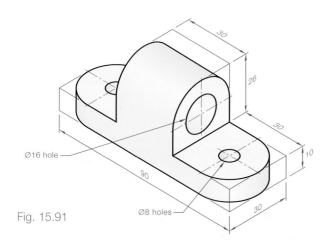

Fig. 15.91

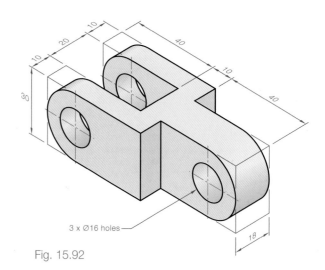

Fig. 15.92

REVOLVED FEATURE

Using the Revolved feature to construct the base shape, model the objects shown from Figures 15.93 to 15.104. Try to match the colours and material appearance used in the diagrams.

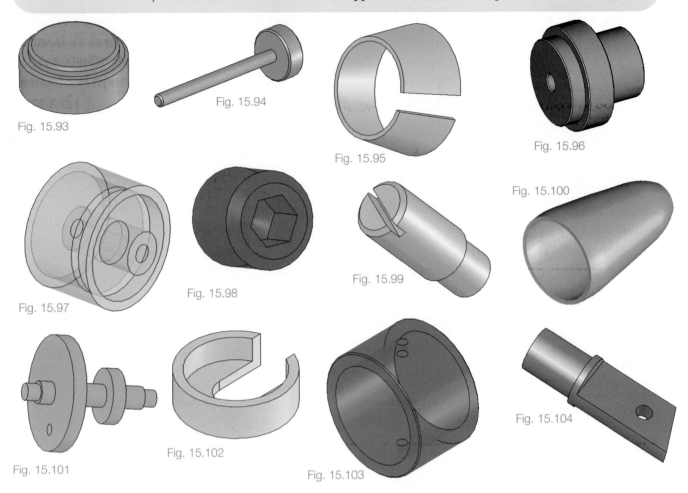

Fig. 15.93

Fig. 15.94

Fig. 15.95

Fig. 15.96

Fig. 15.97

Fig. 15.98

Fig. 15.99

Fig. 15.100

Fig. 15.101

Fig. 15.102

Fig. 15.103

Fig. 15.104

LOFT FEATURE

Fig. 15.105 Model this 3-D shape using a Loft feature between a square and an octagon.

Fig. 15.106 Model this hyperboloid of revolution using the Loft feature. Hollow the centre using the Shell feature.

Fig. 15.107 Model the transition piece shown between a rectangle and a circle. The two ends are extruded.

Fig. 15.108 Model the transition piece between a filleted square on one plane and a filleted rectangle on a perpendicular plane.

Fig. 15.109 Use the Shell command to hollow the centre of this transition piece between a circle and a square on perpendicular planes.

Fig. 15.110 This lofted feature is between a square on the Front Plane, an ellipse on Plane 1 and a rectangle on Plane 2. Produce a similar model.

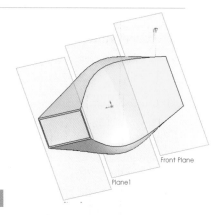

SWEPT FEATURE

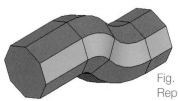

Fig. 15.111 Reproduce the 3-D object shown by sweeping an octagon along the curved path.

Fig. 15.112 Reproduce the pipe shown by using sweep and shell.

Fig. 15.113 Reproduce the handle shown by using a swept ellipse.

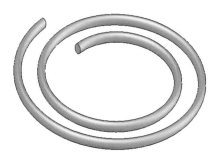

Fig. 15.114 Use Sweep and Shell to produce a piece of tubing shown.

Fig. 15.115 Produce a similar model by using a swept circle, a Loft feature between a circle and square, and the Extrude feature.

COIL FEATURE

Fig. 15.116 Reproduce a similar model using the Coil feature and an ellipse.

Fig. 15.117 Use the Coil feature to model this spring. It has circular section and three revolutions.

Fig. 15.118 Reproduce a similar auger/cutter using the Coil feature and a rectangle.

Fig. 15.119 Model this spring which has a rectangular section and tapers along its length.

Fig. 15.120 A half-pipe section is used to model this coiled feature.

Fig. 15.121 Model this spring by joining a tapered, clockwise coil to a tapered anti-clockwise coil.

Model the objects shown in these diagrams using the features discussed in this chapter.

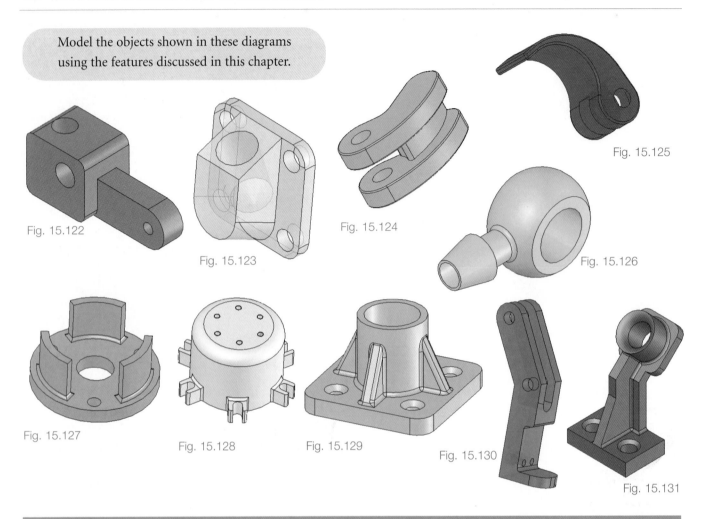

Fig. 15.122

Fig. 15.123

Fig. 15.124

Fig. 15.125

Fig. 15.126

Fig. 15.127

Fig. 15.128

Fig. 15.129

Fig. 15.130

Fig. 15.131

MODELLED PARTS USING PARAMETRIC DIMENSIONS

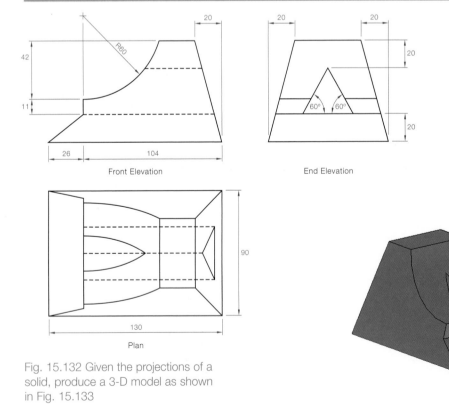

Front Elevation

End Elevation

Plan

Fig. 15.132 Given the projections of a solid, produce a 3-D model as shown in Fig. 15.133

Fig. 15.133

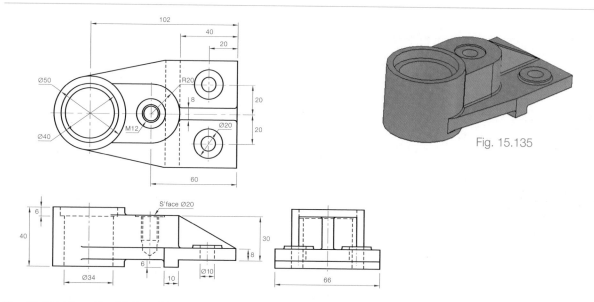

Fig. 15.135

Fig. 15.134 Given the third-angle projections of an axle support, produce a 3-D model as shown in Fig. 15.135.

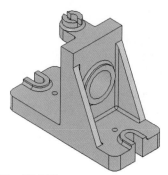

Fig. 15.137

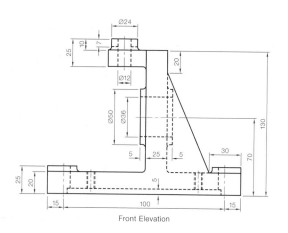

Front Elevation

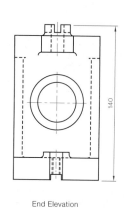

End Elevation

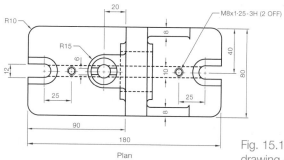

Plan

Fig. 15.136 Given the detailed drawing of a machine part. Produce a 3-D model as shown in Fig. 15.137.

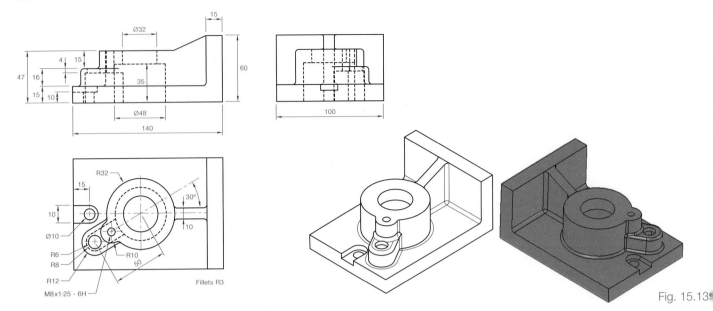

Fig. 15.138 Given the detailed drawing of a machine part.
Produce a 3-D rendered model as shown in Fig. 15.139.

DETAILED DRAWINGS, ASSEMBLY DRAWINGS AND PRESENTATION DRAWINGS

Produce a 3-D model of a bracket as shown in Fig. 15.141 to the dimensions shown in Fig. 15.140. Produce a fully dimensioned, detail drawing of this bracket.

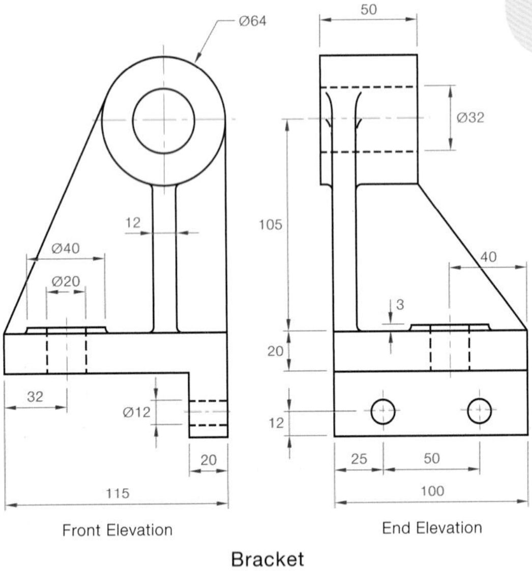

Front Elevation

End Elevation

Bracket

Fig. 15.140

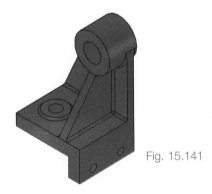

Fig. 15.141

Produce a 3-D model of the axle shown in Fig. 15.143 to the sizes shown in Fig. 15.142. From this model produce a detail drawing of the part.

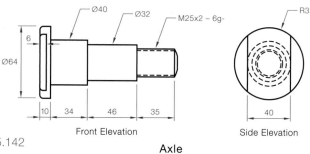

Fig. 15.142

Front Elevation

Side Elevation

Axle

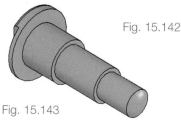

Fig. 15.143

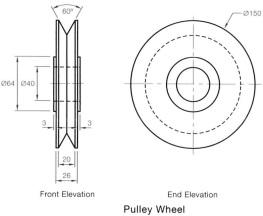

Front Elevation

End Elevation

Pulley Wheel

Fig. 15.144

The pulley wheel shown in Fig. 15.145 is to be modelled to the sizes given in Fig. 15.144. From the 3-D model produce a dimensioned detail drawing.

Fig. 15.145

Produce a 3-D model of the nut shown in Fig. 15.147 using the sizes from Fig. 15.146.

Fig. 15.147

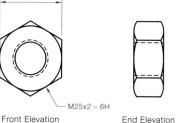

Front Elevation

End Elevation

Nut

Fig. 15.146

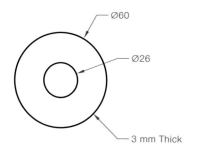

Fig. 15.148

Fig. 15.149

Produce a 3-D model of the washer (Fig. 15.149) to the sizes given in Fig. 15.148.

ASSEMBLY OF PARTS

Assemble the parts produced in Figures 15.141, 15.143, 15.145, 15.147 and 15.149. Produce an assembly drawing, Fig. 15.151, and an exploded isometric of the assembly, Fig. 15.152

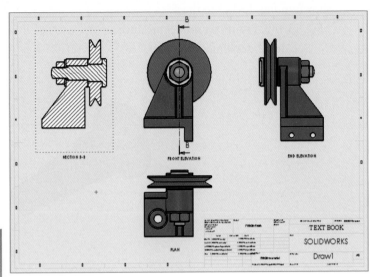

Fig. 15.151

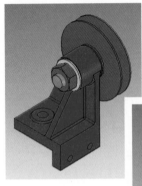

Fig. 15.150

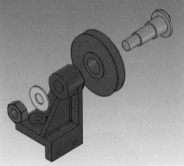

Fig. 15.152

16 Information and Communication Technology

SYLLABUS OUTLINE

Areas to be studied:

• File management and organisation. • File formats and extensions. • Image transfer. • *Image processing, transfer and manipulation.* • Web research. • Presentation techniques using ICT and CAD software.

Learning outcomes

Students should be able to:

Higher and Ordinary levels

• Create folders and save files to designated locations using recognised naming conventions.
• Use and understand the various file formats and images associated with CAD and related ICT software.
• Transfer images from CAD software to ICT packages as an aid to compiling a document, making a presentation (copy/paste) or producing a photo-realistic representation of a model (export/insert, render to file).
• Convert an image from one format to another.
• Use the Internet as a research tool.
• Download text and images from the Internet for analysis, editing and reproduction in a DTP package.
• Capture images using a range of media (e.g. digital cameras, scanners, screen capture, Internet, other).
• Make slides with a CAD package of key steps involved in creating a drawing.

Higher level only

• *Manipulate images to achieve special effects.*
• *Use slides or other animation techniques to illustrate graphic design solutions.*

Files and Folders

In order to function, a computer depends on a large number of **files**. These files are packages of information and instructions for the computer. Each document, drawing or 3-D model you design on the computer can be saved, and so a file is created.

In a traditional office, a great deal of the work is on paper and can be seen, stored and filed away. Each letter, bill, invoice etc., is kept in the appropriate folder in a filing cabinet. If maintained carefully this system means that these items can be found quickly and, after they are used, they are put back in the same place. A disorganised office may have a clutter of files and paperwork leaving it very difficult to find the particular thing you want.

The computer should be thought of as an electronic filing system. Similar files or files related to a particular project, should be grouped together and 'placed' into a folder. The computer will store the files and folders on the hard disk, a floppy disk, a CD, a DVD or some other storage medium.

A folder can contain folders (called subfolders) and each subfolder can contain more files and subfolders and so on. It is extremely important therefore to save your work in an organised manner so that it does not get mislaid within the system. The user can create *their* own set of folders to organise *their* work the way *they* like.

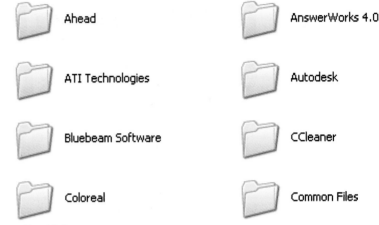

Fig. 16.1
Folder icons.
Icons are small drawings which help to identify the type of object.

Making a Folder

Desktop

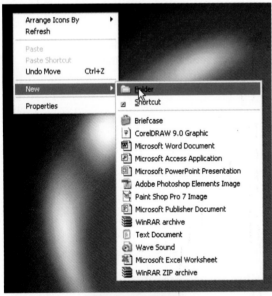

Fig. 16.2
Creating a
new folder on
the desktop

Fig. 16.3 The new
folder is created on
the desktop and is
waiting to be named.

Folders can be created on the desktop and moved at a later stage.

(1)   Right-click the mouse in a blank area of the desktop.

(2)   Click **New** on the menu that appears.

(3)   Click **Folder** on the new submenu.

(4)   A new folder appears on the desktop. The words 'New Folder' are blue and can be changed to any title that you wish. It is good practice to give the folder a name that relates to the files that you will store in this folder.

My Computer

You can use the **My Computer** icon to create a folder anywhere on the computer, for example on the hard drive C:

(1) Double-click on the My Computer icon to open its window.

(2) To make a folder on the C drive, double-click the icon. A new window opens to show the contents of the C drive.

(3) Right-click the mouse on a blank area of this new window to create a folder like we did on the desktop.

Fig. 16.4
Opening the 'My Computer' folder reveals its contents.

Fig. 16.5
Right-click the mouse on the blank area of the C: drive window and create a new folder on the drive.

My Documents

It is good practice to store your work in subfolders of the **My Documents** folder. Using this system your important files and work are easily backed up and are grouped together in one place. The My Documents folder can be opened as above and a new folder placed into it.

Saving Files

Fig. 16.6
'Save As' allows the naming of the file and the selection of the folder in which it is to be kept.

You have been working on a new 3-D model on the computer and you wish to file it away. The computer will have automatically given your work a name, e.g. Part1. **This name should be changed** and the file must be directed to the correct folder. The name chosen must have some relevance to the file to be saved. A name that describes the file would be useful, e.g. Rakehead or Pullyhousing. Once the name is changed the destination for the file is selected and the computer will place the renamed file into the selected folder. For the first saving of work the **Save As** command should be used.

When this file is used again, at a later stage, it must be retrieved from the folder. It is saved using the **Save** command. You do not need to input the name again nor the path to the folder, the computer remembers these from before.

File Formats

Fig. 16.7a shows seven file types generated by the Inventor CAD software.

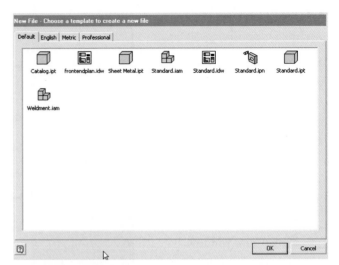

Fig. 16.7a Inventor file type groupings.

Catalog.ipt   This is used to form a part which is to be used as a resource in many future model constructions. A standard bolt would be an example of such a part.

Sheet Metal.ipt   For creating a part made from sheet metal.

Standard.iam   For producing an assembly of Inventor parts.

Standard.idw   A template for producing a detailed drawing of a part or an assembly drawing. A sheet showing a plan, elevation, section etc., can be produced with this file format.

Standard.ipn   For producing a presentation drawing of an assembly. An exploded isometric can be produced.

Standard.ipt   For producing an Inventor 3-D part.

Weldment.iam   For producing an assembly which is to be welded together.

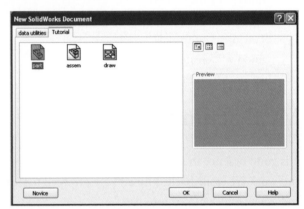

Fig. 16.7b SolidWorks file types.

Fig. 16.7b shows three types of drawing document used by the SolidWorks CAD software.

Part.sldprt   Used to produce a 3-D model of a single part.

Assembly.sldasm   Used to form an assembly of a number of SolidWorks parts.

Drawing.slddrw   Used to produce a detailed drawing of a part or an assembly drawing.

There are many types of CAD software available on the market and it is possible to interchange parts and drawings between these different packages. Each type of software supports a certain number of file formats. It will, of course, support files which have been generated by

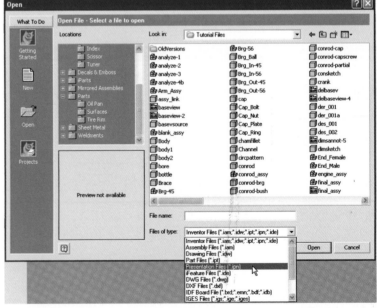

Fig. 16.8a File formats supported by Inventor for Importing files from other CAD packages.

itself but will also support several other file formats. If a drawing or a part file is generated by Software Package A and is saved to a format that is supported by a different software package, Software Package B, then the drawing or part file created in package A is useable in package B. The file format is shown by the three letters after the file name. To take in and use a file from another software package is called **importing** a file. To save a file for use in another package is called **exporting** a file. Figures 16.8a and 16.8b show file formats supported by Inventor for importing files and exporting files, while Figures 16.9a and 16.9b show file formats supported by SolidWorks for importing and exporting files.

Some common file formats explained:

IGES	**I**nitial **G**raphics **E**xchange **F**ormat. This is one of the more widely accepted file translation formats.
SAT	**S**ave **A**s **T**ext. This is AutoCAD's native solid format.
STEP	**ST**andard for the **E**xchange of **P**roduct model data. It is used for translating lines, surfaces and solids.
STL	An STL file is a list of triangular surfaces that depict the 3-D model.
XGL	**X** Windows **G**raphics **L**ibrary is a file format that captures all the 3-D information that can be rendered by the OpenGL rendering library.
ZGL	This is a compressed XGL format.
DXF	AutoCAD Data exchange format.
DWG	AutoCad drawing file format.

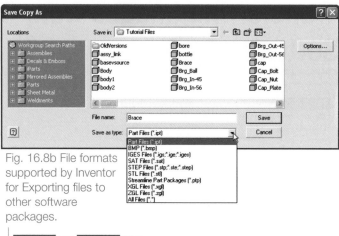

Fig. 16.8b File formats supported by Inventor for Exporting files to other software packages.

Fig. 16.9a File formats supported by SolidWorks for Importing and Exporting files from, and to, other software packages.

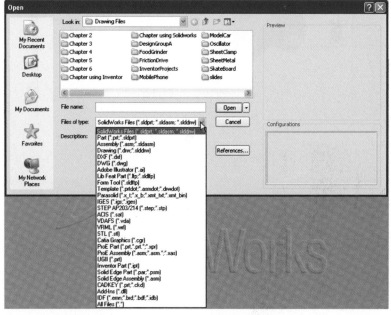

Fig. 16.9b File formats supported by SolidWorks for Importing drawing files from other CAD software packages.

Transferring Images from CAD software to Other Software Packages

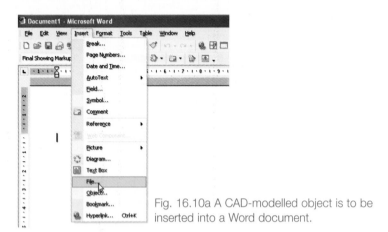

Fig. 16.10a A CAD-modelled object is to be inserted into a Word document.

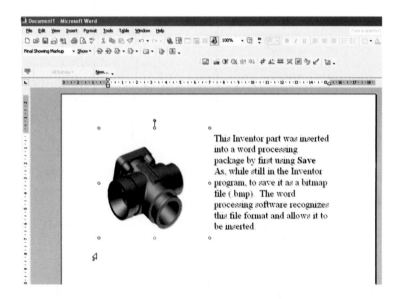

This Inventor part was inserted into a word processing package by first using **Save As**, while still in the Inventor program, to save it as a bitmap file (.bmp). The word processing software recognizes this file format and allows it to be inserted.

Fig. 16.10b The file format used to save the model must be recognised by the word processing software.

As has been said earlier, it is relatively easy to transfer an object/image from one CAD software package to another. They are designed like this to help the design process. They all use similar ways of generating and saving images, and by using the import and export features are able to interchange files.

To place an image into a word processing document or a desktop publishing document is not as easy because these types of software do not recognise as many of the file formats. The first step therefore is to identify the file formats that are supported by **both** types of software. The list will probably be short enough and may include the formats:

- .jpeg
- .pdf
- .tiff
- .bmp

The file is then **Saved As** to one of the compatible file formats when exiting the CAD software. The final step is to insert the file into the document and modify its size and position, Figures 16.10a and 16.10b.

Some CAD files can be inserted as an **object** into the word processing or desktop publishing documents. As an object the CAD image in the document is directly linked to the actual file. If the part file is subsequently modified using the CAD software, then the image in the document will automatically adapt. Figures 16.11a and 16.11b show a SolidWorks part being inserted as an object into a word processing document.

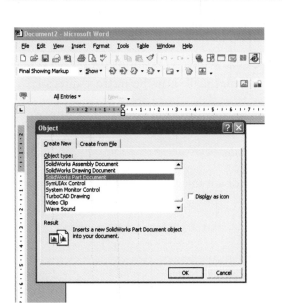

Fig. 16.11a Changing the CAD model into an object.

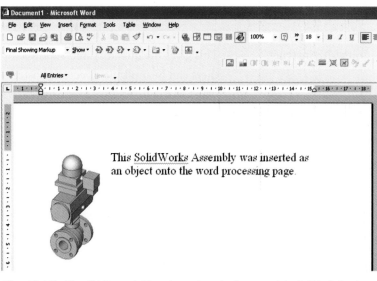

Fig. 16.11b The CAD model has been inserted as an object. It is linked back to the original file.

The Internet: A Brief Explanation

The Internet, in simple terms, is the world's largest computer network. A computer network is a system in which computers are connected so that they can share information. The Internet links thousands of computers and allows the sharing of huge amounts of files, articles and pictures etc. These links cover the whole world and can be accessed by almost anyone with the right equipment. The Internet is not new and has been around for many decades, but its growth and use has mushroomed in recent times.

- The Internet was created by the US military–industrial complex in the late 1960s as a way of enabling government researchers to share computer files.
- The Internet quickly became popular among academic institutions as a communication link.
- By the late 80s and early 90s the personal computer became popular and so did the Internet, and since then it has been growing rapidly by the day.

Using the Internet as a Resource

Using URLs as a Research Tool

First to explain the term URL. A URL is a web address on the Internet. Each page on the web has its own unique address which allows it to be located easily, this address is its URL. URL stands for Uniform Resource Locator.

A URL consists of certain distinct parts. For example, here's a URL:

http://www.poorrichard.com/newsltr/instruct/subsplain.htm

Each part of the URL has a specific meaning.

http://   This stands for Hypertext Transfer Protocol and tells the browser that the address is for a web page.

www.poorrichard.com	This is the host name, the name of the computer holding the web server that is administering the website you wish to visit.
/newsltr/instruct/	This gives the directory and subdirectory in which the web server is storing the file. Of course, there can be multiple directories listed. In this example the file is in the 'instruct' directory which is a subdirectory of the 'newsltr' directory.
subsplain.html	This is the name of the file that makes up the web page. The 'html' file extension stands for Hypertext Markup Language.

Using URLs is a very quick way of finding information from the Internet. The disadvantage of using URLs is that you must know the address from some other source in order to be able to input it.

Search Engines as a Research Tool

First to explain the term 'search engine'. A search engine is a program with which you search a database of web pages. With a search engine you type a keyword, and click a **Search** button or press **Enter**. The search engine then looks through the database for you. Internet sites or web pages that contain the search word are then displayed. There are many search engines available to the user. If you cannot find what you want using one search engine, it is often worthwhile to do a similar search using a different search engine, see examples in Figures 16.12a to 16.12e.

Google	http://www.google.com
Yahoo!	http://www.yahoo.com
Go.com	http://go.com
Lycos	http://www.lycos.com
AltaVista	http://www.altavista.com

How to use a search engine?
Each search engine is a little different and allows you to use different sorts of search terms. You can always search by entering a single word, but the more you know about each search engine, the more efficiently you can search. When you first go to a search engine, look around for some kind of link to a **Help** document, probably labelled **Tips** or **Hints**. Read this document; it will give suggestions and hints for using the search engine. Here are some general guidelines:

- Words between quotation marks will find words in the exact order in which they are typed.
- Proper names can be used but ensure that they are capitalised correctly.

Fig. 16.12a

Fig. 16.12b

Fig. 16.12c

Fig. 16.12d   Fig. 16.12e

- Words separated by hyphens: entering words in this way finds both words as long as they are close together, e.g. geodesic-dome.
- Words in brackets: entering words this way will find the search words but not necessarily in the order in which they have been entered, e.g. (involute gear profiles).

Downloading Text and Images for Use in a Desktop Publishing Package

There are several ways of saving material found on the Internet for use later. Pictures and images off the Internet can be particularly useful when compiling an article or a report.

Saving to File

Images can be copied from an Internet page and saved onto the computer hard drive or removable media as a file. This file can then be inserted into a word processing document or desktop publishing document. The image can then be manipulated within the document in the usual way.

Fig. 16.13a shows a web page on the Hyperbolic Paraboloid. The graphic is to be used as part of a word processing document. Right-click on the image and use the **Save Picture As**... command to save the image as a file, Fig. 16.13b.

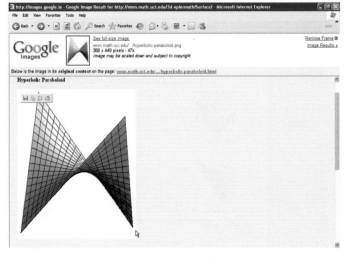

Fig. 16.13a A web page image of a Hyperbolic Paraboloid which we wish to use in a word processing document.

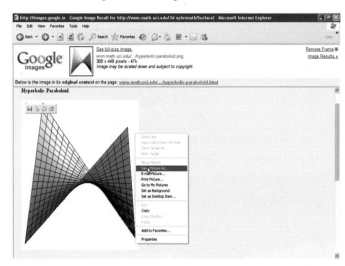

Fig. 16.13b Save the image as a file by Right-clicking on the picture and using the 'Save Picture As...' command.

This file can then be inserted into the word processing document using **Insert**, **Picture**, **From File**, series of commands, Fig. 16.13c.

To finish off, the image may now be manipulated and edited within the document, Fig. 16.13d.

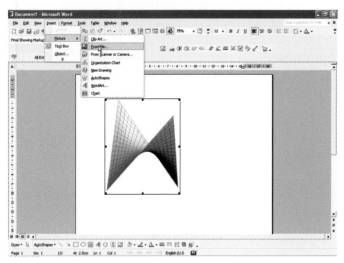

Fig. 16.13c Within the word processing document, the 'Insert', 'Picture', 'From File...' commands are used to insert the picture.

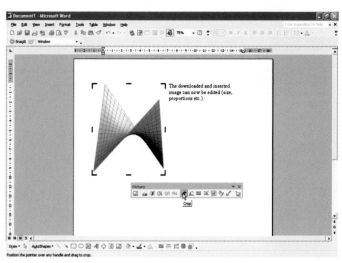

Fig. 16.13d The image can be edited within the document.

Saving to Clipboard

When a file is downloaded and saved on the computer it is available for use at any time in the future until the file is removed. A less permanent way of using material off the Internet is to use the **Copy** command. This will copy the image or text to a temporary holding area called the clipboard. It will remain on the clipboard for use while the computer is switched on but will be lost when the power is switched off (unless it is **Saved** beforehand). Using a word processing package or a desktop publishing package, material can be taken off the clipboard and **Pasted** into a document.

Fig. 16.14a shows a web page. The material from the page which is to be used is highlighted and the **Copy** command is used to save the text and image to the clipboard.

Fig. 16.14b shows a word processing document. The material from the clipboard can be **Pasted** onto this document. Both the graphics and the text can be manipulated and edited as normal once pasted in place.

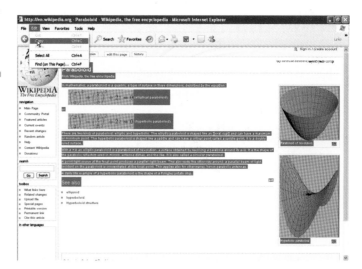

Fig. 16.14a The material to be used from the web page is highlighted and copied to the clipboard.

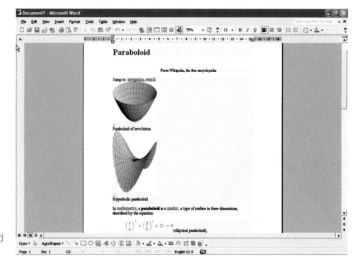

Fig. 16.14a The material from the web page can now be pasted from the clipboard into a word processing document.

Capturing Images from Other Sources

Digital Camera

There are many useful images on the Internet but it is not always possible to find the exact image you want. A digital camera can be used to capture your own images/pictures. The digital camera saves the photographic information as a file which can be used, as explained earlier, for insertion into word processing or desktop publishing documents.

Scanner

A diagram on a sheet of paper can be scanned into the computer, where it can be saved as a file, to be inserted into another application. The scanner reads the sheet of paper and converts the information on the page into a file. This file can be inserted into documents etc. as explained earlier.

Screen Capture

A particularly useful piece of software to have is screen capture software. There are many types available but what they all essentially do is take a snapshot of the display on the computer monitor, or a portion of the display. This software can be left running in the background while you search the Internet or model a 3-D object using a CAD package. Any useful image can then be quickly and easily captured and saved to file.

Making Slides with a CAD Package

A slide is a snapshot of a drawing. Although it contains a picture of the drawing at a given instant, it is not a drawing file. Slides have the following limitations:

- A slide file cannot be imported as part of a drawing file.
- A slide cannot be edited.
- A slide cannot be printed.

- A slide only displays what is visible on-screen. Off-screen portions of the drawing, or parts of a drawing that are frozen or turned off, will not be displayed.

In spite of these limitations, slides are a useful presentation method for two reasons. Firstly, the slides can be viewed in sequence to form a slide show. The slides are displayed with a short interval between each to form a sort of movie. Secondly because the slides are a snapshot of a drawing they are much smaller files and can therefore be loaded quickly.

The making of slides is not supported by all CAD software packages. AutoCAD allows the making of slides using the **Mslide** command. Drawings may be produced in AutoCAD and made into slides, or files can be imported in from other CAD software packages and then made into slides. Fig. 16.15 shows a slide being made using AutoCAD.

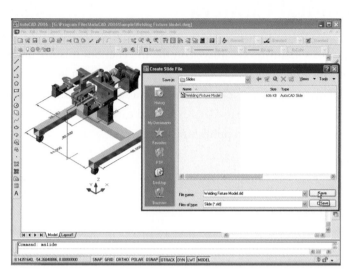

Fig. 16.15

Manipulating Images Using Animation Techniques

There are other interesting ways of presenting your design solutions, depending on which software you are using.

SolidWorks

SolidWorks has two special features for manipulating images:

- Animate an eDrawing.
- Physical Simulation.

The tool **Animate an eDrawing**, Fig. 16.16, begins a continuous animation of the on-screen model in shaded mode. The model may be a single part or an assembly of parts. The animation consists of the model being twisted and turned in space, giving the onlooker a view of all sides of the object.

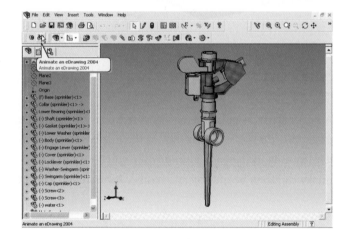

Fig. 16.16

Physical Simulation, Fig. 16.17, allows the user to simulate the effects of:

- linear motors,
- rotary motors,
- springs,
- gravity on an assembly.

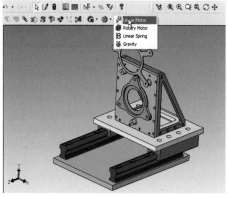

Fig. 16.17

Fig. 16.18 shows the Simulation drop-down menu. The simulation once calculated is recorded like a mini-movie and can be played back showing the parts moving as they are effected by the motor, spring or gravity, Fig. 1619.

Fig. 16.18 Simulation drop-down menu.

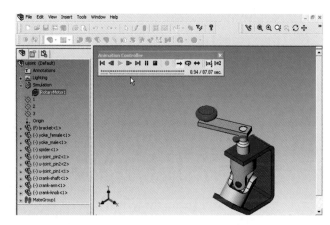

Fig. 16.19 The turning of the handle by a rotary motor being animated.

Inventor

Inventor also has a special animation feature. It is used to animate movement when making exploded isometrics of assembled models. You can develop, play and record these animations to show the order and path of tweaks in a complex assembly. This mini-movie show can be recorded to an external file and replayed later. Fig. 16.20 shows the animate button, and Fig. 16.21 shows an exploded isometric presentation being animated.

Fig. 16.20 The 'Animate...' button is in the Presentation Panel.

Fig. 16.21 An animated movie is playing here, showing the parts of this food grinder moving apart.

Activities

FILES AND FILE FORMAT

Q1. Explain the difference between a computer file and a computer folder.

Q2. Write a brief note comparing a computer filing system and an office filing system.

Q3. Create a new folder on the desktop called **My Folder**. Inside this folder create three subfolders:
(1)   Inventor drawings.
(2)   SolidWorks drawings.
(3)   Downloaded drawings.

Q4. Create a new folder on a blank floppy disk called **Removable Files**. Inside this folder create four subfolders:
(1) Parts.   (2) Assemblies.
(3) Drawings.   (4) Presentation.

Q5. Open an Inventor or SolidWorks part file. Using the **Save As** command rename the file and save it to the Parts subdirectory on the floppy disk.

Q6. Following the same procedure as above, rename an assembly drawing and save it in the A: drive Assembly subfolder.

Q7. Explain the terms:
• file format, • import, • export.

Q8. Explain the link between file formats, the Import command and the Export command.

INSERTING CAD IMAGES INTO WORD-PROCESSING DOCUMENTS

Q9. Produce a document describing how to produce an extruded circle using CAD software (i.e. how to produce a cylinder). The document should include at least one inserted graphic.

Q10. Produce a word processor document that briefly explains the difference between an extruded solid and a revolved solid. A minimum of two CAD images must be inserted into the document to help illustrate your explanation.

Q11. Produce a word processor document that explains the difference between:
• a CAD modelled solid, • a CAD assembly, • a CAD presentation drawing.
Insert an example of each to help illustrate your explanation.

INTERNET

Q12. Find the web homepage for three different search engines and insert these homepages into a word processing or desktop publishing package.

Q13. Find some images from the Internet on the following topics:
- hyperbolic paraboloid, • geodesic domes,
- hyperboloid of revolution,
- gear teeth profiles.

Save two images from each topic to floppy disk.

Q14. Produce a document giving a brief description of a geodesic dome and illustrate this document with images downloaded from the Internet.

Q15. Search for web pages on one-point perspective and two-point perspective. Copy and paste images and text from these web pages into a word processing or desktop publishing package.

DIGITAL CAMERA, SCANNER, SCREEN CAPTURE

Q16. Produce a list of equipment needed for *Design and Communication Graphics,* using a word processing package. This list must be illustrated with inserted digital camera images of each piece of equipment.

Q17. Produce a word processing or desktop publishing document to explain the following engineering terms:
- cam, • screw thread, • undercut, • spot face.

Illustrate each explanation with an image (or images) scanned from this textbook.

Q18. Using a screen capture software package, capture images of ten different CAD toolbar button icons. Insert these images into a word processing document and explain what each button does.

SLIDES

Q19. Make a slide presentation showing the stages involved in producing a cycloid.

Q20. Make a four-slide presentation of a 3-D modelled part.
Slide 1 – Front elevation of Part
Slide 2 – End elevation of Part
Slide 3 – Plan of Part
Slide 4 – Isometric view of Part

ANIMATION

Q21. Using the Inventor software, open a new presentation drawing. Use an existing assembly to create the base view. Tweak the components apart. Use the Animate command to animate the exploded view.

Q22. Open an existing part file or assembly file in the SolidWorks software package. Use the Animate an eDrawing command to animate the part or assembly.

Q23. Find and open the SolidWorks **ujoint** assembly file and use the rotary motor simulation to produce an animation of the crank arm being rotated.

Q24. Open the SolidWorks **toolbox-tutorial** assembly file and use the linear motor simulation to animate the top body sliding along the guide rails.

Q25. Open a new Inventor presentation file. Open the **Carb** assembly file as your initial view. tweak the components apart to produce an exploded isometric view. animate this process.

PART 3

APPLIED GRAPHICS

17 Dynamic Mechanisms

SYLLABUS OUTLINE
Areas to be studied (in an applied context):

- The common geometric loci: involutes, helices, conical spirals, Archimedean spirals, and *logarithmic spirals.*
- Construction of loci defined by the movement of circles relative to lines and circles. • *Construction of tangents at a point on an involute, Archimedean spiral, cycloid, epicycloid, hypocycloid and trochoid.* • Determination of loci from linkage mechanisms. • Construction of cam profiles and displacement diagrams depicting uniform velocity, simple harmonic motion, uniform acceleration and retardation for in-line knife-edge followers.
- *Construction of cam profiles and displacement diagrams depicting uniform velocity, simple harmonic motion, uniform acceleration and retardation for roller and flat in-line followers.*

Learning outcomes
Students should be able to:

Higher and Ordinary levels
- Construct the involute of a circle and regular polygons.
- Construct the helix and conical spiral from given data.
- Construct an Archimedean spiral.
- Use a trammel to solve problems on loci.
- Construct the locus of a point in a link mechanism.
- Construct radial plate cams of given uniform velocity, simple harmonic motion, uniform acceleration and retardation to in-line knife-edge followers.
- Construct cam profiles and displacement diagrams.
- Construct displacement diagrams for given cam profiles.
- Understand the applications for all the curves constructed.
- Construct standard cycloids.

Higher level only
- *Construct epicycloids, hypocycloids and trochoids.*
- *Construct a tangent at a point on an involute, Archimedean spiral, cycloid, epicycloids, hypocycloid and trochoid.*
- *Construct radial plate cams of given uniform velocity, simple harmonic motion, uniform acceleration and retardation to roller and flat in-line followers.*
- *Construct involute and epicycloidal gear profiles.*
- *Construct a logarithmic spiral.*

Dynamic Mechanisms 1

Involutes

Helices

Conical Spirals

Archimedian Spirals

Involute

If a piece of string is wound around a plane figure, being kept taut at all times, the path the end of the string follows is called an involute.

Involute to a square

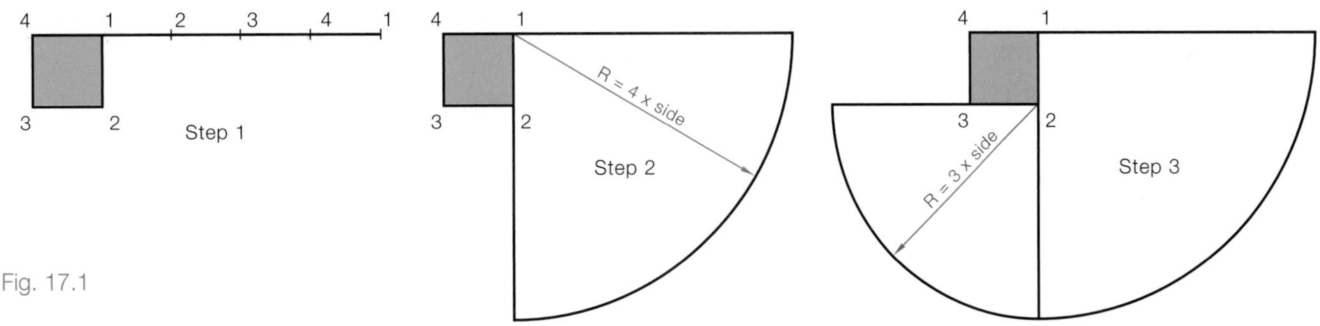

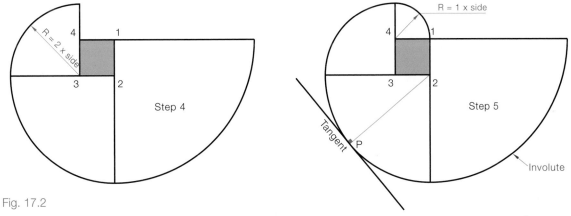

Fig. 17.1

Extend one side and make it equal to the perimeter of the square. With corner 1 as centre, rotate the string until it runs along edge 1,2. The string now bends at corner 2 and pivots. With 2 as centre and radius to the end of the string, rotate until the string is in line with edge 2,3. Continue to complete the involute.

Fig. 17.2

A tangent can be constructed from any point on the curve in the same way as a tangent to a circle. Draw the normal 2,P and construct the tangent perpendicular to it.

Involute to a polygon, e.g. hexagon

Extend one side of the polygon and make it equal to the perimeter in Fig. 17.3. The involute is constructed as before. It pivots on a corner until it reaches the next corner and then proceeds to pivot on it. The path followed therefore is made up of portions of circles. Tangents are constructed as before.

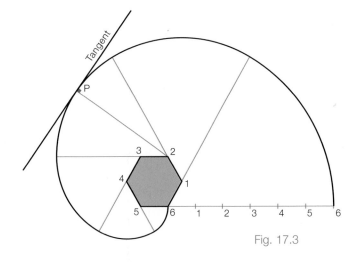

Fig. 17.3

Involute to a circle

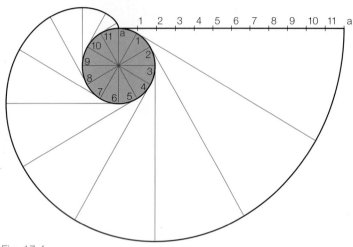

Fig. 17.4

An involute to a circle is different to the previous examples because at no stage does the string pivot about a fixed point.

(1) Divide the circle into twelve equal parts and construct a tangent at the end of each division.

(2) Choose one of these and step-off the circumference as shown in Fig. 17.4.

(3) As the string is wrapped it shortens. By the time the string is wrapped to position 4 on the circle it is only eight divisions long because the remaining four divisions are around the circle. By the time the string reaches 10 on the circle it is only two divisions long because the remaining ten divisions are around the circle.

(4) The curve must be drawn freehand.

Involute to an irregular shape

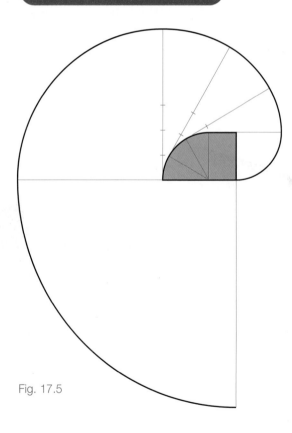

Fig. 17.5

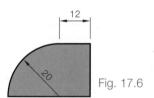

Fig. 17.6

Draw the involute of the following irregular shape.

(1) Most irregular shapes can be broken up and seen as shapes made up of pieces of regular shapes. This particular shape is broken up as a rectangle and a quarter of a circle.

(2) The construction can be seen in Fig. 17.6 and follows the approach used in the involute to a square and the involute to a circle.

The Helix

A helix is the path of a point which moves around a cylinder at a constant rate while moving in the direction of the axis at a constant rate.

To draw a helix of one revolution

Draw the plan and elevation of the cylinder. Divide the plan into 12 equal parts and project up to the elevation. Draw the development of the curved surface of the cylinder. **The development of a helix is a straight line.** The points on the development are projected back to the elevation as shown in Fig. 17.7. The helix can be left-handed or right-handed. Fig. 17.7 shows a left-handed helix.

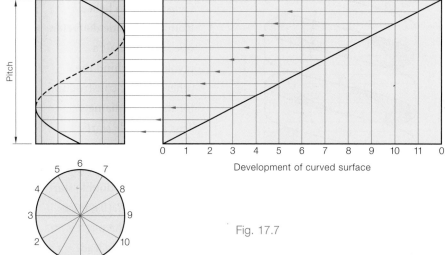

Development of curved surface

Fig. 17.7

To draw a right-handed helix of 1¹/₂ revolutions given the cylinder in Fig. 17.8.

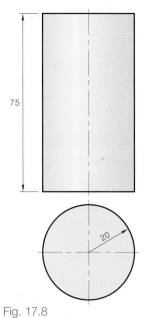

Fig. 17.8

An alternative method to using a development is to divide the height of the cylinder into the required number of equal parts. If the plan is divided into 12 parts then we must divide the cylinder height into 18 equal parts to achieve 1¹/₂ revolutions. The right-handed helix shown in Fig. 17.9 is plotted by projection as shown.

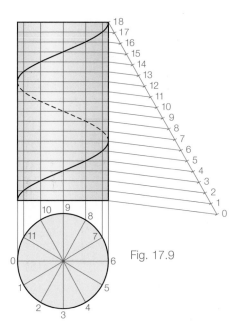

Fig. 17.9

Screw threads and springs

Most screw threads are helices, as are coil springs, worm gears and spiral staircases.

To draw a right-hand screw thread (square) given the inside diameter, the outside diameter and the lead.

The lead is the advancement of the thread after one revolution.

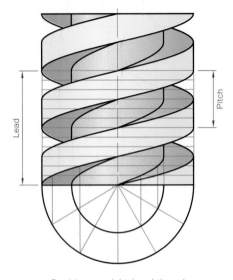

Construct two helices from the outside diameter, one running half a revolution behind the other. Similar construction for the small diameter. This is a single start thread. In a single start thread the pitch is equal to the lead. For a double start thread, Fig. 17.10a, it can be seen that the pitch is equal to half the lead.

Double start right-hand thread

Fig. 17.10a

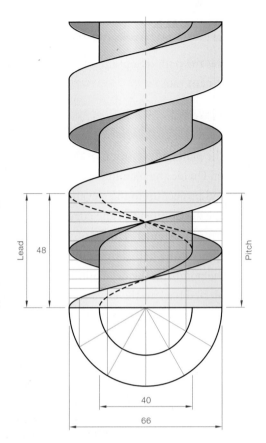

Single start right-hand thread

Fig. 17.10b

Given the plan and elevation of a cylinder with two points on its surface, A and B. Draw a helix starting from the base of the cylinder and finishing at the top of the cylinder and passing through A and B.

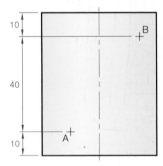

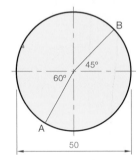

Fig. 17.11

(1) Draw the plan and elevation.
(2) Divide up the plan, draw the generators in elevation and draw the development.
(3) Find points A and B on the development. Point A is on generator 2 and point B is halfway between generators 7 and 8.
(4) Draw a straight line between A and B, on the development, and extend to hit the top and bottom of the development at points t and s. The development of a helix is a straight line.
(5) From the development, project the points on the elevation.
(6) Points s and t must first be found on the plan before being found in elevation.

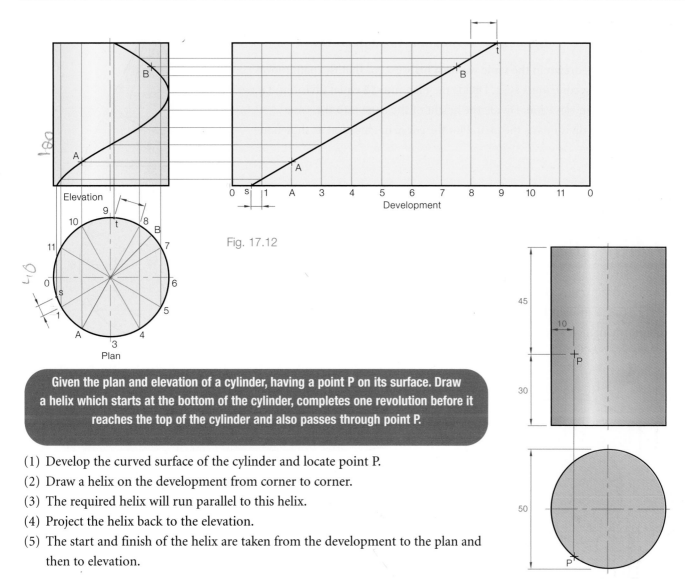

Fig. 17.12

Given the plan and elevation of a cylinder, having a point P on its surface. Draw a helix which starts at the bottom of the cylinder, completes one revolution before it reaches the top of the cylinder and also passes through point P.

(1) Develop the curved surface of the cylinder and locate point P.
(2) Draw a helix on the development from corner to corner.
(3) The required helix will run parallel to this helix.
(4) Project the helix back to the elevation.
(5) The start and finish of the helix are taken from the development to the plan and then to elevation.

Fig. 17.13

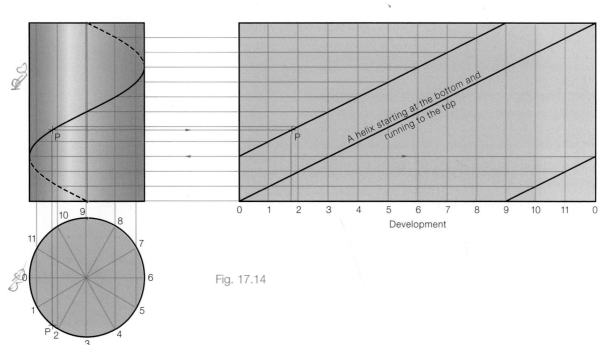

A helix starting at the bottom and running to the top

Fig. 17.14

Conical Spiral

A conical spiral is drawn in the same way as a helix except that the path moves from the base of a cone to its apex. Divide the plan into 12 equal divisions. Draw these generators in elevation. Divide the height of the cone into the same number of equal divisions as the plan. Plot the curve in elevation as shown in Fig. 17.15.

Project to plan.

The points in plan on generator 3 and 9 are found as shown in Fig. 17.15. The curve produced in plan is an **Archimedian Spiral**.

Archimedian Spiral

An Archimedian spiral is the locus of a point which is moving at a uniform velocity along a straight line which itself is rotating about a fixed point, the pole, at a uniform angular velocity.

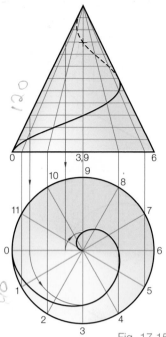

Fig. 17.15

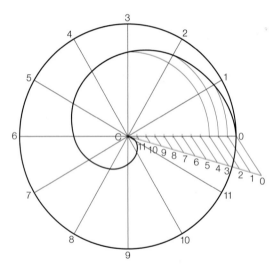

Fig. 17.16

To draw an Archimedian Spiral of one convolution given the longest radius vector as 50 mm and the shortest as 0 mm.

(1) Draw a circle having the radius equal to the longest radius vector. The spiral will start at a point on the circumference of this circle and after one convolution will reach the centre of the circle.

(2) Choose your starting point on the circumference, point 0. Divide the circle into twelve equal divisions from this point 0.

(3) Divide the radius C0 into twelve equal parts.

(4) Swing these points to cut the radials as shown in Fig. 17.16.

(5) Join these points with a freehand curve to form the spiral.

Draw an Archimedian spiral of 1³/₄ convolutions given the largest radius vector of 50 mm and the shortest of 15 mm.

(1) Draw two concentric circles, one of 50 mm radius, the other 15 mm radius.

(2) Divide the circles into 12 equal parts.

(3) The distance between the two circles is divided into 21 equal spaces. Twelve parts for a full convolution and nine for ³/₄ of a convolution.

(4) Plot the spiral as before.

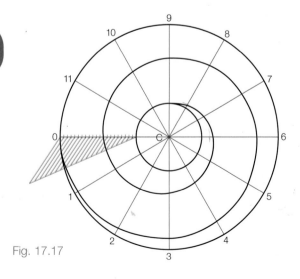

Fig. 17.17

Construct one convolution of an Archimedian Spiral given the shortest radius vector of 15 mm and an increase in vector length of 3 mm every 20°.

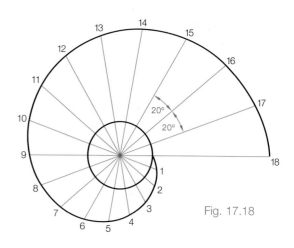

(1) Draw a 15 mm circle.

(2) Choose a starting point on the circumference.

(3) Divide the circle up into 20° sections from this point.

(4) For each radial measure the required distance outside the circumference of the 15 mm circle.

  9 mm for radial 3 (3 × 3 mm)

  24 mm for radial 8 (8 × 3 mm)

  45 mm for radial 15 (15 × 3 mm)

(5) Draw the curve to pass through these points.

Fig. 17.18

Cycloid

A cycloid is the path traced out by a point on the circumference of a circle as it rolls along a fixed straight line without slipping.

To draw a cycloid given the circle, the base line and the point on the circumference.

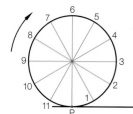

Fig. 17.19

(1) Draw the circle, the base line and point P.

(2) Divide the circle into a number of equal parts, e.g. 12 parts.

(3) The circle is to make one revolution so it will travel a distance equal to the circumference of the circle. Take one-twelfth of the circumference and step it off, from P, twelve times.

(4) Index the points as shown.

(5) As the circle rolls, the centre of the circle will travel parallel to the base line. We are going to look at the circle at twelve stages during its travel. Locate the centre point of the circle for each of these stages by erecting perpendiculars from 1,2,3 etc. on the base line.

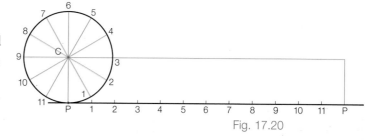

Fig. 17.20

(6) As the circle rolls clockwise, point 1 on the circumference moves onto point 1 on the base line. At the same time the centre will have moved to C_1. Point P will have moved also and can be located by triangulation. Take the distance from point 1 on the circumference to point P. Place the compass on the new point 1 on the base line and scribe an arc. Take a second

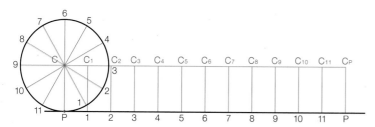

Fig. 17.21

distance from the circle centre to point P (the radius) and scribe an arc from C_1 to intersect the first arc, giving the location of point P_1 on the locus.

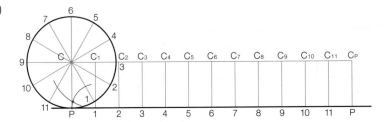

Fig. 17.22

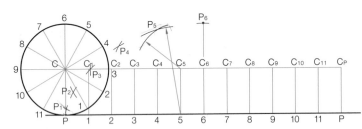

Fig. 17.23

(7) Take a similar approach for the rest of the points. For example P_5 is found by taking the distance from 5 on the circumference. Place the compass on 5 on the line and scribe an arc. Take a second distance from the centre of the circle to point P (the radius) and scribe an arc from C_5. The intersection of the arcs gives P_5, the fifth point on the cycloid.

(8) The right half is completed in the same way with the arcs swung to the right. Join the points up freehand to form a smooth curve, see Fig. 17.24.

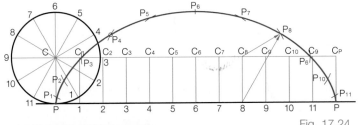

Fig. 17.24

To draw a cycloid given the base line, circle and the point P on the circle circumference. Point P does not fall on one of the twelve divisions.

(1) Divide the circle into twelve equal parts and index.
(2) Take one-twelfth of the circumference and step along the base line twelve times.
(3) Find the twelve centres. Index both sets of points.

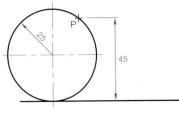

Fig. 17.25

(4) Point P falls between 4 and 5 on the circumference and will therefore hit the base line between 4 and 5. It is also to the right of the centre line. The cycloid will therefore be dropping at the start.
(5) Plot the points as before.

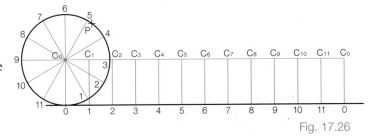

Fig. 17.26

(6) The starting point and the end point must be at the same level.

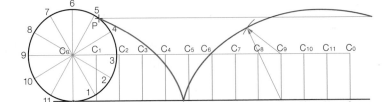

Fig. 17.27

Epicycloid

> If a circle rolls without slipping round the outside of a fixed circle then a point P on the circumference of the rolling circle will produce an epicycloids.

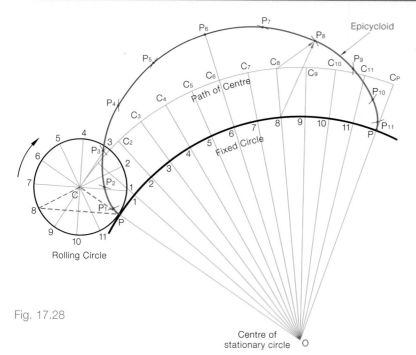

Fig. 17.28

(1) Join the centre of the rolling circle and the centre of the fixed circle.

(2) Divide the circle into twelve using this line as one of the division lines.

(3) Step-off the twelve steps along the outside of the fixed circle and index.

(4) With O as centre, swing an arc from C. This will be the path of the centre as the circle rolls.

(5) Using radians from O through points 1, 2, 3 etc. On the circumference of the fixed circle locate the centres C_1, C_2, C_3 etc.

(6) Plot the locus as before.

Hypocycloid

> If a circle rolls without slipping round the inside of a fixed circle, then a point P on the circumference of the rolling circle will produce a hypocycloid.

(1) Join the centres O and C and extend.

(2) Divide the rolling circle into twelve equal parts relative to this line.

(3) Step-off the twelve steps along the circumference of the fixed circle and index.

(4) With O as centre swing an arc from C giving the path of the centre as the circle rolls.

(5) Locate the centres C_1, C_2, C_3 etc. by using radians from O to points 1, 2, 3 etc. on the circumference of the fixed circle.

(6) Plot the locus as before.

Note: Point P need not be on one of the twelve divisions.

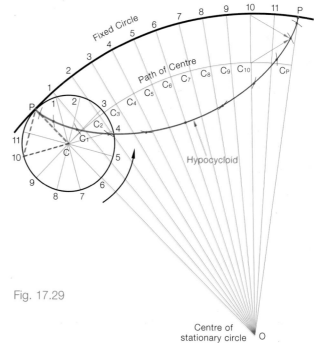

Fig. 17.29

Inferior Trochoid

> When a circle rolls, without slipping, along a straight line, then a point P inside the circle will follow the path of an inferior trochoid.

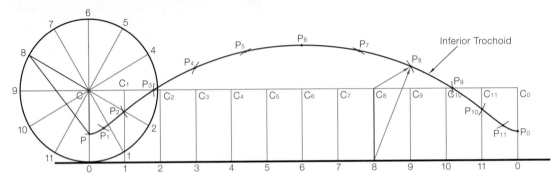

Fig. 17.30

The construction is similar to the cycloid.

(1) Divide the circle into twelve equal parts and index.

(2) Step-off the twelve steps along the straight line to find the length of the circumference.

(3) Find the path of the centre line and locate C_1, C_2, C_3 etc., as shown in Fig. 17.30.

(4) The points along the locus are located as previously described for the cycloid, measuring to point P inside the circle each time.

(5) Join the points to give a smooth curve.

Superior Trochoid

> When a circle rolls, without slipping, along a straight line, then a point P outside the circle will follow the path of a superior trochoid.

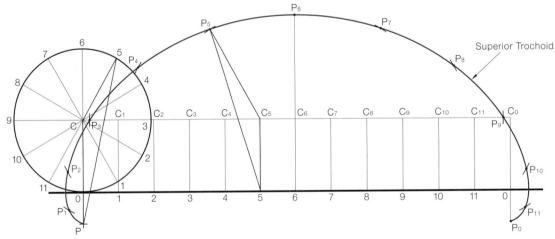

Fig. 17.31

(1) Divide the circle into twelve equal parts and index.

(2) Step-off the twelve steps along the straight line to find the length of the circumference.

(3) Locate C_1, C_2, C_3 etc.

(4) Locate P_1 to P_0 as shown previously.

(5) Draw the locus.

Inferior Epitrochoid

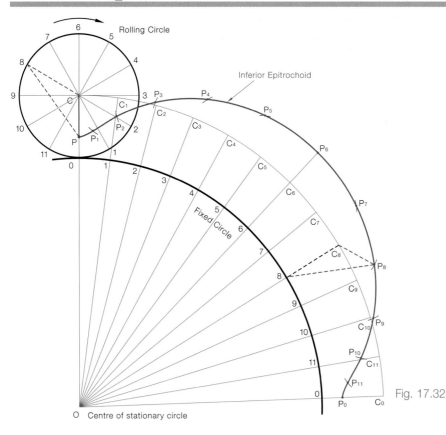

When a circle rolls, without slipping, around the outside of a fixed circle, then a point P inside the circle will follow the path of an inferior epitrochoid.

(1) Divide the circle into twelve equal parts.
(2) Set circumference off on the fixed circle.
(3) Rotate C about O and locate the twelve centres.
(4) Locate the points on the locus as before.

Fig. 17.32

Superior Epitrochoid

When a circle rolls, without slipping, around the outside of a fixed circle, then a point P outside the circle will follow the path of a superior epitrochoid.

The construction of the locus follows the same method as before.

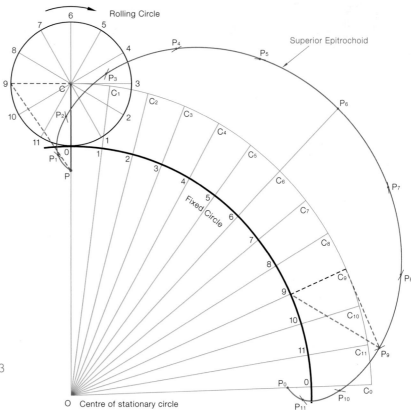

Fig. 17.33

Inferior Hypotrochoid

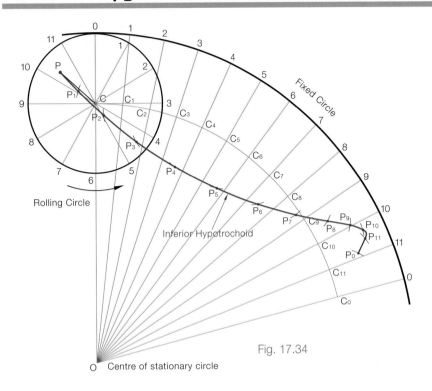

> **When a circle rolls, without slipping, around the inside of a fixed circle, then a point P inside the circle will follow the path of an inferior hypotrochoid.**

Construction as before. Note the position of point P. The position of point P does not effect the method of construction.

Fig. 17.34

Superior Hypotrochoid

> **When a circle rolls, without slipping, around the inside of a fixed circle, then a point P outside the circle will follow the path of a superior hypotrochoid.**

Construction as before.

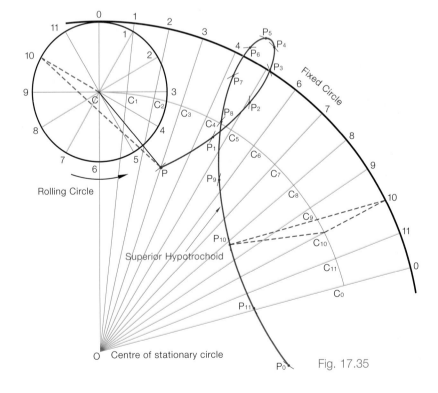

Fig. 17.35

Use of Templates to Solve Problems on Cycloids etc.

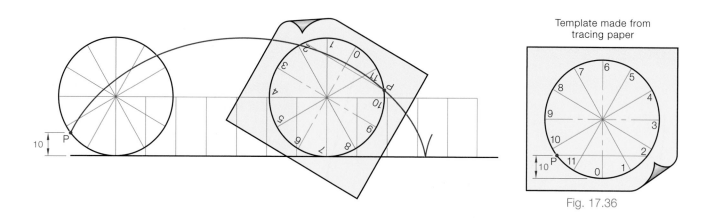

Template made from tracing paper

Fig. 17.36

Most of these loci problems can be solved using a template. The template is moved into position and point P is plotted with a pencil or compass point, see Figures 17.36 and 17.37.

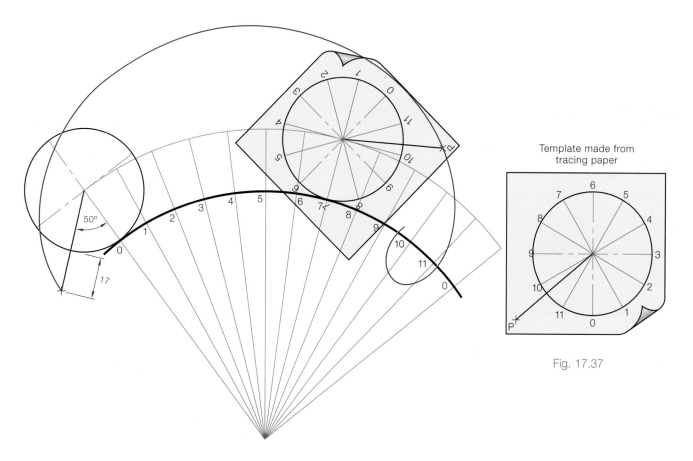

Template made from tracing paper

Fig. 17.37

Tangent to an Involute, Archimedian Spiral, Cycloid, Epicycloid and Hypocycloid

Tangent to an Involute

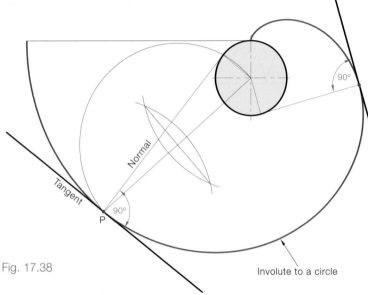

Fig. 17.38

Involute to a circle

For an involute to a circle it can be seen that tangents to the circle will form normals to the involute.

(1) Select any point P on the involute.
(2) From P draw a tangent to the circle.
(3) The tangent to the circle is the normal for the tangent to the involute. Draw the tangent at 90° to the normal.

For an involute of a square the curve is made up of circular portions.

(1) Select any point P on the involute.
(2) Join P back to the centre point of the arc that formed that section of the involute. This is the normal.
(3) Draw the tangent perpendicular to the normal.

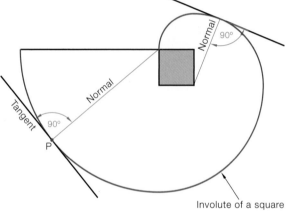

Involute of a square

Fig. 17.39

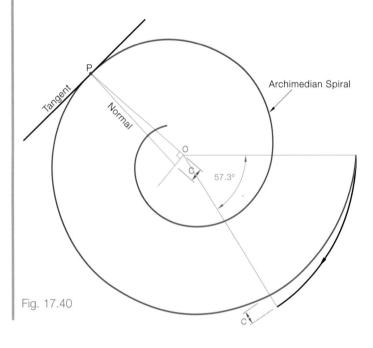

Archimedian Spiral

Fig. 17.40

Tangent to an Archimedian Spiral.

(1) Select any point P on the spiral.
(2) Join P to the pole, point O.
(3) Draw a perpendicular to PO at O.
(4) Measure out the constant C and draw the normal.
(5) The tangent is perpendicular to the normal. The constant c is the distance the spiral has moved closer to the pole over an angular distance of one radian. A radian equals approximately 57.3°, see Fig. 17.40.

Tangent to a Cycloid

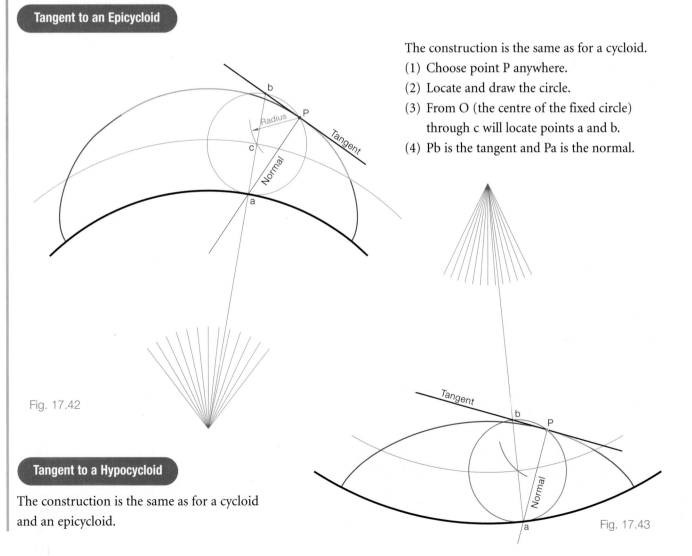

Fig. 17.41

Method 1

(1) Choose any point P on the cycloid.
(2) Draw the circle at the cycloid's highest point.
(3) Project P horizontally to q.
(4) Join q to r.
(5) The tangent will be parallel to qr.

Method 2

(1) Choose any point P_1 on the cycloid.
(2) Using the radius of the circle, strike an arc from P_1 to locate c on the centre line.
(3) Draw the circle.
(4) The circle touches the base line at a. A line drawn from a through c will locate point b.
(5) P_1b is the tangent and P_1a is the normal.

Tangent to an Epicycloid

The construction is the same as for a cycloid.
(1) Choose point P anywhere.
(2) Locate and draw the circle.
(3) From O (the centre of the fixed circle) through c will locate points a and b.
(4) Pb is the tangent and Pa is the normal.

Fig. 17.42

Tangent to a Hypocycloid

The construction is the same as for a cycloid and an epicycloid.

Fig. 17.43

HIGHER LEVEL

Worked Examples on Loci

> In the Figure 17.44 the circle rolls clockwise for one revolution along the line AB. At the same time point P is moving to point C. Draw the path of point P for the combined movement.

(1) There are two movements occurring simultaneously. We will deal with one movement and then combine it with the other.

(2) Since we usually divide the rolling circle into twelve equal portions, it is easiest to break all the movements into twelve equal steps. We divide PC into twelve equal steps and index them. This is one movement. By the time the circle has travelled for half a revolution, point P will have moved to P_6.

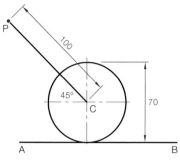

Fig. 17.44

(3) Divide the circle and index.

(4) Step out the twelve steps and index.

(5) Locate the twelve centres, see Fig. 17.45.

(6) The points on the locus are located as before using arcs. We are not measuring to P at the end of the line, we are measuring to P_1, then P_2, then P_3 etc. For example: Take from 4 on the circumference of the circle to P_4 as radius. Place the compass on 4 on the base line and draw an arc. Take from the centre C of the circle to P_4 as radius. Place the compass on C_4 and draw an arc. Where the two arcs cross locates the fourth point on the locus, see Fig. 17.46.

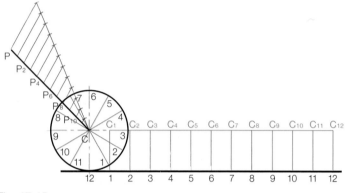

Fig. 17.45

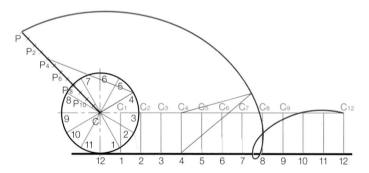

Fig. 17.46

> Fig. 17.47 shows a large circle B which rolls for half a revolution clockwise along the base line. At the same time the small circle A rolls for half a revolution around the circumference of the circle B, in a clockwise direction. Meanwhile point P moves to point D. Plot the locus of point P for the combined movements.

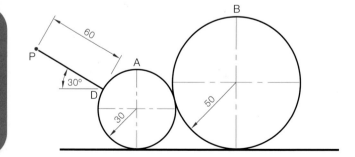

Fig. 17.47

There are three movements occurring simultaneously in this problem. Complete one movement, combine it with the second and finally combine the first two with the third to give the full answer.

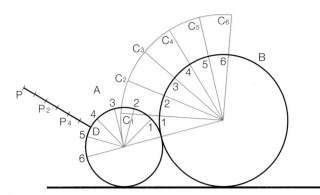

Fig. 17.48

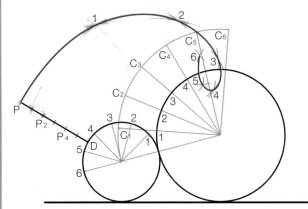

Fig. 17.49

(1) Join the centres of the two circles.

(2) The small circle does a half turn. We divide half of it into six equal parts relative to the line joining the centres. Index these points.

(3) Step these steps off around the large circle.

(4) Locate the centres C_1 to C_6 by radiating from the centre of circle B.

(5) The line PD is now divided. It is divided into six equal parts because the next movement is in six steps.

(6) Plot the path of these two movements combined. Take the radius from 1 on the small circle to P_1. Scribe an arc from 1 on the large circle. Take a second radius from the centre of the small circle to P_1. Scribe an arc, to cross the first arc, from C_1, Fig. 17.49.

(7) We must combine these movements with the movement of the large circle. The large circle rotates for half a turn. Divide the half-circle into six equal parts.

(8) Step these off along the base line.

(9) Locate the six centres.

(10) The points on the locus are located by measuring to the first locus. Take from 1 on the large circle to point 1 on the locus as radius. Scribe an arc from point 1 on the base line. Take from the centre of the large circle to point 1 on the locus as radius. Scribe an arc from C_1 to cross the first arc etc., Fig. 17.50.

(11) Join the points with a smooth curve.

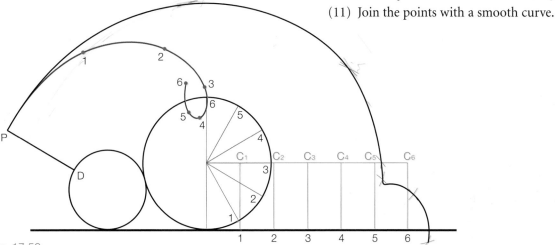

Fig. 17.50

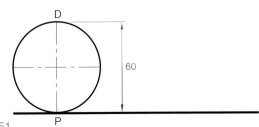

Fig. 17.51

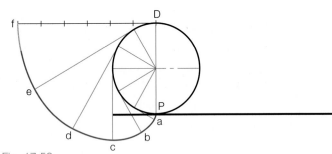

Fig. 17.52

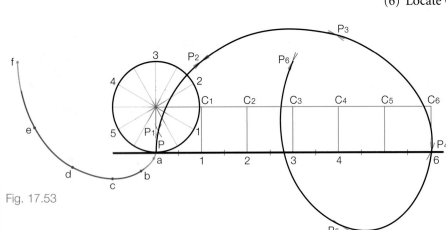

Fig. 17.53

Fig. 17.51 shows a circle which rolls clockwise for one revolution on the given line. During the rolling of the circle an involute is unwound from P to D. Draw the locus of P for the combined movement.

There are two movements involved, the involute and the rolling circle. We start with the involute.

(1) Divide the half-circle into six equal portions. Construct a tangent at the end of each division.

(2) The string is unwinding from P to D, so at D it will be six units long. It shortens by one unit for each tangent moving toward point P.

(3) Divide the circle into twelve.

(4) Step the divisions out on the line.

(5) Index every second point as this will give us six steps, like we have in the involute.

(6) Locate C_1 to C_6.

(7) Plot the points on the combined locus. Take from 1 on the circle to the first point on the involute, point a, as radius. Scribe an arc from 1 on the base line. Take from the centre of the circle to point a on the involute as radius. Scribe an arc from C_1 to cross the first arc etc.

Activities

INVOLUTES

Q1. Draw an involute to a square of 20 mm side.

Q2. Draw an involute to a hexagon of base 18 mm.

Q3. Draw an involute to a circle of 15 mm radius.

Q4. to Q7. Draw an involute to the given shapes. The involute should start at point P and unwind in a clockwise direction.

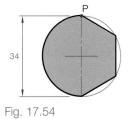

Fig. 17.54

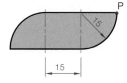

Fig. 17.55

Fig. 17.56

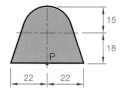

Fig. 17.57

HELICES

Q8. Given the plan and elevation of a cylinder. Draw a left-handed helix of two revolutions starting at point P.

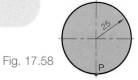

Fig. 17.58

Q9. Given the plan and elevation of a cylinder with two points A and B on its surface. Draw a helix to go from the bottom to the top of the cylinder and to pass through points A and B.

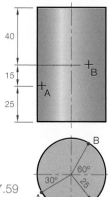

Fig. 17.59

Q10. Draw a single start, right-hand square, screw thread given the inside diameter of 50 mm, outside diameter of 80 mm and the lead of 72 mm.

Q11. Draw a double start, left-hand square, screw thread given the inside diameter of 50 mm, outside diameter of 80 mm and the pitch of 36 mm (lead of 72mm).

CONICAL SPIRALS

Q12. Draw a conical spiral to start at the base of the given cone at point P and to reach the apex in one revolution.

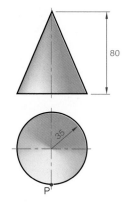

Fig. 17.60

Q13. Draw a conical spiral that passes through point P and completes exactly one convolution from base to apex.

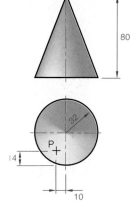

Fig. 17.61

Q14. Draw an Archimedian spiral having its longest radius vector of 50 mm, its shortest radius vector of 14 mm and completing one convolution.

Q15. Draw an Archimedian spiral having 1½ convolutions. The spiral is to have a longest radius vector of 56 mm and a shortest radius vector of 20 mm.

Q16. Construct 1¼ convolutions of an Archimedian spiral given the longest vector as 60 mm and a decrease of 5 mm every 45°.

Q17. Construct ¾ of a convolution of an Archimedian spiral given the shortest radius vector of 15 mm and an increase every 15° of 3 mm.

CYCLOIDS, EPICYCLOIDS ETC.

Q18. The circle rolls clockwise along the given line without slipping. Plot the locus of point P for this movement.

HONOURS
Draw a tangent to the cycloid at the 6th point on the locus.

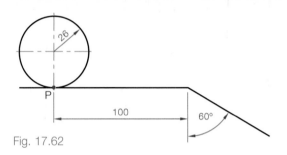

Fig. 17.62

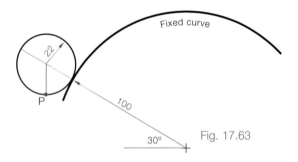

Fixed curve

Fig. 17.63

Q19. In Fig. 17.63 the circle rolls clockwise along the fixed curve for one revolution. Plot the locus of point P for this movement.

HONOURS
Draw a tangent to the epicycloids from a point 30 mm from the fixed curve.

Q20. In Fig. 17.64 the small circle rolls round the inside of the larger circle for one revolution. Plot the locus of point P for this movement

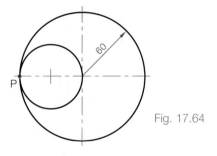

Fig. 17.64

Q21. Plot the locus of point P as the circle rolls clockwise for one complete revolution.

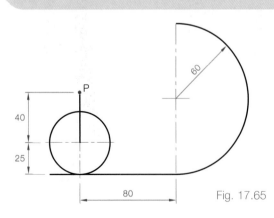

Fig. 17.65

Q22. In Fig. 17.66 the large circle rolls round the small circle for one revolution. Plot the locus of point P for this movement.

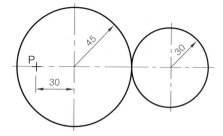

Fig. 17.66

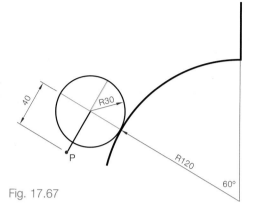

Fig. 17.67

Q23. Plot the locus of point P as the circle rolls without slipping for one revolution.

Q24. Fig. 17.68 shows a small circle which rolls round the large circle for one revolution. At the same time P is unwound as an involute in a clockwise direction for half a revolution to A. Draw the locus of P for the combined movement.

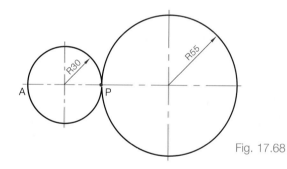

Fig. 17.68

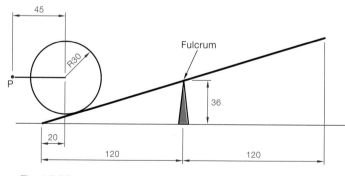

Fig. 17.69

Q25. Fig. 17.69 shows a circle rolling up a see-saw. When the circle reaches the fulcrum the see-saw tips so that the right-hand side touches the ground. Plot the locus of point P for 1¹/₂ turns of the circle.

HIGHER LEVEL

Q26. Fig. 17.70 shows a circle which rolls clockwise along the arc for one revolution. During the rolling of the circle, point P moves at a constant pace to C and then A. Plot the locus of P for the combined movement.

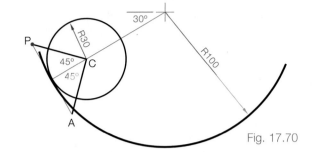

Fig. 17.70

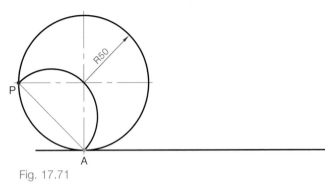

Fig. 17.71

Q27. Fig. 17.71 shows a circle which rolls clockwise along the straight line. During the rolling of the circle, P moves along a semi-circular path to A. Draw the locus of P for the combined movement.

Q28. In Fig. 17.72 the profile rolls for 3/4 of a revolution in a clockwise direction. During the rolling of the profile P moves to A. Draw the locus of P for this combined movement.

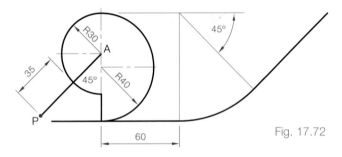

Fig. 17.72

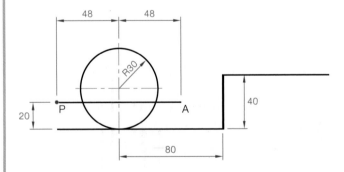

Fig. 17.73

Q29. In Fig. 17.73 the circle rolls clockwise for one revolution. During the rolling of the circle the point P moves to point A. Draw the locus of point P for the combined movement.

Dynamic Mechanisms 2

Linkages

Cams

Gears

Types of Link Mechanisms

Sliding link

End A of the link slides along a set line forcing end B to slide along its set path.

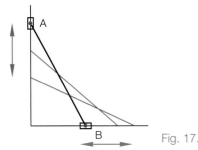

Fig. 17.74

Crank and sliding link

The rod AB rotates about point A. This is a crank. The rotating of the crank causes link C to slide over and back.

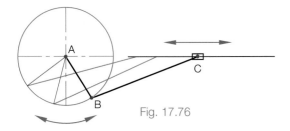

Fig. 17.76

Crank and rocker

As crank AB rotates, rocker arm CD moves forwards and backwards.

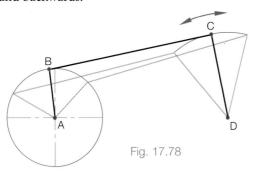

Fig. 17.78

Swinging and sliding link

As the rod swings about point A, the link C is sliding down.

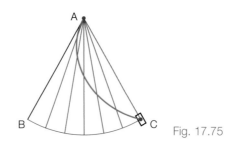

Fig. 17.75

Double crank

This mechanism only works if the length of BC equals that between the centres of A and D. Crank AB rotates. The link between B and C forces C to rotate about D.

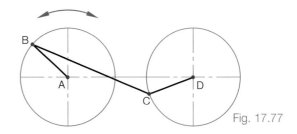

Fig. 17.77

Crank and fixed through link

C is fixed in position but allows BC to slide through it.

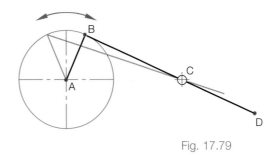

Fig. 17.79

> **A ladder AB is leaning against a wall, with one end against the wall and the other on the floor. Plot the locus of the midpoint of the ladder as it slides to the floor.**

(1) Draw the problem placing the ladder at a steep angle.

(2) Divide the distance from A to the corner into a number of parts.

(3) Draw the ladder in each position and locate point P in each case.

(4) Join all the plotted points to form the locus. This locus is called a **glisette**.

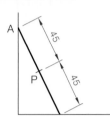

Fig. 17.80

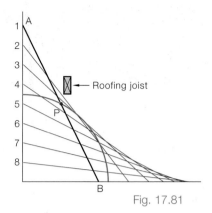

Fig. 17.81

Alternate method

Many of these loci problems can be solved using a trammel.

(1) Mark off the length of the ladder AB and the position of point P.

(2) By moving the trammel so that A slides along the vertical line and B slides along the horizontal line, the locus of point P can be plotted.

This construction may be used to see if a ladder will fit between a gap in roofing joists or if a long object will fit through a doorway.

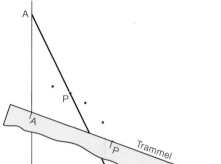

Fig. 17.82

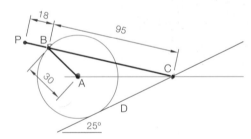

Fig. 17.83

> **Fig. 17.83 shows a crank AB which revolves in a clockwise direction around pivot A. Link PC is pin-jointed at B. End C slides on line DE. Plot the locus of point P for one revolution of the crank.**

(1) Set up the problem.

(2) Divide the circle into twelve equal parts.

(3) For each division draw in the link BC ensuring that C is always on the line DE and 95 mm long.

(4) Point P can be found for each position of the crank arm. The first six steps are shown.

(5) This problem can more easily be solved with a trammel as shown in Fig. 17.85

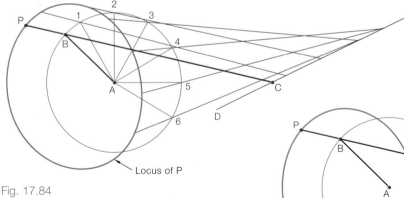

Fig. 17.84

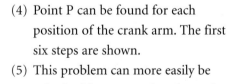

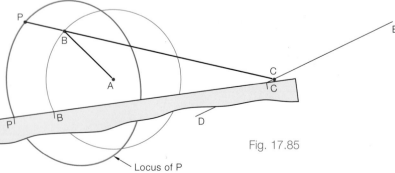

Fig. 17.85

Fig. 17.86 represents an up-and-over garage door in a partly open position. Pivot C slides along line AF while A and B can pivot. Draw the locus of both E and D as the door opens and closes.

(1) Set up the problem as given.
(2) Cut a suitable trammel and on it mark the door length D to E. Mark the pivot points B and C.
(3) Pivot C follows the line AF and pivot B will follow a circular path with A as centre.
(4) Use the trammel to plot all the points.

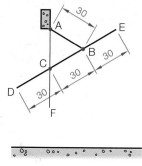

Fig. 17.86

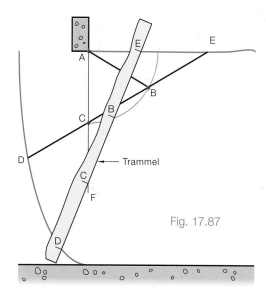

Fig. 17.87

Fig. 17.88 shows a crank AB which rotates about point A. Link BP can slide through the pivot C. Plot the locus of P for one revolution of the crank.

(1) Set up the problem.
(2) Cut a trammel and on it mark B and P.
(3) Use the trammel to plot the points by keeping B on the circle and the line BP passing through C.

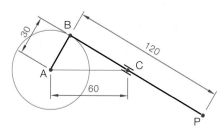

Fig. 17.88

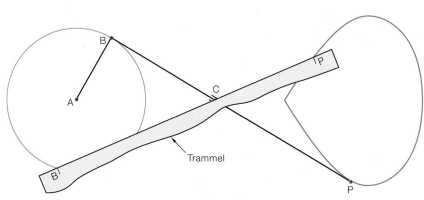

Fig. 17.89

Fig. 17.90 shows a crank DC which rotates about D. AB can rotate about A and is linked to the crank by BC. Plot the locus of point P for one full revolution of the crank.

(1) CD is a crank and AB will be a rocking arm. Set up the problem.
(2) Draw the full circular path of point C.
(3) Draw the arc that point B will follow.
(4) Set up the trammel equal in length to BC and mark the position of point P.
(5) Plot the locus of P by keeping the point C on the trammel on the circle and by keeping the point B on the trammel on the arc.

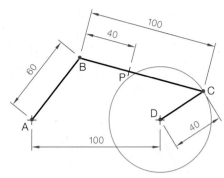

Fig. 17.90

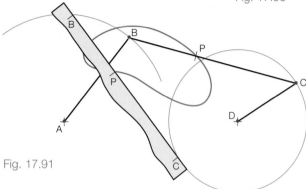

Fig. 17.91

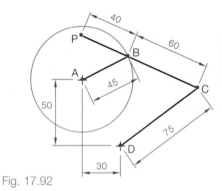

Fig. 17.92

Fig. 17.92 shows a crank AB which rotates for a complete revolution. Link DC rotates about fixed centre D. Plot the locus of point P for the movement.

(1) AB is a crank and DC will be a rocker arm. Set up the problem.
(2) Draw the circle to show the movement of point B.
(3) Draw the arc to show the movement of point C.
(4) The trammel will represent the link CBP.
(5) Point C on the trammel must run along the circle. Point B on the trammel must travel along the arc.
(6) Numerous points on the locus can be plotted and the path drawn.

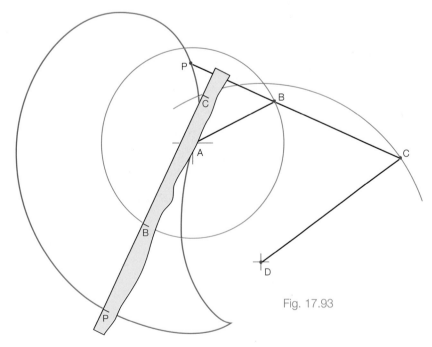

Fig. 17.93

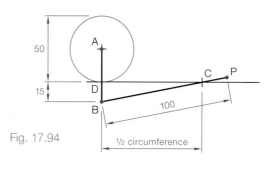

Fig. 17.94 shows a circle, which rolls for one revolution along the line DE. B is a pivot and C is a fixed through pivot. Plot the locus of point P for the motion.

(1) The path of point B must be found first. The locus of B will be a superior trochoid. Construct as explained in Dynamic Mechanisms 1 (first half of this chapter).

(2) Locate point C.

(3) Make the trammel match link BCP.

(4) The locus is plotted by placing point B on the superior trochoid and the edge of the trammel must touch point C at all times.

Fig. 17.94

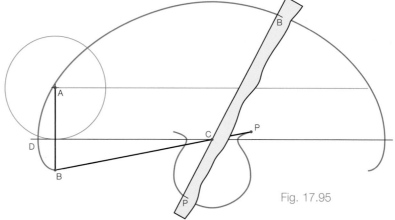

Fig. 17.95

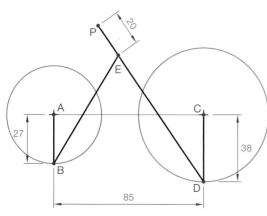

BE = 70 mm   BE = 85 mm

Fig. 17.96

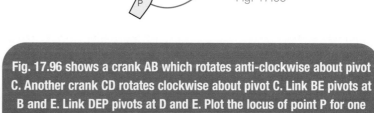

Fig. 17.96 shows a crank AB which rotates anti-clockwise about pivot C. Another crank CD rotates clockwise about pivot C. Link BE pivots at B and E. Link DEP pivots at D and E. Plot the locus of point P for one revolution of the cranks. (Both cranks rotate at the same rate.)

(1) It should be noted that this mechanism has a number of moving parts and is not easily solved using a trammel.
   Divide both crank circles into twelve equal parts and index, remembering that AB rotates anti-clockwise and CD rotates clockwise.

(2) At each position on the circles the full mechanism is constructed finding a point on the locus (construction for P_0, P_3 and P_7 shown).

(3) Join the twelve points on the path with a smooth curve.

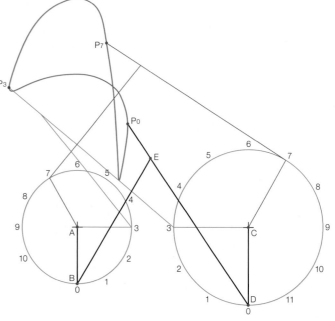

Fig. 17.97

Displacement Diagram

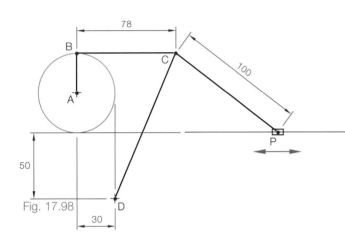

Fig. 17.98 shows a crank AB which pivots about A. A rocker arm DC pivots about D. B and C are pivots and P is a sliding link. Plot the displacement diagram for point P for one complete clockwise revolution of the crank.

Fig. 17.98

The movement of P is linear. The displacement diagram allows the position of P to be plotted for any degree of revolution of the crank. The position of P can also be related to time. If we know how long it takes for one revolution of the crank we can easily calculate the exact location of point P for any moment in time.

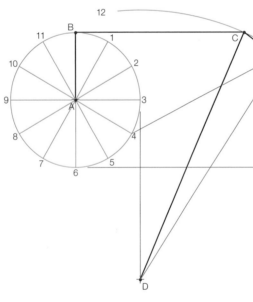

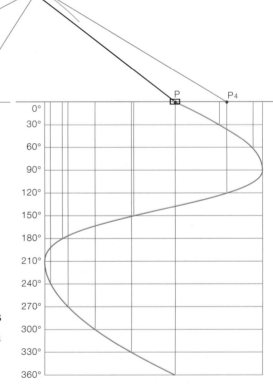

Fig. 17.99

Method

(1) Plot all twelve positions of point P as the crank rotates. This will establish the maximum and minimum positions of point P.

(2) Set out a graph as shown in Fig. 17.99. The height of the graph does not matter as long as it is divided into twelve equal parts. The graph is divided into twelve because the rotation of the crank was broken into twelve equal steps.

(3) The position of point P is plotted for each 30° rotation. This point is plotted on the graph, (P_4 shown.)

(4) Repeat for each of the twelve steps of the crank's rotation.

Activities

Q1. The line AB represents a ladder leaning against a wall. Plot the locus of point P as the ladder falls. End A runs along the wall and end B runs along the floor.

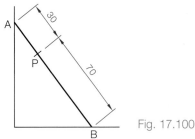

Fig. 17.100

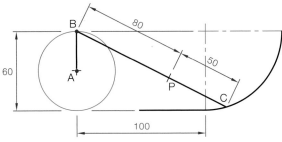

Fig. 17.101

Q2. Fig. 17.101 shows a crank AB which rotates for one complete revolution. Link BC is pin-jointed at B and end C is restricted to the path shown. Plot the locus of P for the movement.

Q3. Crank AB rotates about point A. Link BP is pin-jointed at point B. Point C is a fixed-through pivot. Plot the locus of point P for one full revolution of the crank.

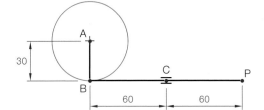

Fig. 17.102

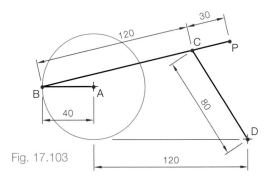

Fig. 17.103

Q4. Crank AB rotates about A. Rocker arm DC rotates about D. Link BCP is pin-jointed at B and C. Plot the locus of point P for one complete revolution of the crank.

Q5. Fig. 17.104 shows a circle which rolls along the line DE for one complete revolution. B is a pivot and C is a fixed through pivot. Plot the locus of point P.

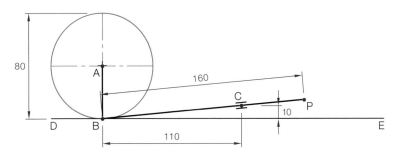

Fig. 17.104

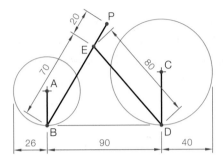

Fig. 17.105

Q6. Fig. 17.105 shows a crank AB which rotates about A. Another crank CD rotates about C. Both cranks rotate at the same rate and in the same direction. Links DE and BEP are pivot-jointed at B, D and E. Plot the locus of point P for one complete revolution of the cranks.

Q7. Fig. 17.106 shows a crank AB which rotates about A. Another crank CD rotates about C. Crank AB rotates clockwise and crank CD rotates anti-clockwise. Both cranks rotate at the same rate. Joint B, E and D are pivot joints. P is a sliding link. Draw the locus of E for one revolution of the cranks.
Draw a displacement diagram for P for the full movement.

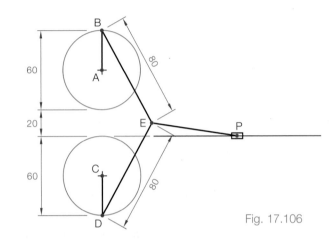

Fig. 17.106

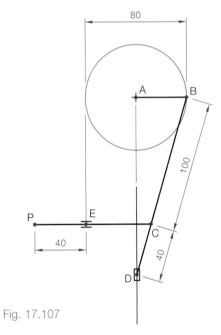

Fig. 17.107

Q8. Crank AB rotates about A. D is a sliding link and B is a pivot. Plot the locus of C for one revolution of the crank. CEP is connected at point C by a pivot joint. E is a fixed-through link. Plot the locus of P for the combined movement.

Q9. Crank AB rotates clockwise for one revolution. During the turning of the crank, D slides at a constant speed to E and back to D again. C and B are pivot joints. Plot the locus of P for one revolution of the crank.

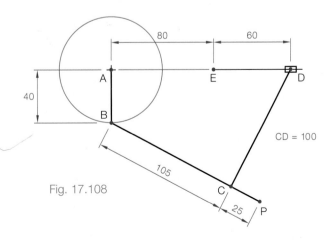

Fig. 17.108

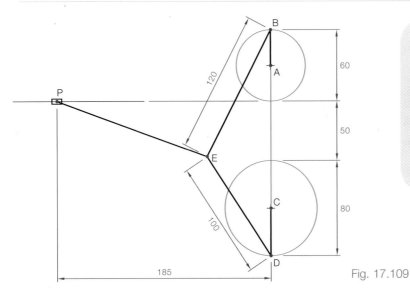

Fig. 17.109

Q10. Fig. 17.109 shows two cranks, AB and CD. AB rotates clockwise and rotates twice for every one revolution of CD, which rotates anti-clockwise. B, D and E are pivot joints and P is a sliding link. Plot the locus of E for one revolution of CD (two revolutions of AB). Draw a displacement diagram for P for the full movement.

Cams

A cam is a shaped component generally used to change rotary movement into linear movement. Cams are used regularly in engine parts and mechanisms. The most usual types are **radial plate cams**. A shaft rotating at uniform speed carries a disk, usually of irregular shape, called the cam. A **follower** presses against the curved surface of the cam, Fig. 17.110. Rotation of the cam causes the follower to move according to the shape of the cam profile. The follower is kept in constant contact with the cam by gravity, or by using a spring. The follower shown in the diagram is a **knife-edge follower**. There are other types of followers which we will look at later on in the chapter. A knife-edge follower can follow very complicated cam shapes but wears rapidly.

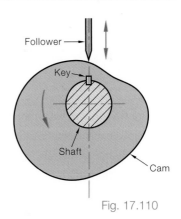

Fig. 17.110

Displacement Diagrams
The movement of the follower is an important consideration in cam design. Its rate of movement and position varies hugely according to the cam profile. A displacement diagram is a means of planning this follower movement before the cam is constructed. It is a graph plotting the movement of the follower for one full revolution of the cam.

Uniform Velocity
The follower rises or falls at a constant speed. The movement will plot as a straight line on a graph.

Uniform velocity gives constant follower speed but produces abrupt changes which may cause the follower to jump. It should be noted that

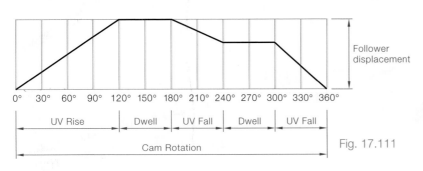

Fig. 17.111

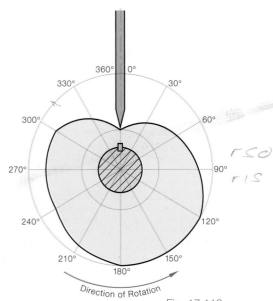

Fig. 17.112

those portions of the cam that give uniform rise or fall to the follower will be portions of Archimedian spirals. When the follower dwells, the cam profile will be a portion of a circle having the same centre as the cam.

Simple Harmonic Motion (SHM)

Simple harmonic motion produces a very gentle transition from one movement to the next. The speed of the follower is not constant. The construction is based on a circle and produces a sine curve on the follower displacement diagram.

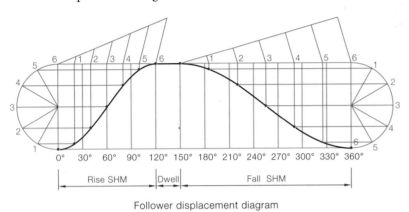

Fig. 17.113

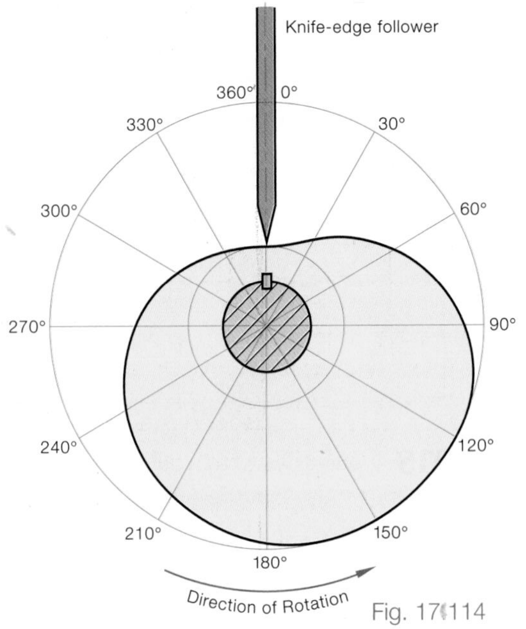

Fig. 17.114

Method

(1) Draw a semicircle to match the rise that is required for the follower. This semicircle is usually placed at the end of the follower displacement diagram.
(2) Divide the semicircle into equal segments, usually six.
(3) Divide the length of rotation it takes for the full movement into the same number of equal parts.
(4) Plot the points as shown in Fig. 17.113.

Uniform Acceleration and Retardation (UAR)

As the name suggests, the follower accelerates smoothly and decelerates smoothly at the start and the end of this movement.

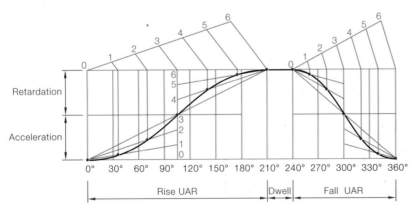

Fig. 17.115

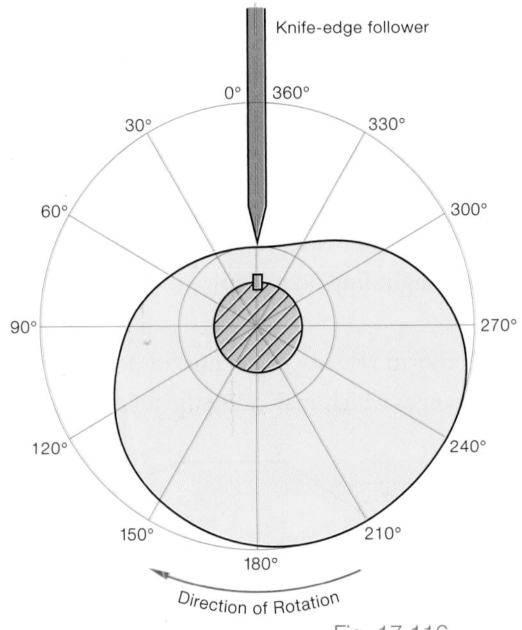

Fig. 17.116

Method

The construction is based on two half parabolas. We use the rectangle method as shown in Fig. 17.115.

Draw the profile of a clockwise cam to give the following displacement to an in-line knife-edge follower:
0° to 120° a UV rise of 36 mm,
120° to 330° a SHM fall of 36 mm,
330° to 360° dwell.
The centre of the cam is 18 mm below the nearest approach of the follower.

(1) Start by drawing the follower displacement diagram. The height of the graph will be 36 mm. The length of the diagram does not matter but should be easily divisible by twelve.
(2) Project across the top and bottom of the follower displacement diagram. The centre of the cam will be 18 mm below the minimum line.
(3) Draw the maximum and minimum circles and divide them into twelve equal segments.
(4) Index these divisions. Since the cam rotates clockwise the divisions on the circles will be indexed anti-clockwise.
(5) Project each point on a degree line on the follower displacement diagram across to the vertical axis of the cam.

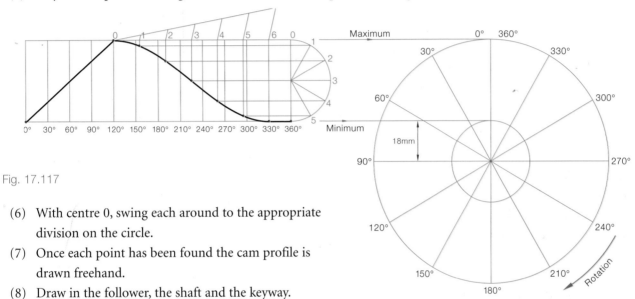

Fig. 17.117

(6) With centre 0, swing each around to the appropriate division on the circle.
(7) Once each point has been found the cam profile is drawn freehand.
(8) Draw in the follower, the shaft and the keyway.

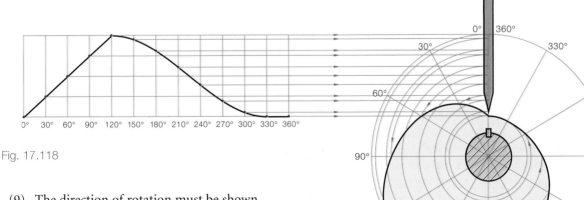

Fig. 17.118

(9) The direction of rotation must be shown.
(10) Divisions can be made smaller than 30° to increase accuracy if required.

Draw the profile of an anti-clockwise cam to give the following displacement to an in-line, knife-edge follower:
0° to 120° simple harmonic rise of 30 mm,
120° to 180° uniform velocity rise of 10 mm,
180° to 330° uniform acceleration and retardation fall of 40 mm,
330° to 360° dwell.
Cam centre 16 mm below nearest approach of the follower.

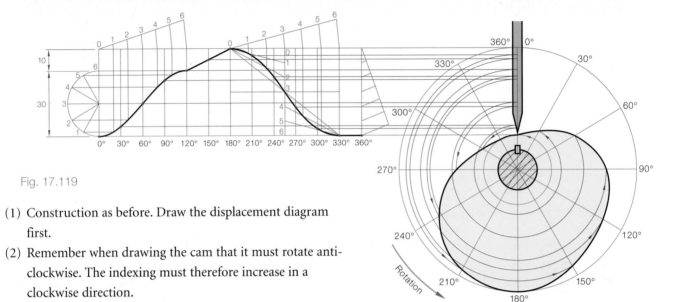

Fig. 17.119

(1) Construction as before. Draw the displacement diagram first.
(2) Remember when drawing the cam that it must rotate anti-clockwise. The indexing must therefore increase in a clockwise direction.

Draw the profile of a clockwise cam to give the following displacement to an in-line, knife-edge follower:
0° to 30° dwell,
30° to 150° uniform acceleration and retardation rise of 30 mm,
150° to 210° uniform velocity fall of 10 mm,
210° to 270° simple harmonic rise of 22 mm,
270° to 360° uniform acceleration and retardation fall of 42 mm.
Cam centre 18 mm below nearest approach of the follower.

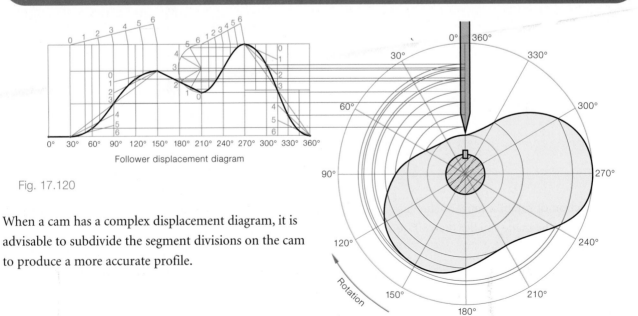

Follower displacement diagram

Fig. 17.120

When a cam has a complex displacement diagram, it is advisable to subdivide the segment divisions on the cam to produce a more accurate profile.

Plot the follower displacement diagram for an in-line, knife-edge follower in contact with the cam profile shown in Fig. 17.121.

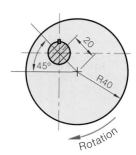

(1) Draw the cam.

(2) With centre C draw the maximum and minimum displacement circles.

(3) Divide the cam into segments and index.

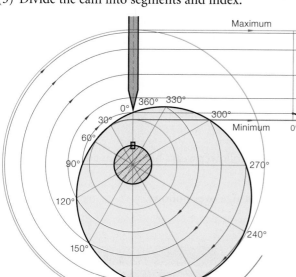

Fig. 17.121

Fig. 17.122

(4) Project the maximum and minimum heights of the follower from the centre line to give the top and bottom lines of the follower displacement diagram.

(5) With C as centre rotate the points on the division lines on the cam around onto the follower centre line.

(6) Project these points across to their corresponding positions on the follower displacement diagram.

(7) Complete the follower displacement diagram by drawing a smooth curve through the points.

Plot the follower displacement diagram for an in-line, knife-edge follower in contact with the cam profile shown in Fig. 17.123.

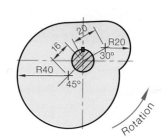

(1) Draw the cam.

(2) Draw the maximum and minimum circles.

Fig. 17.123

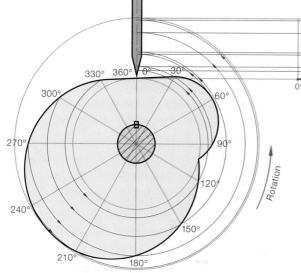

(3) Divide the cam and index clockwise.

(4) Use the maximum and minimum circles to find the top and bottom of the displacement diagram.

(5) Rotate the points on the cam to the follower centre line.

(6) Project across the points to the follower displacement diagram and complete the graph.

Fig. 17.124

Other follower types

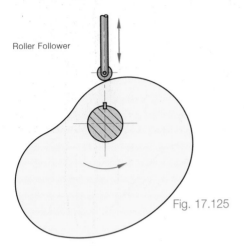

Roller Follower

Fig. 17.125

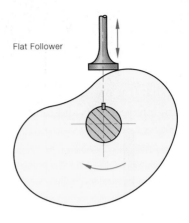

Flat Follower

Fig. 17.126

The roller follower wears less quickly than a knife-edge follower.

It is smoother at high speeds.

It cannot follow intricate shapes.

The flat follower wears better than a knife-edge follower.

It can bridge over hollows.

Given the follower displacement data:
0° to 120° uniform acceleration and retardation rise of 36 mm,
120° to 180° uniform velocity rise of 12 mm,
180° to 240° dwell,
240° to 360° simple harmonic motion fall of 48 mm.
The roller follower is in-line and 12 mm in diameter. Rotation of cam is clockwise. The nearest approach of the roller centre to the cam centre is 20 mm.

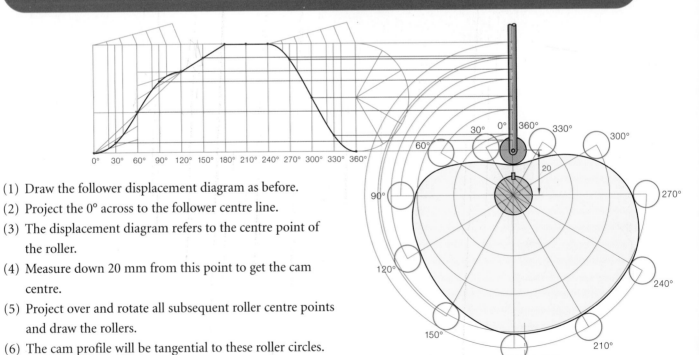

(1) Draw the follower displacement diagram as before.

(2) Project the 0° across to the follower centre line.

(3) The displacement diagram refers to the centre point of the roller.

(4) Measure down 20 mm from this point to get the cam centre.

(5) Project over and rotate all subsequent roller centre points and draw the rollers.

(6) The cam profile will be tangential to these roller circles.

Fig. 17.127

HIGHER LEVEL

Given the follower displacement data:
0° to 60° dwell,
60° to 180° SHM rise of 30 mm,
180° to 240° UV rise of 18 mm,
240° to 360° UAR fall of 48 mm.
The follower is in-line and flat and extends 6 mm to either side of the centre line. The centre of the cam is 16 mm below the nearest approach of the follower. The cam rotates anti-clockwise.

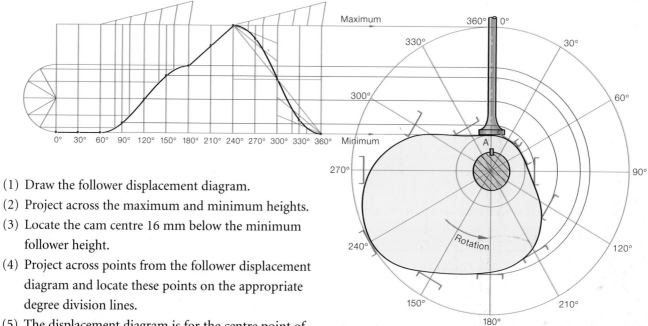

Fig. 17.128

HIGHER LEVEL

(1) Draw the follower displacement diagram.
(2) Project across the maximum and minimum heights.
(3) Locate the cam centre 16 mm below the minimum follower height.
(4) Project across points from the follower displacement diagram and locate these points on the appropriate degree division lines.
(5) The displacement diagram is for the centre point of the base of the follower, point A. At each point located around the circle draw the follower base as shown.
(6) Draw the cam profile so that the follower touches it at each location.

HIGHER LEVEL

Given the follower displacement data:
0° to 120° SHM rise of 30 mm,
120° to 180° UV rise of 6 mm,
130° to 360° UAR fall of 36 mm.
In-line roller follower of 12 mm diameter. Cam rotation anti-clockwise. Cam centre 25 mm below the nearest approach of the roller centre. Draw the cam profile.

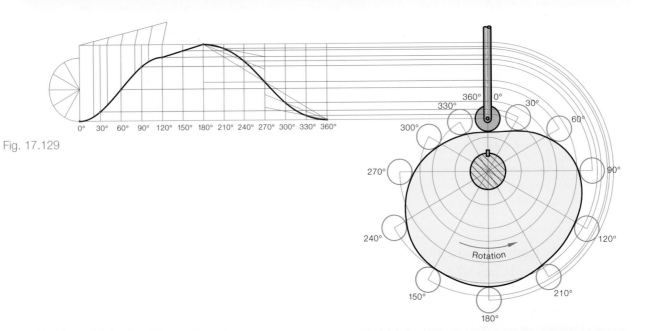

Fig. 17.129

Given the follower displacement diagram as in the previous example.
The follower is in-line, flat and extends 6 mm each side of the centre line.
Cam rotates anti-clockwise.
Cam centre 25 mm below the nearest approach of the follower.
Draw the cam profile.

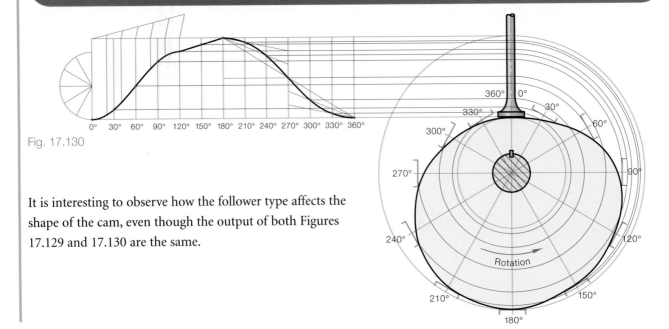

Fig. 17.130

It is interesting to observe how the follower type affects the shape of the cam, even though the output of both Figures 17.129 and 17.130 are the same.

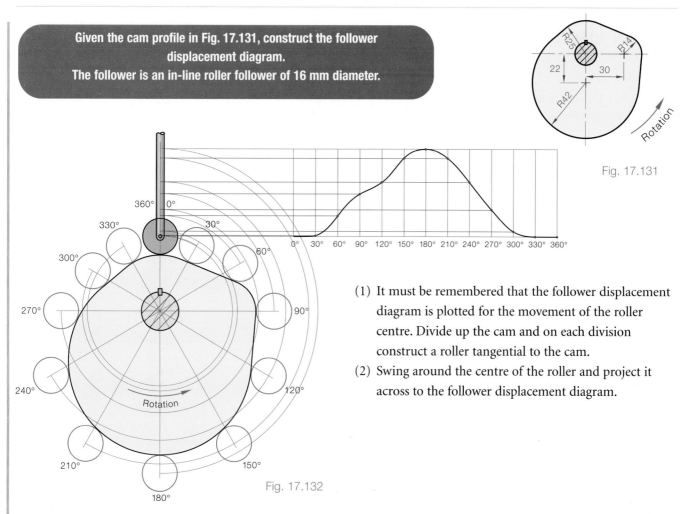

Given the cam profile in Fig. 17.131, construct the follower displacement diagram.
The follower is an in-line roller follower of 16 mm diameter.

Fig. 17.131

(1) It must be remembered that the follower displacement diagram is plotted for the movement of the roller centre. Divide up the cam and on each division construct a roller tangential to the cam.
(2) Swing around the centre of the roller and project it across to the follower displacement diagram.

Fig. 17.132

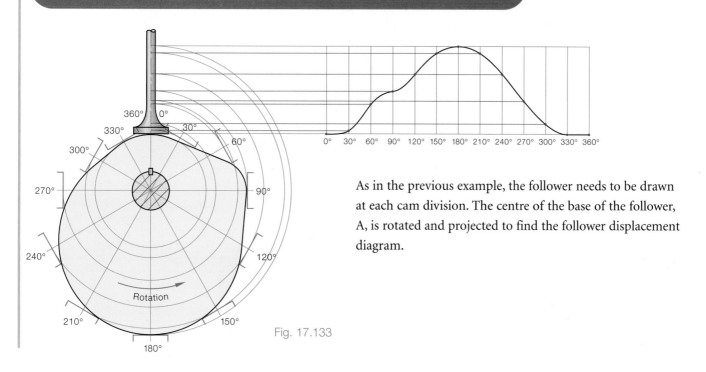

Given the cam profile in Fig. 17.132, construct the follower displacement diagram.
The follower is an in-line, flat follower and extends 8 mm each side of the centre line.

As in the previous example, the follower needs to be drawn at each cam division. The centre of the base of the follower, A, is rotated and projected to find the follower displacement diagram.

Fig. 17.133

Terms Used in Gearing

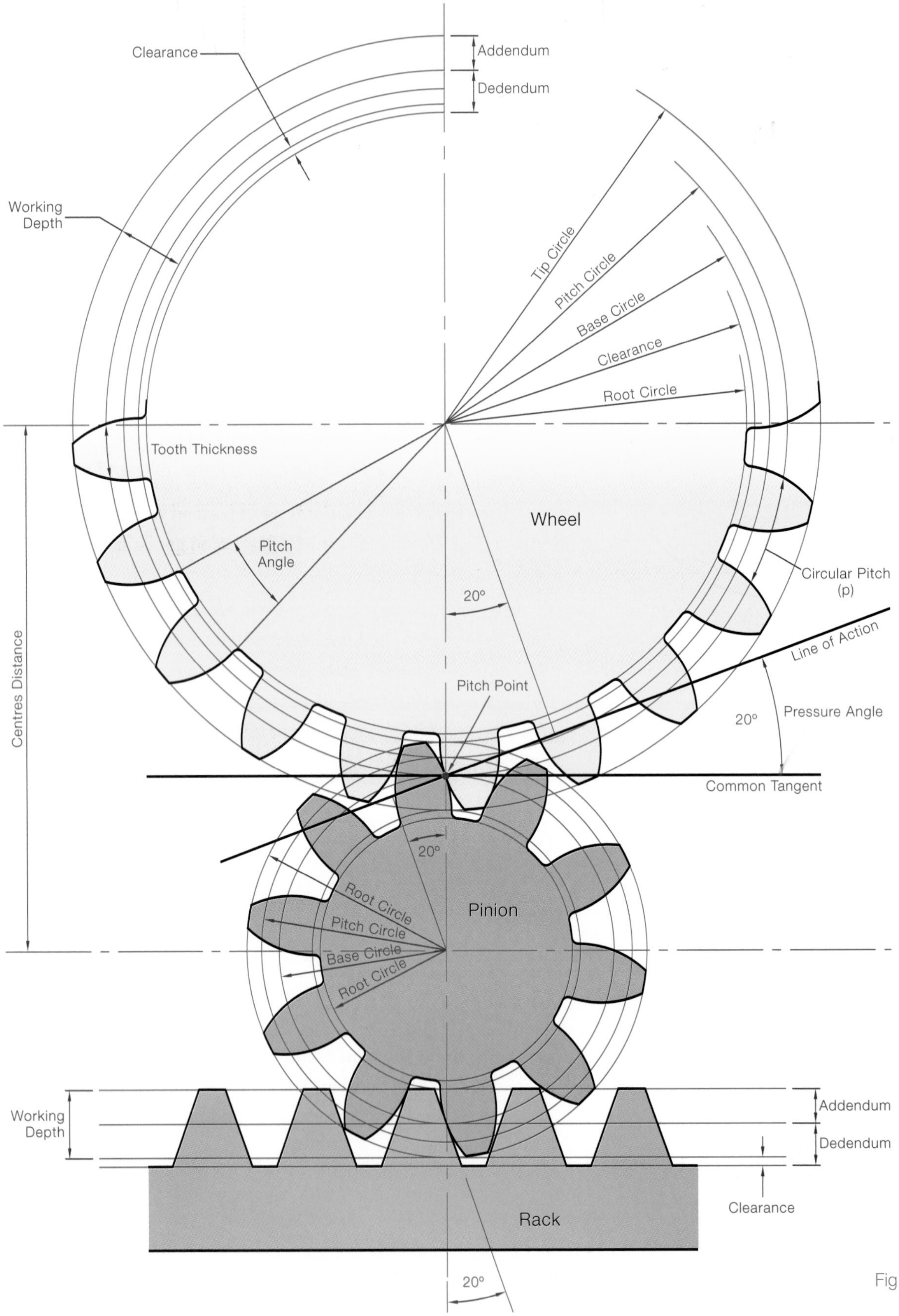

HIGHER LEVEL

Clearance

Addendum

Dedendum

Working Depth

Tip Circle

Pitch Circle

Base Circle

Clearance

Root Circle

Tooth Thickness

Centres Distance

Pitch Angle

Wheel

20°

Circular Pitch (p)

Line of Action

20°

Pressure Angle

Pitch Point

Common Tangent

20°

Root Circle

Pitch Circle

Base Circle

Root Circle

Pinion

Working Depth

Addendum

Dedendum

Clearance

Rack

20°

Fig. 17.134

Addendum (a)	The part of the tooth that extends outside the pitch circle or pitchline. The addendum will always equal the module. **a = m**
Base Circle	An imaginary circle from which the tooth shape is generated. The base circle diameter = the pitch circle diameter × cos (pressure angle) BCD = PCD × cos (pressure angle)
Circular Pitch (p)	Circular pitch is the distance from a point on one tooth to the corresponding point on the next tooth, measured round the pitch circle. **p = πm**
Circular Tooth Thickness	The thickness of a tooth measured along the pitch circle. **Circular tooth thickness** $= \dfrac{p}{2} = \dfrac{\pi m}{s}$
Clearance (c)	Clearance equals one quarter of the addendum. The clearance is the space underneath the tooth when it is in mesh. **c = d − a = 0.25a = 0.25 m**
Dedendum (d)	The part of the tooth which is inside the pitch circle or pitch line. The dedendum equals 1.25 × addendum. **d = 1.25 × a**
Line of Action	Contact between the teeth of meshing gears takes place along a line tangential to the two base circles. This line passes through the pitch point.
Module (m)	The module is the pitch circle diameter divided by the number of teeth. $$m = \frac{PCD}{t} = \frac{\text{Pitch circle diameter}}{\text{No. of teeth}}$$ For example, a gear having a PCD of 200 and 20 teeth will have a module of 10.
PCD	Pitch circle diameter.
Pinion	When two gears are in mesh the smaller gear is called the pinion.
Pitch Angle	360° divided by the number of teeth.
Pitch Circle (PC)	This is the circle representing the original cylinder which transmitted motion by friction.
Pitch Point	When two gears are in mesh their pitch circles will be tangential to each other. The pitch point is the point of contact between these two circles.
Pressure Angle	The angle between the line of action and the common tangent to the pitch circles at the pitch point. The pressure angle is normally **20°** but may be **14.5°**.
Tip Circle	A circle through the tips of the teeth.
Wheel	When two gears are in mesh the larger one is called the wheel.
Whole Depth	This is the depth of a tooth from tip to root. The whole depth equals the addendum and dedendum.
Working Depth	The whole depth minus the clearance.

Gear Basics

We will start by considering the theoretically perfect gears – two toothless disks. These gears touch at a single point. The rotation of one gear is perfectly transmitted to the other. There is no friction between the gears and there is no friction or wear on the bearings. Unfortunately, if these gears are not held tightly together they will slip. Furthermore, when they are held tightly together we will have friction and wear on the gears themselves and on the bearings and we will have a considerable loss of power.

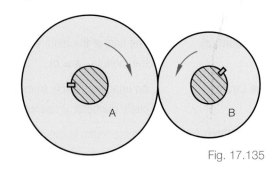

Fig. 17.135

To overcome this difficulty we cut teeth into the disks, so that they will engage each other without slipping and without unduly increasing the friction. **The diameters of these perfect, toothless, gears is the Pitch Circle diameters of the gears.**

Gear teeth

The aim when designing teeth shape is that the faces of the teeth will roll across each other, minimising the sliding friction. There are two types of curves commonly used, epicycloidal (the curve generated by tracing a point on a circle as it rolls around another circle) and involute (the curve generated by unwinding a line from a circle).

Gear ratio

The relative speed of rotation of the two disks is proportional to their radii. Since the circumferences of the circles are in contact a point on the circumference of disk A will move the same distance as a point on the circumference of disk B as they both rotate.

$$\text{Circumference large disk A } 2\pi R \quad : \quad \text{Circumference of smaller disk B } 2\pi r$$
$$2\pi R \quad : \quad 2\pi r$$
$$R \quad : \quad r$$

The ratio of the relational speeds is called the **gear ratio**. If the wheel has a PCD of 100 mm and the pinion has a PCD of 50 mm then the gear ratio will be 2:1. The pinion rotates twice as fast as the wheel. This, of course, will only apply if both **gears have the same pressure angle and module.**

Gear tooth design

As mentioned previously the ideal for all gearing is to have only rolling contact between the tooth surfaces of mating gear teeth, thus reducing both wear and friction. When two teeth interact as a pair of gears rotate, the mating curves must satisfy certain conditions to obtain this rolling action. Given almost any reasonable curve for one tooth, a mating tooth can be derived that will give this rolling action. Such a pair of curves are said to be **conjugate**. It is especially neat if the two conjugate curves are based on the same construction. Involute gears satisfy this requirement.

Involute Gears

A piece of string is wrapped tightly around a disk. Unwind the free end, keeping the string tight at all times. The free end as it unravels will trace out an involute curve, Fig. 17.136. By using the same construction for another disk, another involute is formed which is conjugate to the first. Use these two curves, or parts of them, as the sides of gear teeth and the teeth will roll together as they mesh. Modern machinery uses involute gearing predominantly.

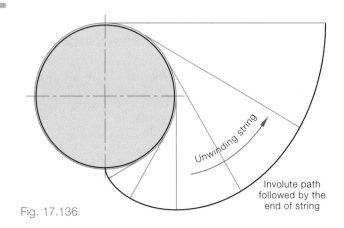

Fig. 17.136

Unwinding string

Involute path followed by the end of string

Epicycloidal Gears

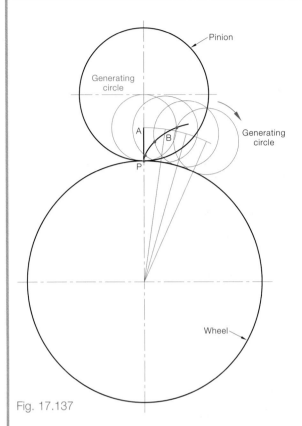

Fig. 17.137

Cycloidal gearing requires two different curves to obtain conjugate action. Fig. 17.137 shows two disks, the wheel and the pinion. A third disk is introduced which is used to generate the tooth profile. If we plot the path of point P on the generating circle as it rolls around the outside of the wheel circle it generates curve B, which is an epicycloid. Using the same generating circle to roll on the inside of the pinion circle a conjugate curve is formed which is a hypocycloid. When the generating circle has a diameter equal to the radius of the pinion circle, the hypocycloid formed is a straight line, A, as shown. The addendum of the wheel is an epicycloid curve B and the dedendum of the pinion is a hypocycloid, straight line A in this example.

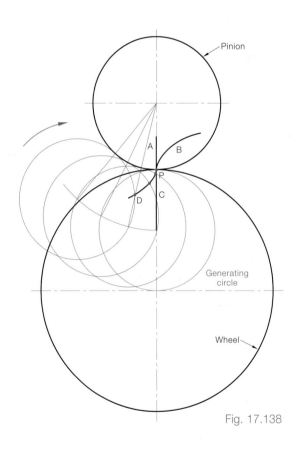

Fig. 17.138

In the same way a generating circle in the wheel generates the flank C of the tooth on the lower gear and the addendum D of the pinion, Fig. 17.138. Between them the two generating circles have generated the tooth shape for each of the two gears. Of particular interest here is that if the sizes of the generating circles are chosen carefully the dedendum of the teeth will be radial straight lines. Fig. 17.139 shows the proof that a hypocycloid generated by a circle rolling inside a circle of twice its radius will be a straight line.

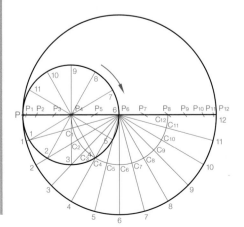

Fig. 17.139

Law of Gearing

Gears are arranged to have sliding contact between pairs of surfaces formed by the teeth of the gears, the rotation of the gears bringing successive pairs into contact. The teeth surfaces in sliding contact have a common tangent and the pressure being exerted between these two teeth will be normal to this tangent. This normal forms the line of action for the gears shown in Fig. 17.140. The line of action and the common tangent between the pitch circles form an angle, the pressure angle. For involute gears this pressure angle is a constant and is usually 20° or 14.5°. For cycloidal gear teeth the pressure angle is variable, becoming zero for contact at the pitch point.

In order that gear motion is smooth, quiet and free from vibration, the Law of Gearing must be satisfied.

> **Law of Gearing**
> The normal to the common tangent between two gear teeth surfaces must pass through the pitch point of the gears.

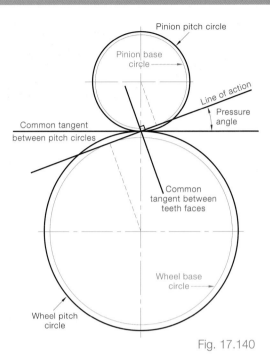

Fig. 17.140

HIGHER LEVEL

Some Things to Note about the Size of the Generating Circle

We have already noted that by using a pair of generating circles having radii equal to half that of the pitch circles, it produces the neat result of generating **radial dedenda** for each gear tooth. If the generating circle is **smaller** than half the radius of the pitch circle, the roots of the teeth are wider and stronger but not radial. A generating circle **larger** than half the radius of the pitch circle produces undercut, necked teeth which may be weak.

The teeth of a cycloidal rack are cycloids generated by the rolling generating circle. They are not straight, like they are in an involute rack, and their shape depends on the radius of the generating circle.

Worked Examples

> Given a pitch circle diameter of 160 mm and a module of 10 construct the spur gear. Show teeth on half the gear and use conventions for the other half. Teeth to be constructed by the involute method. Pressure angle 20°.

(1) Draw the pitch circle, tip circle and root circle. We are given the pitch circle diameter of 160 mm or radius 80 mm. The addendum equals the module. Therefore the addendum equals 10 mm. The tip circle radius will be equal to the radius of the pitch circle plus the addendum, 80 mm + 10 mm = 90 mm. The root circle radius will be equal to the radius of the pitch circle minus the dedendum. The dedendum will be 12.5 mm, therefore the root circle radius will be 67.5 mm (dedendum = 1.25 module).

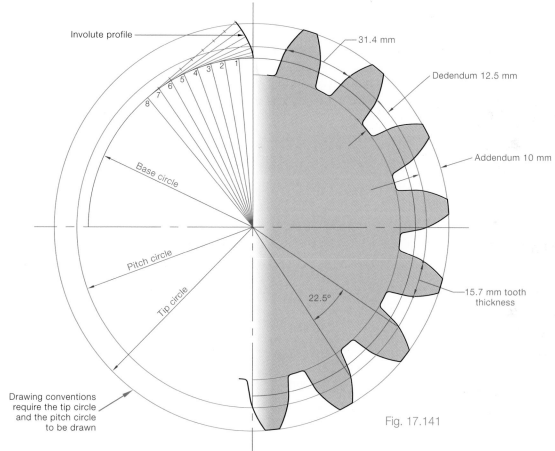

Fig. 17.141

(2) Calculate the radius of the base circle, the circle from which the tooth profile is generated.

Base circle diameter = Pitch circle diameter × cos (pressure angle)

$$BCD = 160 \text{ mm} \times \cos 20°$$
$$BCD = 150.4 \text{ mm}$$

Draw the base circle.

(3) Calculate the number of teeth.

$$PCD = \text{module (m)} \times \text{number of teeth (t)}$$
$$\Rightarrow \quad \frac{PCD}{m} \quad t$$
$$\frac{160}{10} = 16 \text{ teeth}$$

(4) Calculate the circular pitch, the distance from one point on a tooth to a similar point on the next.

$$p = \pi m$$
$$p = 31.4 \text{ mm}$$

The tooth thickness measured on the pitch circle equals half of this, 15.7 mm.

The angular pitch equals $\dfrac{360°}{t} = \dfrac{360°}{16} = 22.5°$

(5) Set out the teeth spacing on the pitch circle either by angular measurement or by measurement along the circumference.

(6) Generate one involute from the **base circle** which is used to draw all the teeth profiles. The construction of an involute has been covered earlier and is shown on Fig. 17.141. The involute is unwound until the tip circle is reached.

(7) The portion of the dedendum inside the base circle usually radiates toward the centre or can curve slightly.

(8) For the other half only the pitch circle and the tip circle are drawn.

> **Draw two involute spur gears showing the gears in mesh. Show five teeth on each gear. The gear ratio is 5:4.**
> **Driver gear details: module 10, 20 teeth, pressure angle 20°.**
> **Tabulate all necessary data for the two gears.**

Driver Gear			Driven Gear		
Module (m)		10	Module (m)		10
No. of teeth (t)		20	No. of teeth (t)	5:4 = 20:16	16
Pressure angle (θ)		20°	Pressure angle (θ)		20°
Pitch circle diameter	m × t	200 mm	Pitch circle diameter	m × t	160 mm
Base circle diameter	PCD × cos θ	188 mm	Base circle diameter	PCD × cos θ	150.4 mm
Addendum (a)	a = m	10 mm	Addendum (a)	a = m	10 mm
Dedendum (d)	1.25 × a	12.5 mm	Dedendum (d)	1.25 × a	12.5 mm
Clearance	0.25 × m	2.5 mm	Clearance	0.25 × m	2.5 mm
Tip circle diameter	PCD + a + a	220 mm	Tip circle diameter	PCD + a + a	180 mm
Root circle diameter	PCD – d – d	175 mm	Root circle diameter	PCD – d – d	135 mm
Circular pitch (p)	π × m	31.4 mm	Circular pitch (p)	π × m	31.4 mm
Tooth thickness	$\frac{p}{2}$	15.7 mm	Tooth thickness	$\frac{p}{2}$	15.7 mm
Pitch angle	$\frac{360°}{t}$	18°	Pitch angle	$\frac{360°}{t}$	22.5°

HIGHER LEVEL

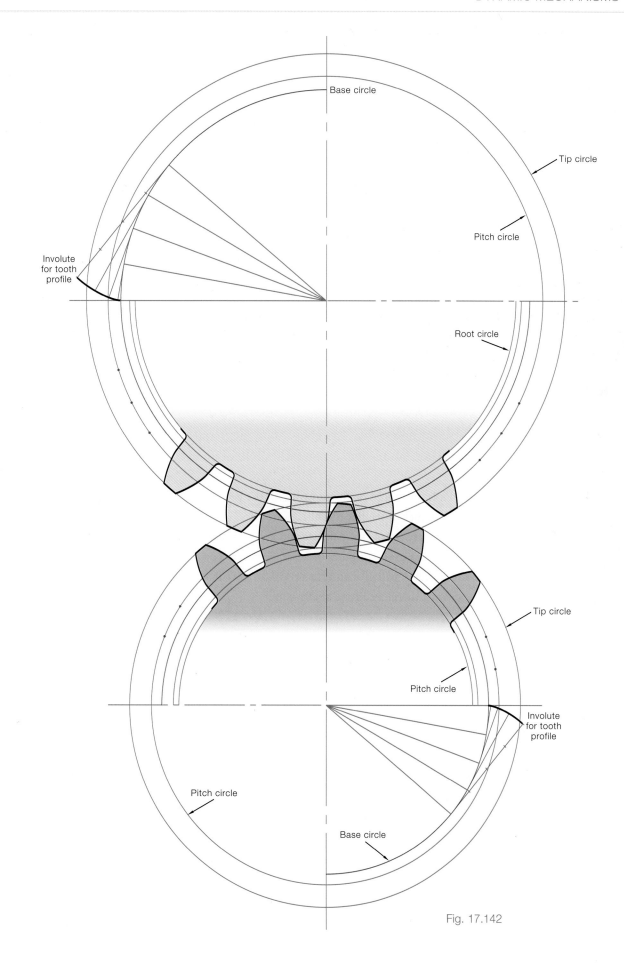

Base circle

Tip circle

Pitch circle

Involute
for tooth
profile

Root circle

Tip circle

Pitch circle

Involute
for tooth
profile

Pitch circle

Base circle

Fig. 17.142

Fig. 17.143 shows a spur gear train. Draw the following table. Complete it by inserting the missing gear train information.

Gear	Teeth	Module	PCD	Rotation	Speed rpm
A	36	6		Clockwise	300
B	24				
C	12				

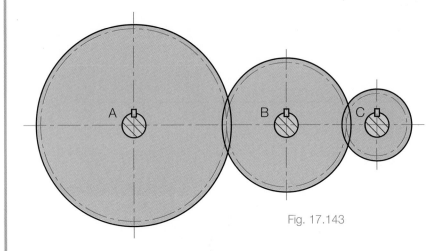

Fig. 17.143

Solution

(1) The module for meshing gears in a train should be the same for all the gears or they will vibrate and wear badly.

(2) The PCD, pitch circle diameter = number of teeth × module.

(3) The rotation of gears in a train alternates between clockwise and anti-clockwise.

(4) The speed of the rotating gears is related to the number of teeth. For every complete turn of gear A, gear B must rotate 1.5 times. An rpm of 300 for gear A will give an rpm of 450 for gear B. Gear C rotates twice for every complete turn of gear B. The smallest gear must therefore rotate at 900 rpm.

Gear	Teeth	Module	PCD	Rotation	Speed rpm
A	36	6	216	Clockwise	300
B	24	6	144	Anti-clockwise	450
C	12	6	72	Clockwise	900

An involute gear wheel with 24 teeth, 20° pressure angle and module 10 is in mesh with a rack. Draw full-size, the gear and rack in mesh, showing five teeth on the gear and five teeth on the rack.
Tabulate all relevant information and calculations.

Gear Wheel			Rack	
Module (m)		10	Module	10
No. of teeth (t)		24	Pressure angle	20°
Pressure angle (θ)		20°	Addendum	10 mm
Pitch circle diameter	m × t	240 mm	Dedendum	12.5 mm
Base circle diameter	PCD × cos θ	225.5 mm	Clearance	2.5 mm
Addendum (a)	a = m	10 mm	Pitch	31.4 mm
Dedendum (d)	1.25 × a	12.5 mm	Tooth thickness	15.7 mm
Clearance	d × a	2.5 mm		
Tip circle diameter	PCD + 2a	260 mm		
Root circle diameter	PCD − 2d	215 mm		
Circular pitch (p)	π × m	31.4 mm		
Tooth thickness	$\dfrac{p}{2}$	15.7 mm		
Pitch angle	$\dfrac{360°}{t}$	22.5°		

(1) Draw the pitch circle, tip circle and root circle.

(2) The base circle can be found by calculation or by finding the circle that is tangential to the line of action.

(3) Draw the pitch line, tip line and root line for the rack. The pitch line and pitch circle are tangential at point P.

(4) Construct the involute tooth profile from the base circle and using tracing paper reproduce this curve to pass through point P.

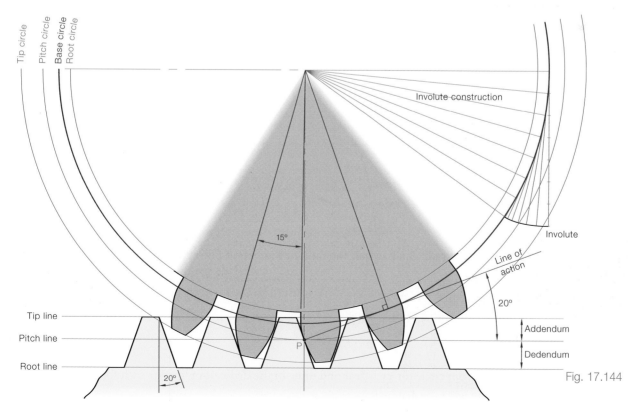

Fig. 17.144

(5) The circular pitch, measured along the pitch circle, is 31.4 mm or 15°. Construct five teeth using these spacings.

(6) The rack should be considered to be a gear of infinite radius. The tooth thickness is measured along the pitch line and the tooth angle is 20° as shown in Fig. 17.144.

> **A cycloidal gear wheel with 18 teeth and a module of 10 is in mesh with a cycloidal pinion gear with 12 teeth and module of 10. Draw full-size, the gears in mesh showing five teeth on each gear. The generating circles used are to produce radial dedenda on each gear.**

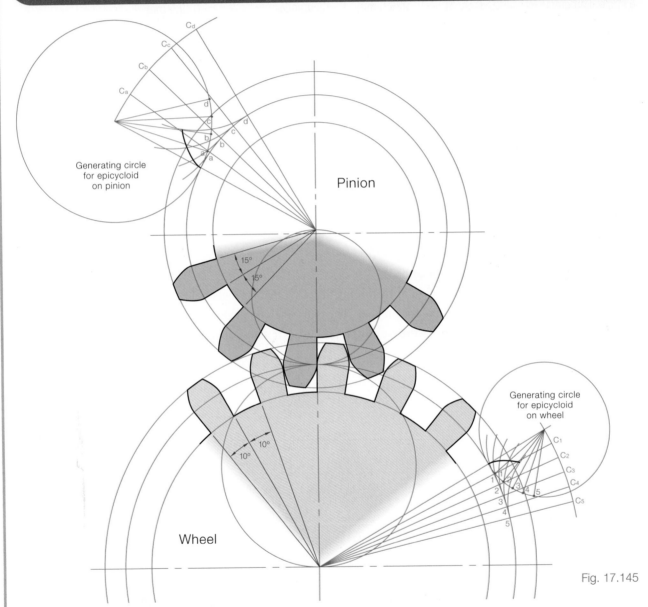

Fig. 17.145

(1) The generating circles will have radii equal to half the radii of the pinion pitch circle and the wheel pitch circle.

(2) Wheel PCD = 18 × 10 = 180 mm.

Pinion PCD = 12 × 10 = 120 mm.

(3) Draw the two pitch circles tangential to each other.

(4) Pitch angle for the wheel 360° ÷ 18 = 20°

Pitch angle for the pinion 360° ÷ 12 = 30°

(5) Draw the tip circle and the root circle for each gear and draw in the dedendum line for each tooth based on the pitch angle and the fact that they will be radial lines.

(6) Use the generating circle rolling along the pitch circle to produce the epicycloidal curve for the gear tooth.

(7) Use tracing paper to duplicate the curves.

> A cycloidal pinion with 20 teeth and a module of 10 is in mesh with a rack. Draw full-size, the rack and pinion in mesh showing five teeth on the pinion and six teeth on the rack. The pinion is to have radial dedenda.

HIGHER LEVEL

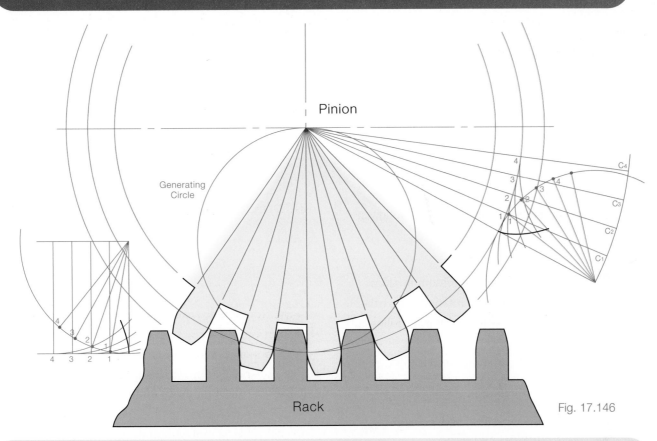

Fig. 17.146

Pinion Details

Module (m)		10
No. of teeth (t)		20
Pressure angle (θ)		20°
Pitch circle diameter	m × t	200 mm
Base circle diameter	PCD × cos θ	225.5 mm
Addendum (a)	a = m	10 mm
Dedendum (d)	1.25 × a	12.5 mm
Clearance	d × a	2.5 mm
Tip circle diameter	PCD + 2a	220 mm
Root circle diameter	PCD − 2d	175 mm
Circular pitch (p)	π × m	31.4 mm
Tooth thickness	$\frac{p}{2}$	15.7 mm
Pitch angle	$\frac{360°}{t}$	18°

Rack Details

Module	10
Addendum	10 mm
Dedendum	12.5 mm
Clearance	2.5 mm
Tooth thickness	15.7 mm

> The construction of the solution is similar to the previous example. Note that the same sized generating circle is used for the pinion and rack. The teeth of the rack have parallel-sided dedenda and cycloidal addenda.

Activities

CAMS

Q1. A plate cam rotating clockwise is to give an in-line, knife-edge follower the following motion.

0–120°   lift 32 mm with uniform velocity
120–180°   dwell
180–360°   fall 32 mm with simple harmonic motion

(i) Draw the cam profile if the minimum cam radius is 38 mm and the camshaft diameter is 24 mm.
(ii) Draw the displacement diagram for the follower.

Q2.
(i) Draw a radial cam with minimum radius of 36 mm and clockwise rotation to give the following motion to a knife-edge follower.

0–120°   rise 30 mm with simple harmonic motion
120–210°   rise of 22 mm with uniform velocity
210–360°   fall of 52 mm with uniform acceleration and retardation

(ii) Draw the displacement diagram for the follower.

Q3. Draw a radial cam with a minimum radius of 30 mm and anti-clockwise rotation to give the following motion to an in-line, knife-edge follower.

0–90°   rise 30 mm with uniform velocity
90–120°   dwell
120–210°   rise 20 mm with simple harmonic motion
210–360°   fall to initial position with uniform acceleration and retardation

Q4. Draw a radial cam with minimum radius of 30 mm and clockwise rotation to give the following motion to an in-line, knife-edge follower.

0–90°   rise 30 mm with simple harmonic motion
90–240°   rise 24 mm with uniform acceleration and retardation
240–360°   fall 54 mm with uniform velocity

Q5. Fig. 17.147 shows the profile of a radial cam, which operates a knife-edge follower.
(i)   Draw the cam.
(ii) Draw the displacement diagram for this cam showing displacement per second. The cam rotates at 6 revolutions per minute.

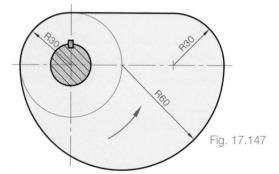
Fig. 17.147

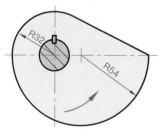
Fig. 17.148

Q6. Fig. 17.148 shows the profile of a radial cam, which operates a knife-edge follower.
(i)   Draw the cam.
(ii) Draw the follower displacement diagram showing displacement per second. The cam turns once every 18 seconds.

Q7. Fig. 17.149 shows the profile of a radial plate cam, which operates a knife-edge follower.

(i) Draw the cam.

(ii) Draw the follower displacement diagram showing displacement every second. The cam rotates 2 times per minute.

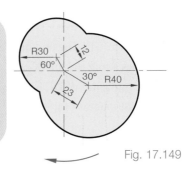

Fig. 17.149

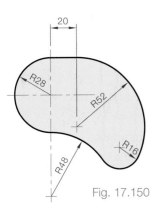

Fig. 17.150

Q8. Fig. 17.150 shows the profile of a radial plate cam which operates a knife-edge follower and rotates 3 times per minute.

(i) Draw the cam.

(ii) Draw the follower displacement diagram showing displacement every second.

MECHANISMS

Q9. Crank O₁A rotates about O₁. Arm O₂A rotates about O₂. The joints A, B and C are pin joints. D slides along the path indicated.

(i) Draw the locus of C for one revolution of crank O₁A.

(ii) Draw a displacement diagram for slider D.

O₁A = 25 mm   CD = 62 mm
AB = 74 mm   O₂A = 62 mm
BC = 50mm

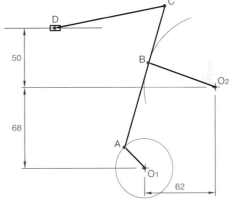

Fig. 17.151

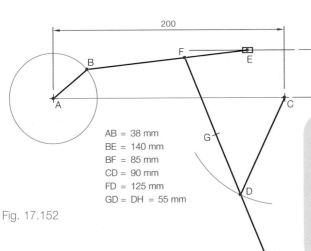

AB = 38 mm
BE = 140 mm
BF = 85 mm
CD = 90 mm
FD = 125 mm
GD = DH = 55 mm

Fig. 17.152

Q10. Crank AB rotates about A for one revolution. Arm CD rotates about C. Joints B, D and F are pin joints. E slides along the path shown.

(i) Draw the locus of point G and point H for the movement.

(ii) Draw the displacement diagram for slider E for one revolution of the crank.

Q11. Crank AB rotates about A. Arm CD rotates about point C. Joint B slides along the arm CD. The end of the connecting rod DE slides along the line X–X.

(i)   Plot the locus of the midpoint of DE for one full revolution.

(ii)   Draw the displacement diagram for point E.

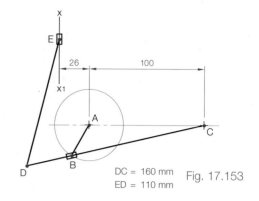

DC = 160 mm
ED = 110 mm

Fig. 17.153

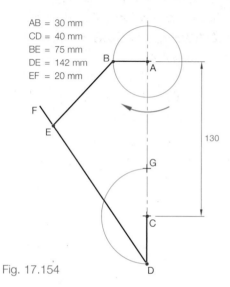

AB = 30 mm
CD = 40 mm
BE = 75 mm
DE = 142 mm
EF = 20 mm

130

Fig. 17.154

Q12. Crank AB rotates about A for one revolution. Arm CD rotates about C. Arm CD rotates to G and back for one revolution of AB. Joints B, D and E are pin joints.

Draw the locus of F for one full revolution of the crank.

CAMS

Q13. Draw the profile and displacement diagram for a cam rotating in an anti-clockwise direction. The cam has a minimum radius of 40 mm. The follower is a 24 mm diameter roller and has the following motion:

0–90°	rise of 30 mm with uniform velocity
90–180°	dwell
180–270°	rise of 20 mm with simple harmonic motion
270–300°	fall of 15 mm with simple harmonic motion
300–360°	fall of 35 mm with uniform velocity

Q14. Construct a cam profile to give an in-line, flat-ended follower the following motion. Follower base extends 8 mm each side of the centre line.

0–60°	dwell
60–180°	rise of 40 mm with uniform acceleration and retardation
180–210°	dwell
210–360°	fall of 40 mm with simple harmonic motion

The cam rotates clockwise and its minimum radius is 30 mm.

HIGHER LEVEL

Q15. Draw the profile and follower displacement diagram for a cam rotating in a clockwise direction. The cam has a minimum radius of 40 mm and has an in-line roller follower of 20 mm diameter.

0–120°	rise of 40 mm with uniform acceleration and retardation
120–210º	fall of 20 mm with simple harmonic motion
210–270°	dwell
270–360°	fall of 20 mm with uniform velocity

Q16. A plate cam rotates anti-clockwise at 5 rpm. The cam gives an in-line roller follower of 9 mm radius the following motion:

Lift of 40 mm with simple harmonic motion in 3 seconds. Dwell for 1.5 seconds.
Fall 18 mm with uniform velocity in 2 seconds.
Fall 22 mm with uniform acceleration and retardation in 4 seconds. Dwell for the remainder of the revolution.

The nearest approach of the roller centre to the cam centre is 52 mm.

Given the above information, draw the cam profile and the follower displacement diagram.

Q17. Draw the follower displacement diagram and the cam profile of a plate cam rotating clockwise which gives a flat-ended follower the following motion:

0–120°	rise 30 mm with uniform acceleration and retardation
120–180º	dwell
180–240°	rise 16 mm with uniform velocity
240–360°	fall 46 mm with simple harmonic motion

The follower extends 7 mm each side of the centre line. The minimum diameter of the cam is 40 mm.

GEARS: INVOLUTE TEETH

Q18. Draw full-size, five teeth of an involute gear. The gear is to have 32 teeth of module 6 and a pressure angle of 20°.

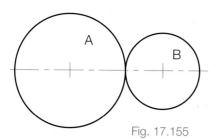

Fig. 17.155

Q19. Gear A has 24 teeth and a module of 8. Gear B has 16 teeth and a module of 8. Show 4 teeth in mesh on each gear and use conventions for the rest of the gears.

HIGHER LEVEL

Q20. The centre distances of two involute spur gears is 180 mm. The gear ratio is 5:4. The module is 10 and the pressure angle is 20°.

(i) Calculate all relevant information and show it in tabular form.

(ii) Draw the profile of the gear wheels showing three teeth from each wheel in mesh.

Q21. A pinion with 16 teeth is to mesh with a rack whose teeth have a pressure angle of 20° and an addendum of 12 mm. The travel of the rack is to be 250 mm.

Draw all the teeth on the rack and five teeth in mesh on the pinion. Tabulate all necessary data. The teeth of the pinion are of involute form.

GEARS: EPICYCLOIDAL TEETH

Q22. A cycloidal gear wheel with 20 teeth and module of 12 is in mesh with a cycloidal gear pinion. The gear ratio is 5:3. Both gears have radial dedenda.

(i) Calculate all relevant information and show it in tabular form.

(ii) Draw the profile of the gear wheels in mesh, showing five teeth on each gear.

Q23. A pinion with 15 teeth is to mesh with a rack. The pinion has cycloidal teeth form and a module of 12. Its dedenda are to be radial.

(i) Calculate all relevant data and show it in tabular form.

(ii) Draw the profile of the rack and pinion in mesh showing five teeth on each.

18 Structural Forms

SYLLABUS OUTLINE

Areas to be studied (in an applied context):

- Structural forms, natural and manufactured. • Singly and doubly ruled surfaces. • The hyperbolic paraboloid as a ruled surface. • *The hyperbolic paraboloid as a surface of translation.* • Plane directors. • The hyperboloid of revolution, projections and sections. • Sections through singly and doubly ruled surfaces. • *The geodesic dome of not more than four points of frequency.*

Learning outcomes

Students should be able to:

Higher and Ordinary levels
- Investigate the development of structural forms in a historical context.
- Identify the key structural forms including arches, domes, vaults, frames and surface structures.
- Produce line drawings of the basic structural forms.
- Produce two-dimensional drawings of arches, domes, vaults and surface structures.
- Construct a hyperbolic paraboloid as a ruled surface.
- Determine the true shape of sections through curved surfaces.
- Project views and sections of a hyperboloid of revolution.

Higher level only
- *Relate the key properties of structural forms to their design and construction.*
- *Produce three-dimensional drawings of arches, domes, vaults and surface structures.*
- *Determine plane directors for ruled surfaces, and construct ruled surfaces given plane directors and directrices.*
- *Project views of a hyperbolic paraboloid defined as a surface of translation.*
- *Construct geodesic domes of not more than four points of frequency.*
- *Investigate and represent structural forms as they occur in the environment.*

In this chapter we will be looking at the historical development of some common structural forms including the arch, the dome and the vault. We will then move on to look at some structural forms of special interest, the hyperbolic parabaloid and the hyperboloid of revolution.

Column and Beam

Using columns and beams is the simplest way to make an opening in a wall. The column or post is the vertical member and the beam is the horizontal member. The beam supports the weight (load) above it and its own weight. This weight is then transferred to the columns and from these to the lower structure. This type of construction was used in prehistoric times and is still used in modern day structures.

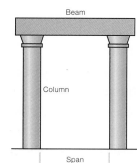

Fig. 18.1

The range of materials available to ancient Romans, Egyptians and Greeks was quite limited (timber and stone) and therefore the spans that could be crossed with beams were relatively short. Stone, in particular, is weak in bending. The longer the beam is, the more likely it is to bend. Long stone beams would be susceptible to failure. Furthermore, since a beam is a single member, it was difficult to obtain in long lengths. Modern day materials such as steel and concrete allow longer spans, particularly when used together.

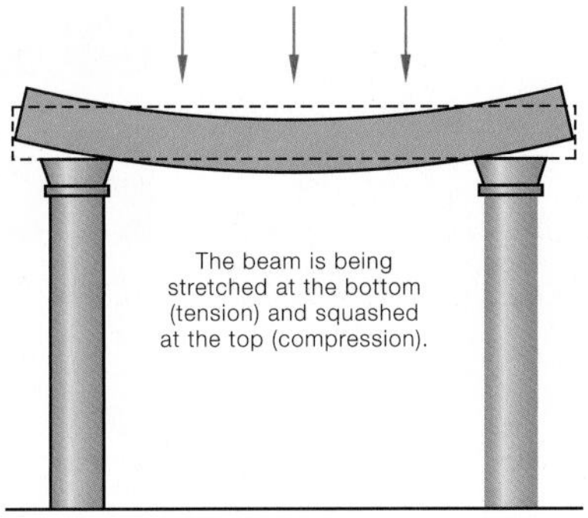

A bending beam is under compression at the top and under tension at the bottom. Concrete is very strong in compression and is good at the top of the beam. Steel is strong in tension and is good at the bottom of the beam. Steel and concrete together make a strong beam.

The construction of columns presented less problems in ancient times for two reasons. Firstly, columns are fundamentally members under compression and the main building material, stone, is excellent under compression. Secondly, columns could be made up from small segments stacked on top of each other. The load when applied actually compresses the joints making it stronger.

Fig. 18.2

The Arch

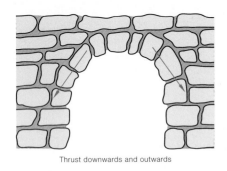

Thrust downwards and outwards

Fig. 18.3

The arch was developed as a means of crossing larger spans than was practical/possible with monolithic stone beams. The arch spans an opening without using any beams at all, just a lot of small stones or bricks. These smaller building elements support each other.

The invention of the arch is credited to the Etruscans, before the Roman Empire was established. The Etruscans used the arch for gates, bridges and drains. When the Roman Empire conquered the Etruscans, they adopted the arch into their architecture and used it widely when building bridges, aqueducts, gates, entrances etc.

The forces exerted by an arch, because of its bend upwards, tend to be both downwards and outwards. The walls to the side of an arch must be of sufficient mass to counteract this diagonal thrust. A single arch therefore will not be stable on two columns unless the columns are heavy enough to buttress against these forces. A series of arches will buttress each other and may be supported on light columns.

Arch Terminology

Centre – the centre(s) from which the curve(s) of the arch is drawn.
Extrado – the top or outer surface of a voussoir.
Intrado – the bottom or inner surface of a voissoir.
Rise – the vertical distance from the spring line to the highest point on the inner curve of the arch
Span – the inner width of the arch.

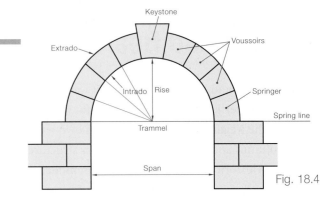

Fig. 18.4

Spring Line – the line from which the curve of the arch starts.

Springer – the first voussoir on the left and the right of the arch.

Voussoirs – the individual elements that make up the arch. Usually tapered.

Arch Shapes

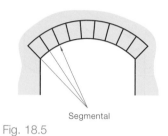

Segmental

Fig. 18.5

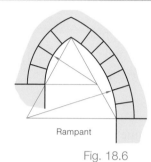

Rampant

Fig. 18.6

A segmental arch forms a curve which is a segment of a larger arch.

A rampant arch is one that starts at one level and finishes at another.

There are a large variety of arch shapes. Some of these are shown below. For each arch shape the joint lines of the voissoirs are generally normals to the inside curve.

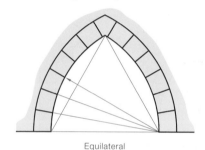

Equilateral

Fig. 18.7a

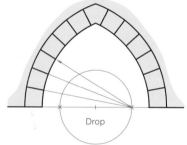

Drop

Fig. 18.7b

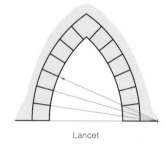

Lancet

Fig. 18.7c

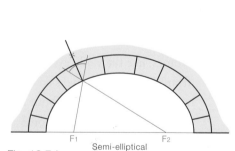

F₁   Semi-elliptical   F₂

Fig. 18.7d

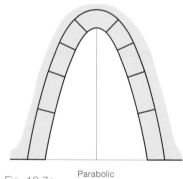

Parabolic

Fig. 18.7e

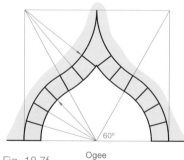

60°

Ogee

Fig. 18.7f

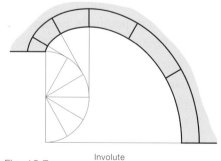

Involute

Fig. 18.7g

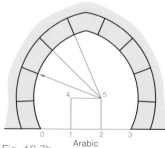

4   5

0   1   2   3

Arabic

Fig. 18.7h

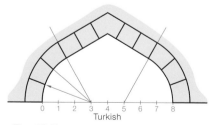

0 1 2 3 4 5 6 7 8

Turkish

Fig. 18.7i

The Vault

The logical progression from the arch is the vault. When the arch is deepened enough to form a part of a cylinder or barrel we have a vault.

The Egyptians were one of the first civilisations to have a widespread use of the vault. They used the vault in tombs, storage rooms and drains. The Romans later adopted the vault into their architecture and developed it further to form the groined vault.

A groined vault is made up from two barrel vaults of the same size and height joining each other at right angles. It will cover a square area. The lines of intersection are called the groins. For a groined vault the whole roof area is supported on four corner piers. This opened up the floor area and was used to great advantage in the construction of large buildings. Many medieval cathedrals show great examples of both barrel and groined vaults.

The construction of a vault consisted of building an arch at the ends. Between the arches a long tunnel was formed from concrete. Centerings or temporary supports were introduced to support the concrete while the vault was being constructed. Buttresses were often used to give the heavy vaults support.

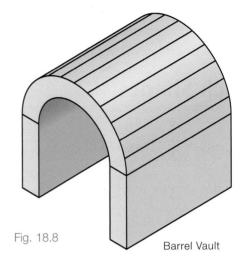

Fig. 18.8

Barrel Vault

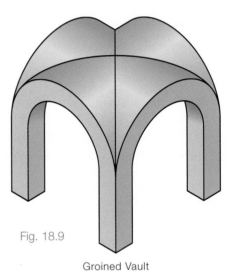

Fig. 18.9

Groined Vault

Domes

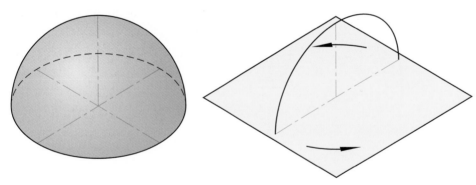

Fig. 18.10

Domes, like the vault, evolved from the arch. A dome is an arch which has been rotated about its centre line. The masonry dome was first constructed around 100 AD by the Romans. The forces exerted by a dome are equal all around its perimeter. Because of the limited variety of building materials available at these times (stone and cement), the domes that were constructed were heavy, requiring extensive buttressing.

The availability of steel to architects and builders in the nineteenth century made dome construction less difficult. Steel has a high strength-to-weight ratio compared to stone and it can also be made into continuous forms. For awkward shapes like domes, this is a great advantage.

The geodesic dome, which is a skeletal frame of a spherical dome, was developed by Buckminster Fuller in the 1940s. It is a lightweight construction and generally sits at ground level.

Most domes are created by rotating a semicircle or similar curve about a centre line.

A parabola, hyperbola, semi-ellipse or similar but non-regular curve will produce a dome. However, the curve must be convex as opposed to concave. In other words, it must bulge outwards.

The geodesic dome is a dome created with triangles. It is structurally very stable and can be built to a very large scale. Its construction is not based on rotation of a curve about an axis but rather on the platonic solids. More on the geodesic dome later.

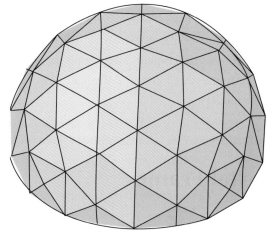

Fig. 18.11

Frames

There are many examples in modern architecture where frames of one type or another are used to speed up and expand the limits of the construction process. The prefabricated frame can be made in ideal conditions, with exact accuracy and to a uniform standard.

Lattice Girder

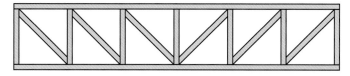

Fig. 18.12

It is only common sense that the wider the span that a beam has to cross, the larger that beam must be in cross-section. As the span widens it will eventually become uneconomical to span across it with solid section beams because of the amount of material used. The lattice girder (Fig. 18.12) provides a strong, light alternative. The lattice girder will be deeper and wider than the solid beam, yet uses less actual material and is stronger if constructed properly.

The lattice girder is broken into triangles. The triangle is the most stable geometric shape and will not be distorted in shape unless one of its sides is lengthened or shortened. Pin-jointing at the ends of each member produces a well-braced, stable frame.

Truss

The triangular truss also bases its strength on triangulation. The larger triangle is often broken into smaller triangles using struts (members under compression) and ties (members under tension). The resulting frame has very high strength in relation to the amount of material used. The truss, when in place, produces a vertical downward force on the walls. This type of frame is well-suited to the light wall construction of the modern day.

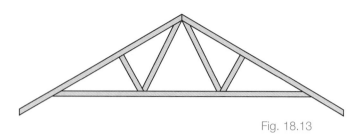

Fig. 18.13

Roof trusses may be constructed from timber or steel and vary hugely in shape and size.

Portal Frames

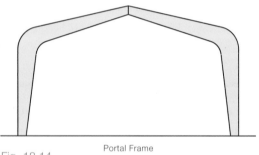

Fig. 18.14

Portal Frame

Portal frames may be constructed of reinforced concrete, steel and often laminated wood. The frame is thickened at the corners to help transfer the load from the top section to the vertical section. This type of frame is widely used in factory and warehouse construction because it forms walls and roof frame in the same unit. The portal frame is a relatively modern form of construction.

Surface Structures

A surface structure is one whose surface both encloses a space and provides support. The material used is usually reinforced concrete because of its strength and because of the versatility it offers in shape.

Slab

The simplest form of surface structure is the horizontal slab or the vertical panel. A slab combined with columns or vertical panels will quickly create a structure which is self-supporting.

By folding or corrugating thin materials their stiffness can be increased enormously. This property has been applied to the simple slab to produce many varied types of surface structures called shell structures.

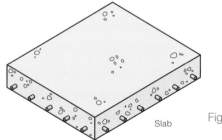

Slab

Fig. 18.15

Shell Structures

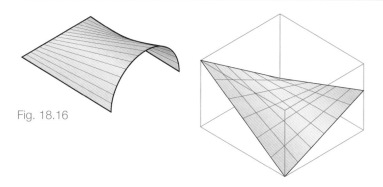

Fig. 18.16

These generate their strength from their shape rather than the thickness of material used. They are generally made from thin concrete with a mesh of steel reinforcement. Shell structures, as a building form, were first used in the twentieth century and were a result of improvements in cement and concrete production. The shapes produced by single shells or combinations of shells can be aesthetically pleasing and produce free-flowing designs. It is these shell structures which form our main topic of interest in this course and they will be examined in detail later on in this chapter.

Structures: Properties, Design and Construction

The Column

A column is a member under compression. The load is vertical downwards and is resisted by an equal upwards force. Columns do not, however, resist lateral thrust because of their height and slenderness. Concrete is an ideal material for building columns because of its high resistance to compression. Steel reinforcing would be used in the column to help prevent it from bulging under heavy load conditions. A thickening of the column at the head and base helps the transfer of loads from the beam above to the floor/foundation below. The column itself is often tapered inwards slightly for the top two-thirds of its height. This idea was developed by the ancient Greek architects and produced a column that appeared straight with parallel sides. If there is an increase in height of a column there must be a corresponding increase in thickness. This ratio, height to thickness, is called the Slenderness Ratio.

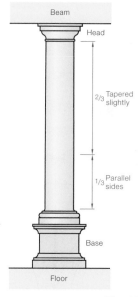

Beam
Head
2/3 Tapered slightly
1/3 Parallel sides
Base
Floor

Fig. 18.17

The Beam

A beam is a member under both tension and compression. The loads applied are usually perpendicular to the longitudinal axis. The beam develops internal stresses to resist these applied loads. Fig. 18.18 shows a loaded beam which is deflecting. The bottom of the beam is stretching and is therefore under tension. The top of the beam is shortening and is under compression. There is a neutral axis in the centre and both these forces increase as the top and bottom of the

HIGHER LEVEL

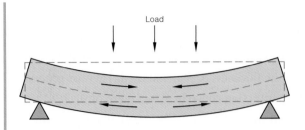

Fig. 18.18

beam are approached. A properly sized beam will bend very little but the load is supported by the beam's resistance to these forces.

Stone as a building material is weak under tension and therefore is not suitable for the construction of long beams – concrete is similar. Reinforced concrete, where the reinforcing is placed toward the bottom of the beam, produces a good beam because the steel provides good tensile strength where the concrete is at its weakest.

The Arch

The shape of the arch means that its upper edge (extrado) is longer than its inner edge (intrado). Each of the individual blocks or elements of the arch must therefore be wedge-shaped. They press against their neighbours on either side and are under compression. The load supported by the arch is passed from element to element until the sides of the arch are reached. The resulting downward and outward thrust must be resisted by the walls at the side, buttressed columns or the next arch in a row of arches.

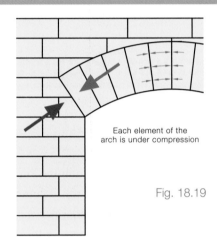

Each element of the arch is under compression

Fig. 18.19

The Vault

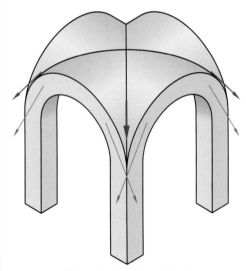

Oblique thrust from three different directions at each corner

Fig. 18.20

The barrel vault exerts the same forces on its supports as an arch does and must have heavy buttressing walls at the sides. The groined vault focuses these forces into the corners where heavy buttressed columns are used. A series of these groined vaults together will help support each other and in this case the columns will only need to support vertical forces and can be lightened considerably. Fig. 18.20 shows how the diagonal arch and two side arches direct the load in three different directions at each corner. Groined vaults are usually built to a square, grid, plan, layout and support each other.

HIGHER LEVEL

The Dome

The traditional masonry dome exerts thrust evenly all the way around its circumference. The supporting walls must be buttressed or be of very large mass to counteract these forces. The geodesic dome is usually of extremely light construction and because of all the triangulation is very stable. The geodesic dome will exert a downward force on its supports.

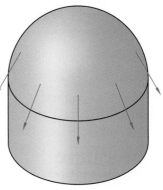

Fig. 18.21

Frames

HIGHER LEVEL

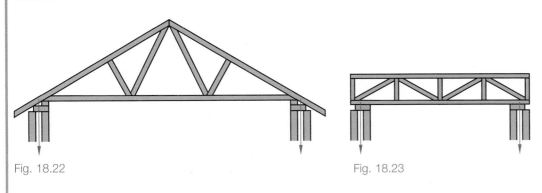

Fig. 18.22   Fig. 18.23

Lattice girders and trussed rafters base their strength on a series of triangles. The individual members may be struts (members under compression) or ties (members under tension). Both the lattice girder and the triangular truss are self-contained units and exert only a vertical load on their supports.

Shell Structures

When you think of shell structures, of whatever type, you think of thin, curved shells of concrete. They get their strength from their shape, not from their thickness. The shell of a bird's egg is both thin and brittle yet can withstand very large, evenly distributed loads. The curved shape helps distribute the load. Many shell structures used in modern architecture have a curved shape and yet can be made up from straight-line elements. This is helpful when constructing a reinforced concrete shell as the reinforcing bars do not need to be bent. It can also be helpful in the making of the framework.

Surface Structures

A surface may be considered to be generated by the motion of a line, the **generatrix**. Surfaces are divided into two groups:
(1)   Those that are generated by a moving straight line are called **Ruled Surfaces**.
(2)   These that are generated by a moving curved line are called **Double Curved Surfaces**.

Any position of the generatrix, be it a straight line or a curve, is called an **element** of the curve.

Ruled Surface

There are three types of ruled surface:

(1)   the plane,

(2)   the single curved surface,

(3)   the warped surface.

1. The Plane

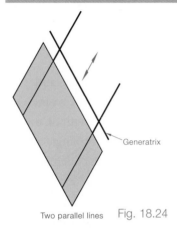

Two parallel lines   Fig. 18.24

The plane is generated by a straight line moving so as to touch two other parallel, straight lines, Fig. 18.24.

It can also be seen as a straight line moving so as to touch two intersecting straight lines, Fig. 18.25.

Alternatively, it can be seen as a straight line moving so as to touch a plane figure at two places at all times, Fig. 18.26.

By definition a plane is a surface such that when any two points are taken on it, the straight line joining them will lie completely on the surface.

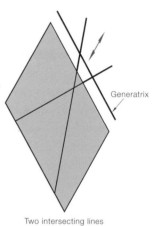

Two intersecting lines

Fig. 18.25

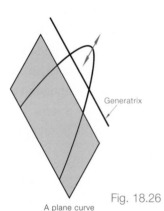

A plane curve   Fig. 18.26

2. The Single Curved Surface

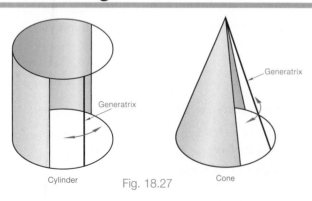

Cylinder   Fig. 18.27   Cone

This is a developable ruled surface. The surface can be unrolled to lie on a plane. The straight line elements are parallel or intersecting. Examples of single curved surfaces are the cylinder and the cone. This category would also include oblique cylinders and cones and surfaces generated by moving the generatrix around elliptical curves as well as circles.

3. Warped Surface

A warped surface is a ruled surface that is not developable. No two consecutive elements are parallel or intersecting. No two adjacent positions of the generatrix lie in the same plane. There is a huge variety of warped surfaces. Common examples are the conoid, cylindroid, hyperboloid of revolution and the hyperbolic paraboloid.

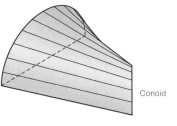

Conoid

Fig. 18.28

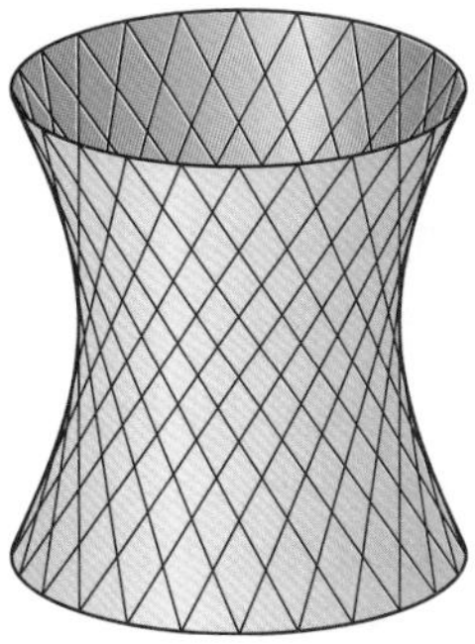

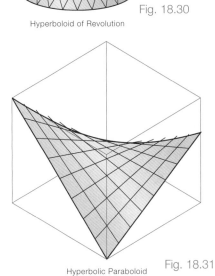

Fig. 18.30

Hyperboloid of Revolution

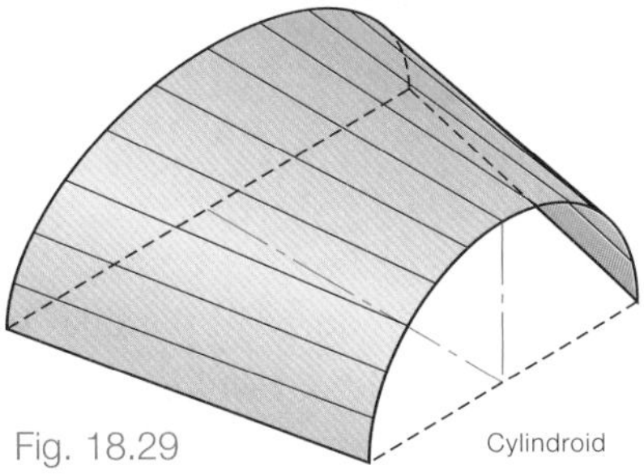

Fig. 18.29   Cylindroid

Hyperbolic Paraboloid   Fig. 18.31

Double-curved Surfaces

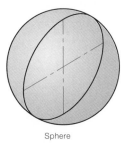

Sphere

Fig. 18.32

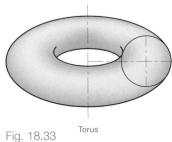

Fig. 18.33   Torus

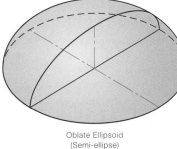

Oblate Ellipsoid
(Semi-ellipse)

Fig. 18.34

Double-curved surfaces are generated by a curved line moving according to a certain law. The most common double-curved surfaces are formed by revolving a curve about an axis in the same plane. Examples of these would be the sphere, torus, oblate ellipsoid, prolate ellipsoid, paraboloid and hyperboloid.

Prolate Ellipsoid
(Semi-ellipse)

Fig. 18.35

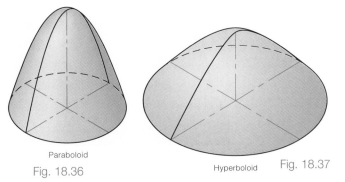

Paraboloid

Fig. 18.36

Hyperboloid   Fig. 18.37

Hyperboloid of Revolution

The hyperboloid of revolution is a ruled surface. It is generated by revolving a straight line about another non-parallel, non-intersecting line as its axis. Figures 18.38 and 18.39 show this arrangement. It is clear from the diagram that any section of a hyperboloid of revolution which is perpendicular to the axis will produce a circle.

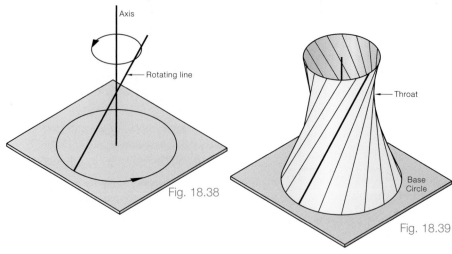

Fig. 18.38

Fig. 18.39

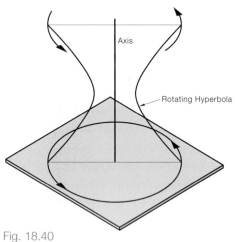

Fig. 18.40

The curves produced at the sides are hyperbolas. The narrowest part of the hyperboloid of revolution is called the throat or the throat circle.

The extreme limits of this shell structure are the cylinder and cone. As the throat circle and the base circle became closer to each other in size the hyperboloid of revolution becomes more cylindrical. As the throat circle decreases in size and nears a radius of zero the hyperboloid becomes more cone-like.

A hyperboloid of revolution can also be constructed by rotating one arm or both arms of a double hyperbola about the conjugate axis. Figures 18.40 and 18.41 show such a double hyperbola.

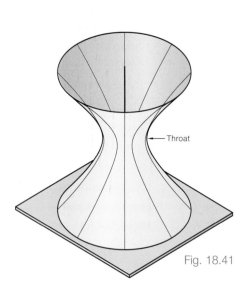

Fig. 18.41

As mentioned already, the hyperboloid is a ruled surface. A ruled surface is a surface that for every point on it, there is a straight line passing through it, which lies on that surface for its entire length. When a point on the surface has two such lines passing through it, it is called a **doubly ruled surface**. The hyperboloid of revolution is such a surface as is evident from Fig. 18.43 on the next page. There are only three doubly ruled surfaces: the hyperboloid of revolution, the hyperbolic paraboloid and the plane.

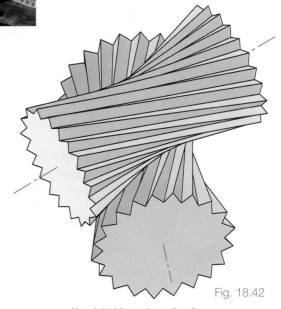

The hyperbolic paraboloid is a shell structure – one of many types. Shells are as old as nature and derive their strength not from the thickness of the shell but from the shape. A good example of this is an egg. The shell of an egg is relatively thin and is composed of a brittle material. In spite of this, an egg will withstand a huge load as long as it is evenly distributed. The strength is derived from the doubly curved surface.

Fig. 18.42

Hyperboloidal gears transmit motion
to a skew shaft

Construction of a Hyperboloid of Revolution

Method 1
Given the base circle, throat circle and height of a hyperboloid of revolution. Construct the shape using elements.

(1) Draw the plan as given and the elevation. The narrowest part of the structure is the throat.

A hyperboloid of revolution can be made up straight-line elements. Each element will form a tangent to the throat circle in plan.

(2) In plan draw an element which starts on the base circle, is tangential to the throat circle and continues to hit the base circle again, e.g. element 1.

(3) In this example the larger circle in plan represents both the base circle and the top circle of the structure. Project point 1 to the base of the elevation and point 'a' to the top of the elevation. Join these points.

(4) At suitable spacing around the circle draw more elements in plan and project to elevation.

(5) The shape forms as the elements are plotted.

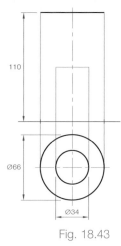

Fig. 18.43

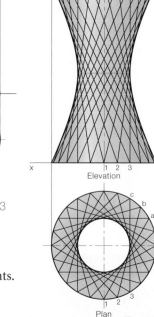

Fig. 18.44

Method 2
Given the same information as in the previous example, construct a hyperboloid of revolution using the rectangle method.

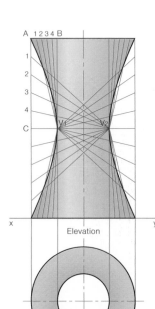

Fig. 18.45

This method is based on the construction of a double hyperbola using the rectangle method.

(1) Draw the given plan and mark off the heights in elevation.

(2) Project up the outer extremities of the circles from the plan thus creating the rectangles into which the curves will fit.

(3) Mark V_1 and V_2 the vertices of the curves.

(4) In rectangle $ABCV_1$ we divide edge AB into a number of equal parts and edge AC into the same number of equal parts.

(5) Join the divisions on AB to vertex V_1.

(6) Join the divisions on AC to vertex V_2.

(7) Where line $V_1 1$ and line $V_2 1$ cross gives a point on the hyperbola. Similarly for lines $V_1 2$ and $V_2 2$ etc.

(8) Repeat construction for other sections of the curves.

Method 3
Given the same information as in Method 1 construct a hyperboloid of revolution using the asymptote method.

The asymptotes to the curves are elements which are seen as true lengths in elevation.
The hyperbola will get closer to the asymptote as it extends but will never touch it.
The asymptotes will always cross at throat level.

(1)   Draw the given plan and set off the heights in elevation.
(2)   Since the asymptotes are true lengths in elevation they must be horizontal in plan. Draw the horizontal line AB in plan tangential to the throat circle.
(3)   Projecting A and B from plan to the top and bottom of the elevation will find the asymptotes AB.
(4)   Pick any number of points on the asymptote in plan, e.g. points 1 to 4.
(5)   Project these points onto the asymptote in elevation.
(6)   Rotate point 3 for instance, in plan, onto the central axis.
(7)   Project the rotated point to elevation and across from point 3 on the asymptote in elevation. This locates a point on the curve.
(8)   Repeat for the other points.
(9)   The shape is completed by using symmetry.

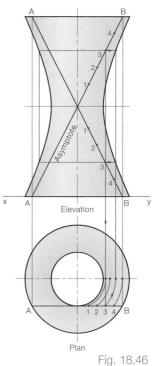

Fig. 18.46

Important Things to Remember about the Hyperboloid of Revolution

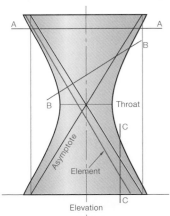

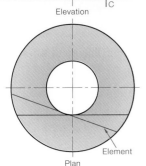

Fig. 18.47

(1)   Sections cut perpendicular to the axis will be circles.
(2)   A straight line on the surface is an element and will be a tangent to the throat circle in the plan.
(3)   The asymptotes are elements which are seen as true lengths in elevation.
(4)   The asymptotes cross each other where the axis and the throat meet.
Hyperbolas of revolutions are used in cooling towers and in gear profiles.

Section A–A is a circle
Section B–B is an ellipse
Section C–C is a hyperbola

Worked Examples

Fig. 18.48 shows the outline plan and elevation of a cooling tower. It is in the form of a hyperboloid of revolution.

(i)   Draw the given plan and elevation.

(ii) Determine the true shape of the section S–S.

Scale 1:500

(1)   Draw the plan, the axis in elevation and the height in elevation.

(2)   Construct the hyperboloid of revolution as described earlier.

Section S–S

(1)   Select a number of points on the section line, e.g. a, b and c.

(2)   Take horizontal sections through each of these points. These horizontal sections will produce circles in plan. The radii of these sections are r_1, r_2 and r_3.

(3)   Project points a, b and c from elevation onto the appropriate circles in plan.

(4)   The section can now be drawn by projecting perpendicular to the section line. Widths W_1, W_2 and W_3 are taken from plan. The section is an ellipse.

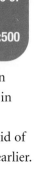

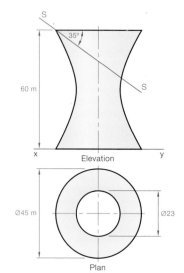

Fig. 18.48

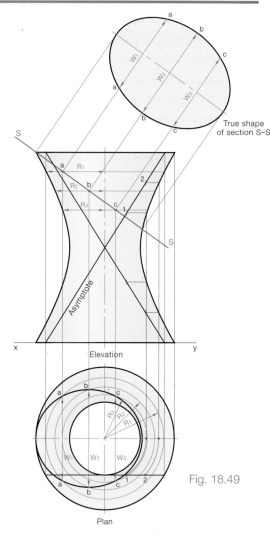

Fig. 18.49

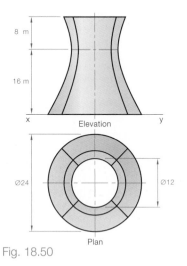

Fig. 18.50

Fig. 18.50 shows the outline plan and elevation of a building. It is in the form of a hyperboloid of revolution. The joint lines on the surface are shown in plan and elevation. Draw the given views.

Scale 1:200

(1)   In plan, draw the base circle and the throat circle as given. The medium-sized circle cannot be drawn yet as we do not know its radius.

(2)   Draw the xy line, throat line, top line and axis in elevation.

(3)   Draw the asymptotes in plan. These are seen as a horizontal line in plan tangential to the throat circle.

(4)   Where the asymptote line in plan hits the base circle at P will give the starting points of the asymptotes in elevation on the xy line at P_1.

(5)   The asymptotes always cross at the centre of the throat line in elevation. Draw the asymptotes.

(6)   Construct the outer curves of the elevation as explained before.

(7)   Where the asymptote meets the top surface at 2 is projected down to point 2 on the asymptote in plan. This is a point on the medium-sized circle. Draw the circle.

JOINT LINES

(1)   Rotate points 1, 2 and 3 on the asymptote in plan onto the joint line, giving 5, 6 and 7. These points on the joint line, because they are on the same horizontal section, can be projected to elevation as shown.

(2)   Points 4 and 8 are on the throat circle and base circle respectively and can be projected to elevation. The right joint line is a symmetrical image of the left.

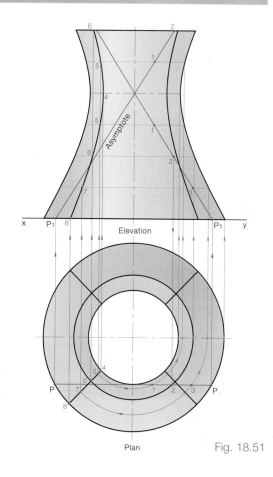

Fig. 18.51

Hyperbolic Paraboloid

A hyperbolic paraboloid surface is obtained by translating a parabola with a downward curvature (ABC) along a parabola with an upward curvature (RST). The vertex of parabola ABC stays in contact with the parabola RST and the parabola hangs vertically at all times.

> **Horizontal sections produce a double hyperbola while vertical sections produce a portion of the parabola ABC.**

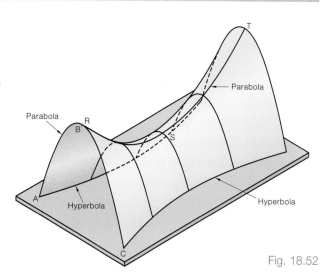

Fig. 18.52

The hyperbolic paraboloid surface can also be generated by straight lines as shown in Fig. 18.53. It is called a **doubly ruled**

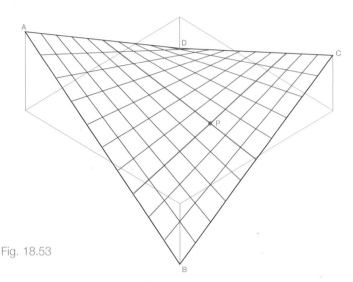

Fig. 18.53

surface. A singly ruled surface is one in which a point on the surface can have a straight line drawn through it which lies on the surface. A cone, for example, is a singly ruled surface as any point on the curved surface can have a straight line drawn through it from the apex. This straight line rests on the cone surface throughout its length. A hyperbolic paraboloid has two such lines running through any point on its surface and is thus doubly ruled.

The diagrams Fig. 18.54 and Fig. 18.55 show that the structures shown in Fig. 18.52 and that shown in Fig. 18.53 are portions of the same structure. The diagonals AC and BD form upward and downward curving parabolas. Vertical sections parallel to these will produce similar parabolic sections.

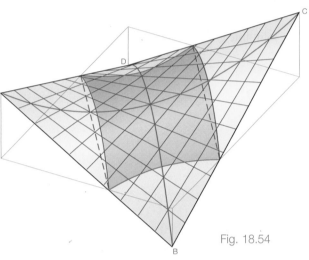

Fig. 18.54

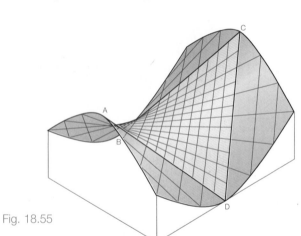

Fig. 18.55

The hyperbolic paraboloid shown in Fig. 18.54 is often referred to as a **low saddle type** and that shown in Fig. 18.55 as a **high saddle type**.

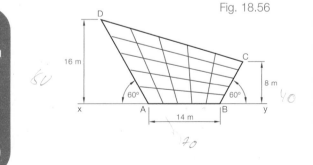

Fig. 18.56

Fig. 18.56 shows the outline plan of a hyperbolic paraboloid roof surface ABCD. The corners A and C are at ground level. Corner B is 12 m above ground level and corner D is 20 m above ground level.

(i)　Draw the given plan and project an elevation.

(ii)　Draw an end view of the roof.

(iii)　Show the curvature of the roof along a line joining A to C.

Scale 1:200

(1)　Draw the outline of the plan as given.

(2)　Each of the sides must be divided into five equal spaces as shown. This can be done by measuring or by division of lines as described before.

(3) Join the elements as shown. It is worth noting here that these structures must have four sides. The division marks on one edge must be joined to division marks on an opposite side, e.g. AB divisions join to CD divisions, and BC divisions join to AD divisions.

(4) Project the elevation of the corners using the heights given in the question. A joins to B to C to D back to A.

(5) The sides in the elevation can be divided by projecting the divisions up from the plan or by measuring.

(6) By indexing the first in a set of elements in plan the corresponding element in elevation can easily be found.

(7) Complete the elevation.

(8) The end view is found in the same way with the division points being found by projection from the front elevation, from the plan or by measuring.

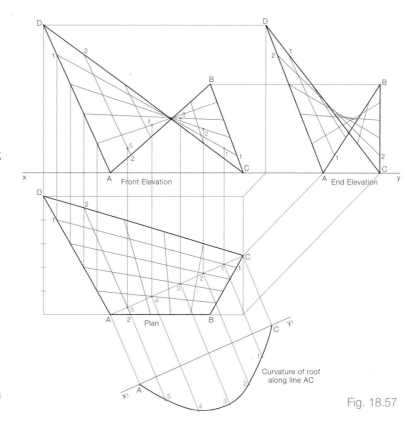

Fig. 18.57

CURVATURE

(1) Join A to C in plan and identify points 1 to 5 where the section lines cross the elements. The more horizontal elements in plan are most suitable.

(2) Draw an x_1y_1 line parallel to the AC line.

(3) Project points AC and 1 to 5 out onto the sectional view. The projection lines must be perpendicular to the AC line and the x_1y_1 line.

(4) The heights of each point must be found from the elevation. Point 1 in plan on element 1, must be projected to elevation onto element 1. The height of this point is taken from elevation and transferred to the sectional view.

(5) Repeat for the other points and join to give the curve.

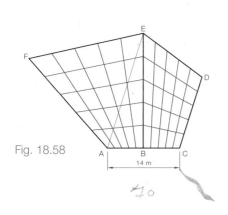

Fig. 18.58

Two adjoining hyperbolic paraboloid roof surfaces ABEF and BCDE are shown in plan. BCDE makes up half a pentagon and AEF is an equilateral triangle. The corners A, C and E are at ground level. Corners D and F are 16 m above ground level and corner B is 20 m above ground level.

(i) Draw the plan and project an elevation.

(ii) Project an end elevation.

(iii) Show the curvature of the roof along the line AE.

Scale 1:200

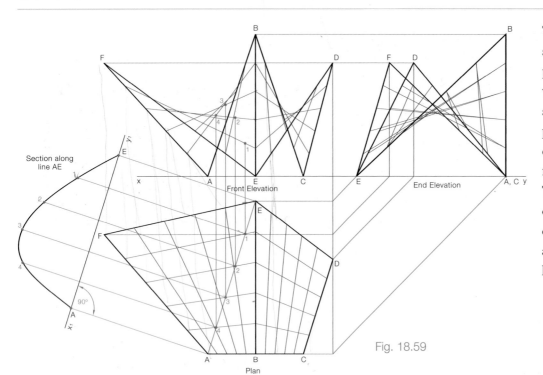

Fig. 18.59

The construction is very similar to that for the previous example. It is worth noting that in the solving of these problems we do not concern ourselves with finding hidden lines. The whole framework is considered during drawing as a wire frame and hence has no hidden lines.

Fig. 18.60 shows the outline plan of two adjoining hyperbolic paraboloid roof surfaces ABCD and ADEF. The corners B, C, E and F are at ground level. The corner A is 3 m above ground level and the corner D is 20 m above ground level.

(i)   Draw the given plan and project the elevation.

(ii)   Project an end elevation of the roof.

(iii)   Find the true shape of the section S–S.

(iv)   Draw a new auxiliary of roof ABCD that will show the true length of edge CD.

Scale 1:200

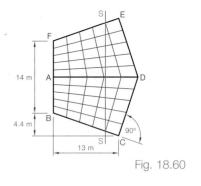

Fig. 18.60

The solving of parts (i), (ii) and (iii) of this problem are the same as in previous examples.

New elevation showing true length.

(1)   To see the true length of edge CD we must view it straight on. The viewing angle is perpendicular to edge CD.

(2)   Draw an x_1y_1 which runs parallel to CD in plan.

(3)   Project the corners in the direction of the arrow. Draw the outer frame and insert the elements. It can be seen from the auxiliary that edge CB is seen as a point view and that one set of elements will appear parallel in this view.

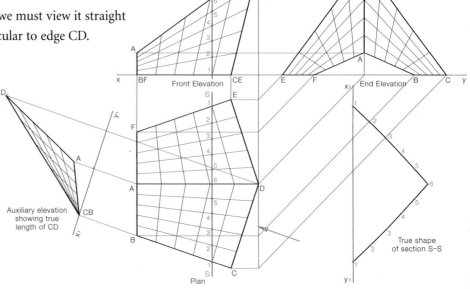

Hyperboloid of Revolution (contd.)

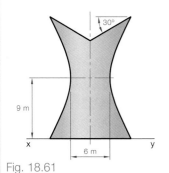

Fig. 18.61

Fig. 18.62 shows the elevation of a hyperboloid of revolution which has been cut at the top. The true length of all full elements on the surface of this structure is 21 m.

(i) Draw the plan and elevation of the building.

(ii) Project an end view.

(iii) Find the true shape of one side of the cut section.

Scale 1:100

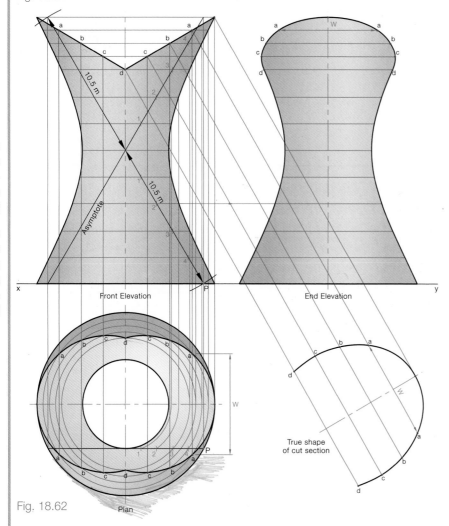

Fig. 18.62

(1) Set up the xy line, axis, throat line and overall height in elevation.

(2) Draw the throat circle in plan.

(3) The true length of all full straight line elements is 21 m. The asymptotes are elements and are seen as true lengths in elevation. The asymptotes always cross in the middle of the throat. Set the compass to half the length of the asymptote, place it at the centre of the throat and draw an arc to hit the xy line at P. Draw a horizontal line tangential to the throat circle in plan. Project P onto this line. Point P is on the base circle.

(4) Draw the hyperboloid as explained earlier.

(5) To find the points on the section in plan we take horizontal sections which produce circles in plan onto which the appropriate points are projected.

(6) The end view and auxiliary are found by taking widths from the front elevation and plan.

The elevation of a piece of sculpture is shown in Fig. 18.63. It is in the form of two solid semi-hyperboloids of revolution. Any straight line element on the full hyperboloid of revolution would measure 17 m.

(i)   Draw the front elevation, end elevation and plan of the sculpture.

(ii)   Determine the true shape of section S–S.

Scale 1:100

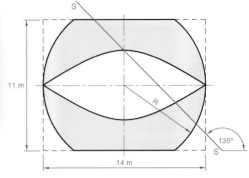

Fig. 18.63

H I G H E R   L E V E L

(1)   The asymptotes will be 17 m long. Since they are only semi-hyperbolic paraboloids we only use half of this distance. Swing an arc from P to cut the side at Q. Point P is projected to the end view and the asymptote is drawn vertically. The throat circle is tangential to the asymptote in end view.

(2)   The hyperboloid is constructed in the usual way.

(3)   The shaped ends are found in end view and plan by taking sections perpendicular to the axes which appear as circles in end view.

(4)   The section S–S is also found by using sections (construction not shown).

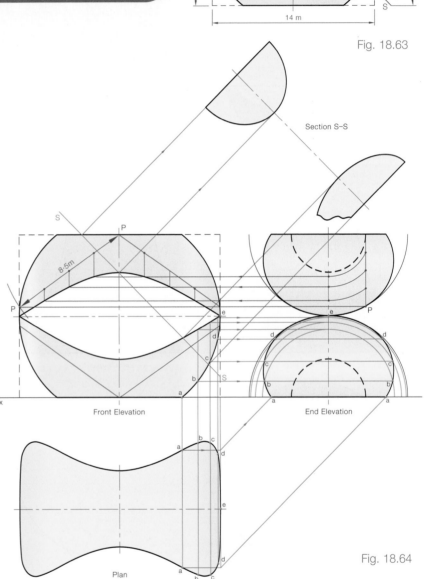

Fig. 18.64

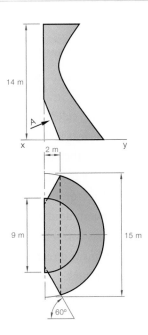

14 m

2 m

9 m   15 m

60°

Fig. 18.65

Fig. 18.65 shows the plan and elevation of a semi-hyperboloid of revolution.

(i)   Draw the plan and elevation of the structure.

(ii) Project a new elevation that will show the true shape of surface A.

Scale 1:100

(1)   Draw the two semicircles in plan and project to elevation.

(2)   The straight line in plan projects as a straight line in elevation and is therefore a portion of an element. As an element it will form a tangent to the throat circle in plan. Extend the line and draw the throat circle.

(3)   Draw the asymptote in plan and project to elevation. Where the asymptote crosses the axis gives the position of the throat.

(4)   Complete the plan and elevation.

(5)   The new elevation is projected perpendicular to surface A. Surface A, when projected, will be made up of straight lines. The widths are found in the plan.

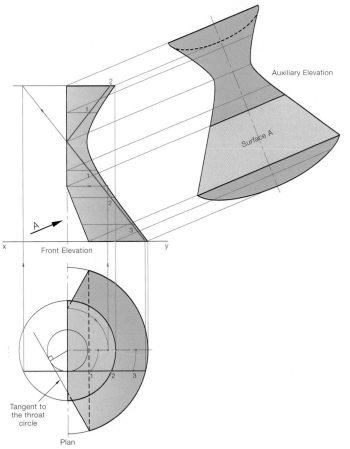

Fig. 18.66

Hyperbolic Paraboloid (contd.)

The hyperbolic paraboloid is a warped surface and therefore cannot be developed. It can also be referred to as a warped quadrilateral. We have seen earlier that it can be considered to be a surface generated by a straight line. The straight line is called a **generatrix**. This straight line moves along two non-parallel, non-intersecting lines (skew lines) called **linear directrices**. All this can be clearly seen from the previous work on this surface. What perhaps is not so clear is that the generatrix, as it slides along the linear directrices, must always stay parallel to a plane, called the **plane director.** In fact, because the hyperbolic paraboloid is a doubly ruled surface, it has two sets of generatrices, two sets of linear directrices and two sets of plane directors.

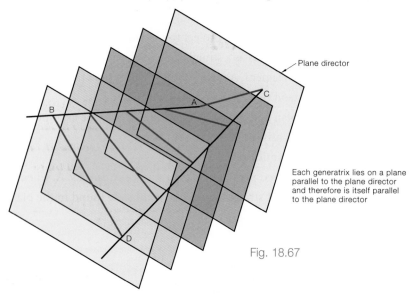

Plane director

Each generatrix lies on a plane parallel to the plane director and therefore is itself parallel to the plane director

Fig. 18.67

Fig. 18.68 shows the plan and elevation of a hyperbolic paraboloid having two linear directrices ad and bc. The vertical plane is the plane director. Since the xy line in plan represents the edge view of the vertical plane, all the generatrices will be parallel to the xy line in plan.

No matter what hyperbolic paraboloid we have, we can get an edge view of its plane director by getting auxiliary views which will show its generatrices as parallel.

The plane director need not be one of the reference planes. In Fig. 18.69 the plane director is a vertical plane that is simply inclined. In plan we see the edge view of the plane director and all the elements appear parallel to it.

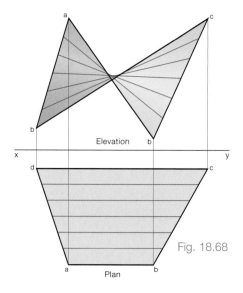

Elevation

Plan

Fig. 18.68

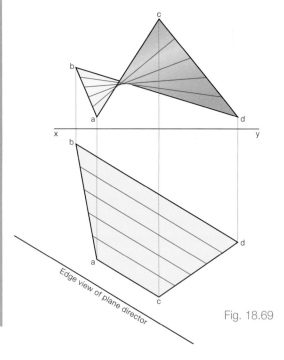

Edge view of plane director

Fig. 18.69

In both Figures 18.68 and Fig. 18.69 the elements of the structure appear parallel either in plan or elevation. If the plane director is an oblique plane, the elements will not appear parallel in either of these views and the use of an auxiliary view is required.

Fig. 18.70 shows an example of such a hyperbolic paraboloid. In order to find the plane director we must find a view of the structure that will show the generatrices as appearing parallel. The extreme elements ab and cd are used in Fig. 18.69 to find this view. The construction used is exactly that used in skew lines problems to show the two lines as parallel.

Generatrices ab and cd

(1) Draw a level line from c and from d draw a line parallel to ab to intersect at x.

(2) Project x down to plan. In the plan draw a line from d parallel to ab in plan to intersect at x in plan.

(3) Join c to x and view in this direction to project a view of the structure showing all elements as parallel.

(4) The plane director can be drawn in the auxiliary. It is seen as an edge view and will be parallel to the generatrices.

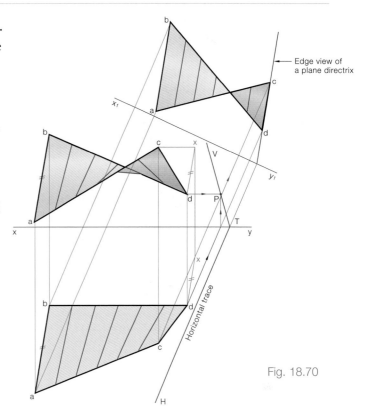

Fig. 18.70

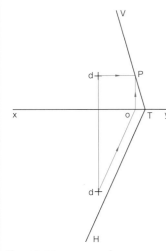

Fig. 18.71

(5) In Fig. 18.70 the plane director is containing element cd. Extend the edge view of the plane director to hit the x_1y_1. This point is a point view of the horizontal trace. Project the horizontal trace back to plan.

(6) The vertical trace is found by using a point on the plane director, e.g. point c or point d. We have point d in plan and elevation, we have the horizontal trace and we require the vertical trace.

(7) Project d in plan, to the xy line, parallel to the horizontal trace to give point o.

(8) Project vertically and from d in the elevation project horizontally to give point p. Point p is a point on the vertical trace.

There is an infinite number of plane directors for any hyperbolic paraboloid surface. They will all be parallel to each other but their position can vary.

HIGHER LEVEL

Given two skew line directrices ab and cd and the traces of the plane director of a hyperbolic paraboloid. To determine the elements of the surface.

$$a = 30, 10, 68$$
$$b = 75, 21, 40$$
$$c = 18, 45, 10$$
$$d = 82, 9, 27$$

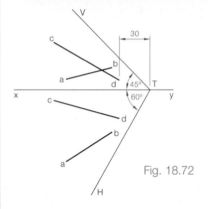

Fig. 18.72

(1) Find the edge view of the plane director by projecting an auxiliary view in the direction of the horizontal trace.

(2) Draw the directrices ab and cd in this auxiliary.

(3) The elements can now be drawn in the auxiliary, parallel to the edge view of the plane director. The most extreme elements are found first and further elements spaced out evenly between these.

(4) Project the elements back to plan and project to elevation.

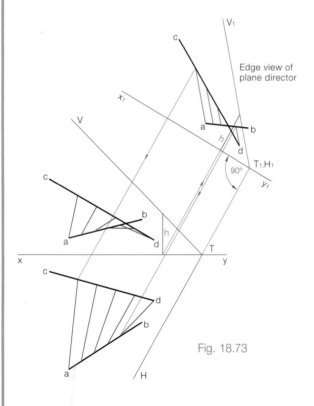

Fig. 18.73

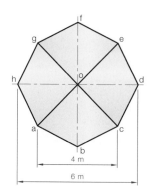

Fig. 18.74

Fig. 18.74 shows the outline plan of a rain shelter. The structure is in the form of four hyperbolic paraboloid surfaces, abco, cdeo, efgo and ghao. Points b, d, f and h are at ground level. Points a, c, e and g are 5 m above ground level and point o is 6 m above ground level.
(i) Draw the plan and elevation of the surfaces ghao, abco and cdeo.
(ii) Find the curvature of the roof along the line joining b to e.
(iii) Find the traces of the plane director for the edges ab and co and having its horizontal trace containing point b.

Scale 1:50

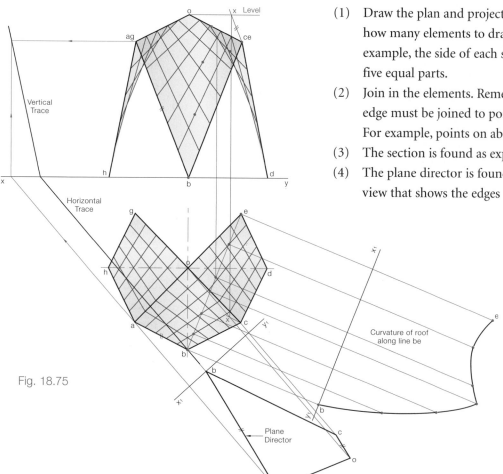

Fig. 18.75

(1) Draw the plan and project the elevation. Decide on how many elements to draw on each surface. In this example, the side of each structure was divided into five equal parts.
(2) Join in the elements. Remember that points on one edge must be joined to points on its opposite side. For example, points on ab join to points on oc.
(3) The section is found as explained before.
(4) The plane director is found by finding an auxiliary view that shows the edges ab and co as parallel. This is a skew lines problem and the construction is as explained earlier.
(5) Where the plane director meets the x_1y_1 gives the horizontal trace which is projected back to plan.
(6) Point 'a' which is also on the plane director is used to find the vertical trace.

HIGHER LEVEL

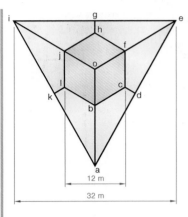

Fig. 18.76

Fig. 18.76 shows the outline plan of a roof made up of nine adjoining hyperbolic paraboloid surfaces. The outline is an equilateral triangle and the three internal surfaces make a regular hexagon in plan.

(i) Draw the plan and elevation of the three surfaces abcd, cdef and bcfo.

(ii) Determine the curvature of the roof along a line joining A to C.

(iii) Determine the plane director for the elements cf and de. Find the traces of the plane director having its horizontal trace passing through e.

Scale 1:200

H I G H E R   L E V E L

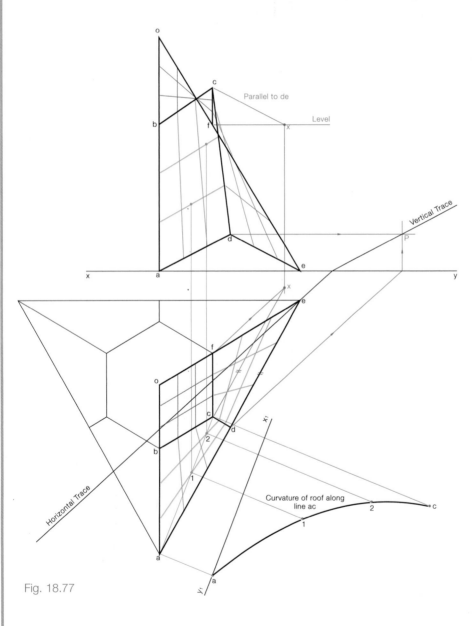

Fig. 18.77

(1) Because of the complexity of the drawing we have only shown a limited number of elements.

(2) The plane director is to be found for cf and de. Draw a level line from f in elevation and draw from c parallel to de giving x. Drop x to plan.

(3) In plan, draw from c parallel to de in plan to locate the exact position of x.

(4) Join x back to f. This is the direction of the horizontal trace. Draw the trace through e.

(5) Draw from d parallel to HT to xy. Project vertically.

(6) Project from d in elevation, horizontally to find P. Point P is a point on the vertical trace. Draw the trace.

Fig. 18.78 shows the plan of a shell structure in the form of a hyperbolic paraboloid. Curve DBA is semi-elliptical in plan. Curves DE and BF are found by extending the surface ABCD until it meets ground level.

(i)   Draw the plan and elevation of the structure.

(ii)   Project the end view.

Scale 1:200

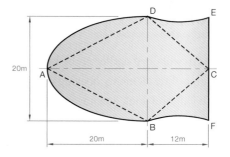

Fig. 18.78

(1)   Set up ABCD in plan and elevation.

(2)   Draw the semi-ellipse in plan using the trammel or similar method.

(3)   Divide the sides of the hyperbolic paraboloid into a suitable number of equal spaces, both in plan and elevation.

(4)   The curve DAB is found in elevation by extending the elements in plan to reach the semi-ellipse at 1, 2, 3 and 4. These points are projected to elevation to meet the elements extended.

(5)   The curves DE and BF are found by extending the elements in elevation to meet the xy line at p and q.

(6)   p and q are projected to plan to intersect the elements extended.

(7)   The end view is found by projection from the other two views.

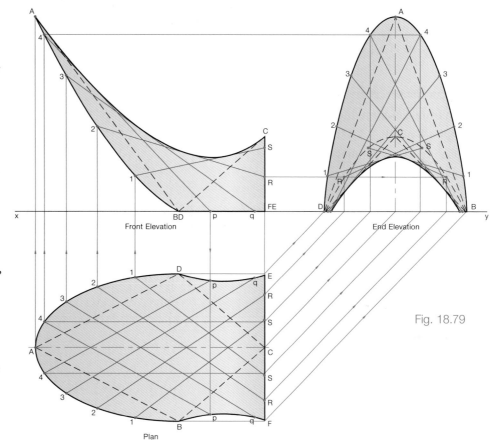

Fig. 18.79

Hyperbolic Paraboloid as a Surface of Translation

As has been explained earlier at the introduction to this topic, the hyperbolic paraboloid can be seen as a structure made up of straight line elements obeying certain rules or as a parabolic curve sliding on its vertex along an inverted parabolic curve. We will now look at some problems based on this type of model.

Fig. 18.80 shows a pictorial view of a shell structure. The surface of the structure is generated by translating the parabola ABC in a vertical position along the parabola BE whose vertex is at E.
Draw the plan and elevation of the structure.

Scale 1:200

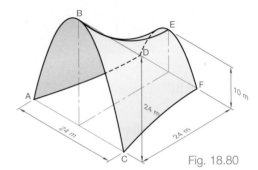

Fig. 18.80

HIGHER LEVEL

(1) Draw the parabola ABC.

(2) In front elevation draw point B and E.

(3) Construct the parabola BE ensuring that the vertex is at E.

(4) All vertical sections will produce parabolas which are part of the ABC parabola. The end curve DEF is part of the ABC parabola. The width w is found in plan by stepping height h down from the top of parabola ABC giving width w.

(5) Curves AD and CF are hyperbolas and are constructed as explained earlier.

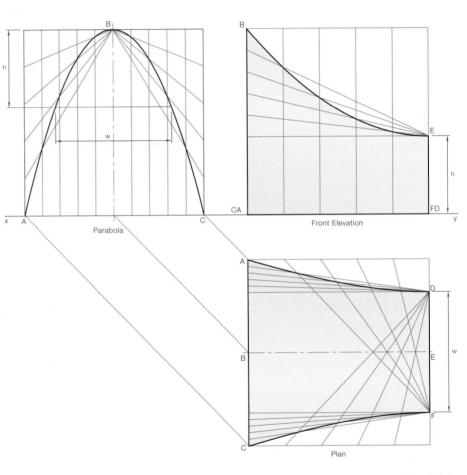

Fig. 18.81

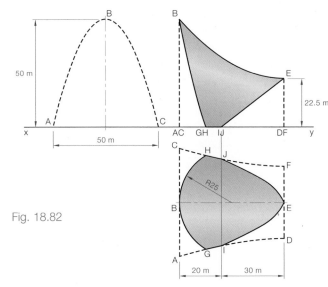

Fig. 18.82

Fig. 18.82 shows the plan and elevation of a shell structure which is in the form of a hyperbolic paraboloid. It is formed by sliding parabola ABC in a vertical position along the parabola BE whose vertex is at E. The shell has been cut as shown.

(i)   Draw the plan and elevation of the unit.

(ii)   Project an end view of the unit.

Scale 1:500

(1)   Draw the parabola ABC.

(2)   Construct the parabola BE in elevation having its vertex at E.

(3)   In the plan, the width of the end DEF is not given and must be found. Take the height of E in elevation and step it **down** from the top of parabola ABC. This gives the **width** of DF in plan.

(4)   The left side of the plan can be completed and the right side of the elevation.

(5) w_1 and w_2 are taken from plan, stepped out from the axis of parabola ABC to find h_1 and h_2 which are stepped down from BE.

(6) h_3 and h_4 are taken from elevation, stepped down from the vertex of parabola ABC to find w_3 and w_4 which find points in the plan.

(7)   The end view is projected from front elevation and plan.

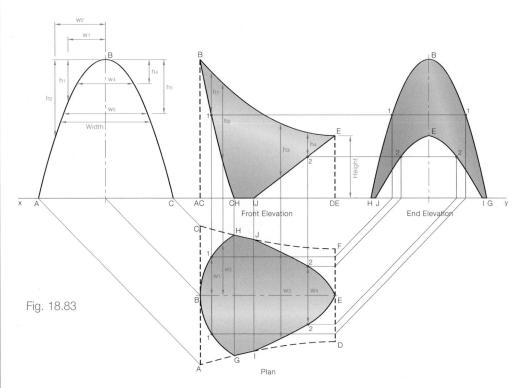

Fig. 18.83

HIGHER LEVEL

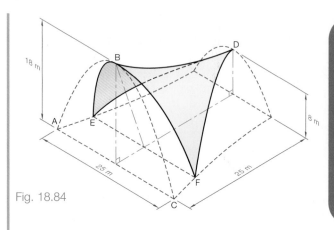

Fig. 18.84

Fig. 18.84 shows a pictorial view of a shell structure. Six of these units are combined to form a total roof surface as shown in plan in Fig. 18.85. The surface of the unit is generated by translating the parabola ABC in a vertical position along the parabola BC whose vertex is at D.

(i)   Draw the plan and elevation of the unit.
(ii) Project an end view of the unit.
(iii) Find the true shape of curve DF.

Scale 1:200

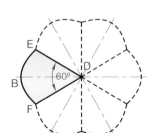

Fig. 18.85

HIGHER LEVEL

(1) Draw parabola ABC.

(2) Draw the rectangle that contains the front elevation and construct the half parabola BD.

(3) Draw the plan of the uncut shell structure by taking heights from parabola BD to the xy line (e.g. H_1) and step these heights **down** from the top of parabola ABC to give widths (e.g. W_1) which are used in the plan.

(4) Cut the shell structure in plan to form an inclusive angle of 60° thus finding E and F.

(5) Project E and F to the xy line and join to B. The left of the front elevation is completed and the right of the plan is completed.

(6) Take heights in elevation from parabola BD to straight line BFE (e.g. H_2).

(7) Step these heights **down** from the top of parabola ABC to find widths which are used in the plan (e.g. W_2).

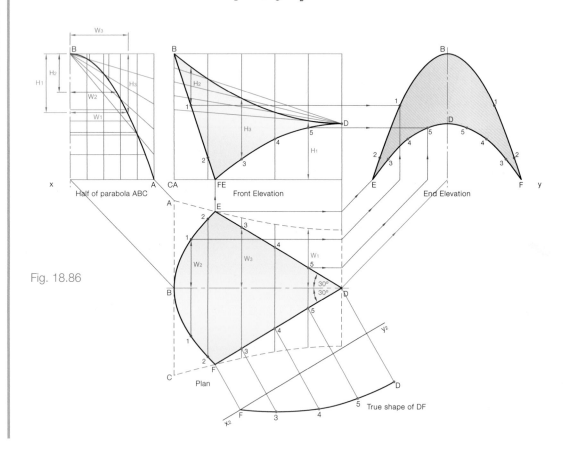

Fig. 18.86

(8)   Widths are now taken in plan from the axis to line DE (e.g. W_3).

(9)   Use these widths on the parabola ABC to find heights **from the top of the parabola down** to the curve (e.g. H_3).

(10) The end view is projected in the normal way.

(11) The true shape of curve DF is found by projecting an auxiliary elevation with $x_1 y_1$ parallel to line DF in plan.

Geodesic Domes

A geodesic dome is a type of structure shaped like a piece of a sphere. This structure is made up of a complex network of triangles that form a roughly spherical surface. The more triangles, the more closely the dome approximates the shape of a true sphere. The geodesic dome was invented by Buckminster Fuller in the late 1940s. He hoped to use such domes to improve the housing of humanity and envisaged that giant domes would cover whole cities.

Geodesic domes are light structures yet very rigid and inherently strong. They have no need for internal supports, as they are self-supporting and therefore leave the internal floor area completely open and unobstructed. They are attractive aesthetically and philosophically because you are getting more internal area using less building materials. There are, unfortunately, some severe practical difficulties in constructing these 'perfect buildings', which has limited their use to public spaces, exhibition halls and enthusiast projects. With so many edges and joints it is difficult and expensive to waterproof these domes. Rain seems to find a way in, no matter what precautions are taken. Furthermore, the fact that the internal surfaces are curved can lead to its own problems in a man-made world that favours rectangular, more modular furniture.

Spherical Geometry

The term 'geodesic' comes from the Greek *geo*, earth, and *daiesthai*, to divide. We have earth-dividing domes. For a sphere, the shortest distance between two points A and B on the surface, travelling along the sphere's surface, is called a **geodesic**. A geodesic is always part of the circumference of a circle which has its centre at the centre of the sphere. Such a circle is called a **great circle**. An unlimited number of great circles can be drawn on the sphere's surface. Other smaller circles can be drawn on the surface but their centres will not coincide with the sphere's centre. These lesser circles play little or no part in dome theory.

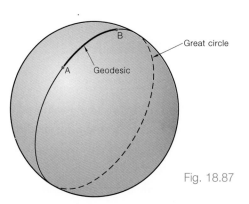

Fig. 18.87

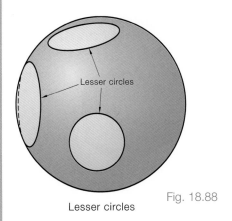

Fig. 18.88

The two points on a sphere that the geodesic line connects can also be connected by a chord that cuts through the sphere. Geodesic domes use these chords as struts. The struts form triangles and it is from these triangles that the dome forms its strength.

Before looking at the make-up of the triangles in a geodesic dome we must first look at much more simple shapes, on which the more complex geodesic shapes are based, **the platonic solids**.

HIGHER LEVEL

The Five Regular Polyhedra

There are only five regular polyhedra: the tetrahedron, cube, octahedron, dodecahedron and icosahedron. For each of these solids all the faces are similar regular polygons, all the edges are equal in length and the same number of faces meet at every vertex.

Why only five regular polyhedra?

> **In any convex polyhedron the sum of the face angles at a vertex is always less than 360°.**

In order to form a three-dimensional solid there must be a minimum of three faces meeting at any one vertex. By looking at the interior angles of regular polygons which can act as faces, it is evident that only three polygons may be used.

(1)   Equilateral triangle with interior angles of 60°.
(2)   Square with interior angles of 90°.
(3)   Regular pentagon with interior angles of 108°.

A regular hexagon which is the next polygon in line has an interior angle of 120°. Three hexagonal faces meeting at a vertex will have interior angles adding up to exactly 360°, not less than 360° and therefore do not obey the rule.

By using equilateral triangles to form a regular polyhedron, there can be three, four or five of them meeting at a vertex, any more and the rule will be broken. From this we get the tetrahedron, octahedron and isosahedron. By using squares, there can only be three at each vertex, thus forming a cube. Finally, by using pentagons, again only three can meet at each vertex, thus forming a dodecahedron.

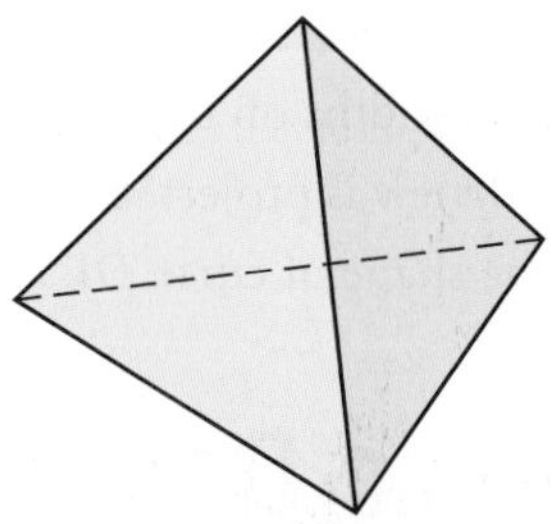

HIGHER LEVEL

Fig. 18.89

Tetrahedron
4 faces, 4 vertices, 6 edges

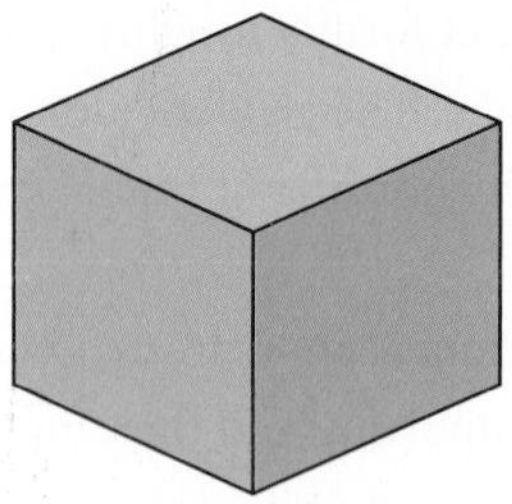

Fig. 18.90

Cube
6 faces, 8 vertices, 12 edges

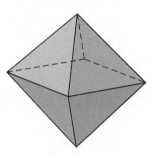

Fig. 18.91

Octahedron
8 faces, 6 vertices, 12 edges

Fig. 18.92

Dodecahedron
12 faces, 20 vertices, 30 edges

Fig. 18.93

Icosahedron
20 faces, 12 vertices, 30 edges

Faces, Vertices and Edges

There is obviously a relationship between the number of faces, vertices and edges for each of these regular polyhedra. This relationship was discovered by Leonhard Euler (1707–83).

$$\text{Faces} + \text{Vertices} - \text{Edges} = 2$$
$$F + V - E = 2$$

This relationship stands true for the five regular polyhedra mentioned earlier, but also for any polyhedra, regular or not, which can be enclosed in a sphere having each vertex touching the sphere surface.

This formula is useful when working on domes because it can help to count vertices.

Platonic Solids and the Sphere

Each of the platonic solids can be circumscribed by a sphere, such that each vertex of the solid rests on the sphere surface and each edge of the surface forms a chord joining two such points. As such these five solids form the basis of geodesic dome construction. They are, however, poor approximations to a sphere. Of the five the tetrahedron, octahedron and icosahedron offer better stability because of their triangular make-up. If we look at the icosahedron which has 20 triangular faces, the vertices are all equidistant from the centre so they determine a sphere. If we subdivide each of the triangular faces into smaller triangles, then some of the vertices of the smaller triangles lie inside the sphere rather than on it. By pushing these points radially outwards from the icosahedron until they meet the sphere, we arrive at the vertices of our geodesic sphere. Obviously by pushing the corners of the smaller triangles out to the sphere surface we are both changing the lengths of the triangle sides and their angles.

Frequency of a Geodesic Dome

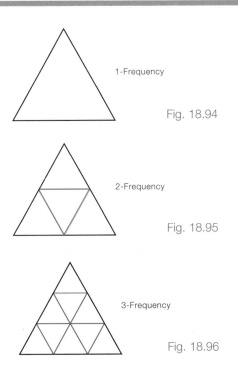

1-Frequency

Fig. 18.94

2-Frequency

Fig. 18.95

3-Frequency

Fig. 18.96

The frequency of a geodesic dome is the measure of the number of triangles into which each face is subdivided. A 1-frequency dome or sphere is just an icosahedron (for example) or part of an icosahedron whose faces have not been subdivided. For a 2-frequency dome, the sides of each icosahedral face are divided into two so that each face is divided into four smaller triangles. For a 3-frequency dome the sides are divided in three, so that the faces become nine smaller triangles and so on.

HIGHER LEVEL

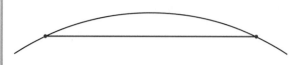

Fig. 18.97

The roundness of the dome is improved by dividing the edges into shorter lengths and raising more points to the surface of the sphere. Raising the midpoint of an edge to the sphere creates two shorter edges, both equal, which give a better approximation to the curvature of the sphere. Increasing the subdivisions to 3-frequency or 4-frequency produces better approximations and struts of varying lengths. The lengths of these struts may be calculated or can be found from tables.

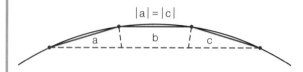

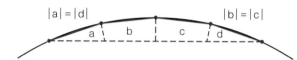

Fig. 18.98

Strut Factor and Tables

The lengths of the sides of the various triangles making up a dome may be calculated from tables. The tables are generally given based on a dome/sphere of one-metre radius. To make a dome of another radius it is simply a matter of multiplying the chord factor by the required radius.

Strut length = Dome/Sphere radius × Strut factor

1-FREQUENCY (ICOSAHEDRAL)

Strut	Strut factor	Req. for dome	Req. for sphere
A	1.05146	25	30

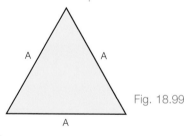

Fig. 18.99

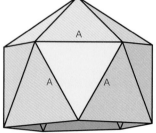

Fig. 18.100

Icosahedral dome
1-frequency

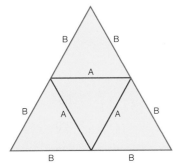

Fig. 18.101

2-FREQUENCY (ICOSAHEDRAL)

Strut	Strut factor	Req. for dome	Req. for sphere
A	0.61803	35	60
B	0.54653	30	60

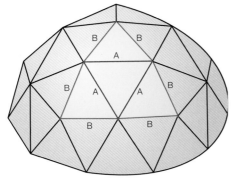

Icosahedral dome
2-frequency

Fig. 18.102

3-FREQUENCY (ICOSAHEDRAL)

Strut	Strut factor	Req. for dome 3/8	5/8	Req. for sphere
A	0.34862	30	30	60
B	0.40355	40	55	90
C	0.41241	50	80	120

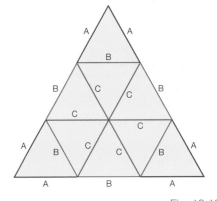

Fig. 18.103

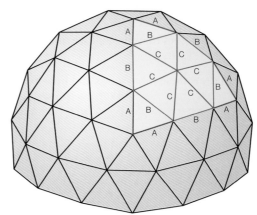

Fig. 18.104

5/8 Icosahedral dome
3-frequency

HIGHER LEVEL

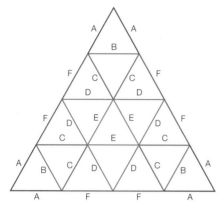

Fig. 18.105

4-FREQUENCY (ICOSAHEDRAL)			
Strut	Strut factor	Req. for dome	Req. for sphere
A	0.25318	30	60
B	0.29524	30	60
C	0.29453	60	120
D	0.31285	70	120
E	0.32492	30	60
F	0.29859	30	60

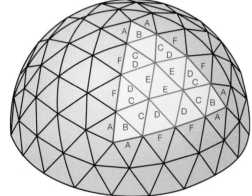

Fig. 18.106

Icosahedral dome
4-frequency

How to Draw a Geodesic Dome

As has been mentioned earlier, all geodesic domes are derived from one or other of the platonic solids. Of these five solids, the three that are made up with triangles are most favoured:

the tetrahedron – 4 faces,
the octahedron – 8 faces,
the icosahedron – 20 faces.

The icosahedron produces domes that most closely match a sphere.

We first look at how to draw these three solids and how to find their circumscribing spheres.

Tetrahedron

(1) The plan of a tetrahedron resting on one of its faces is an equilateral triangle and its apex 0 is found by bisecting the angles.

(2) The end view can be used to find the tetrahedron's height as it shows edge 0,3 as a true length.

(3) Complete the front elevation.

(4) The centre of the circumscribing sphere lies on the axis of the solid and touches all vertices. In the end view, bisect true length 0,3 to intersect the axis through 0 to locate c. Draw the sphere in all views.

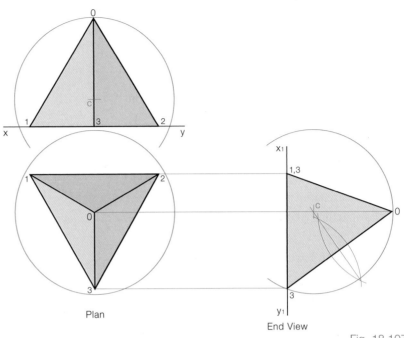

Plan

End View

Fig. 18.107

HIGHER LEVEL

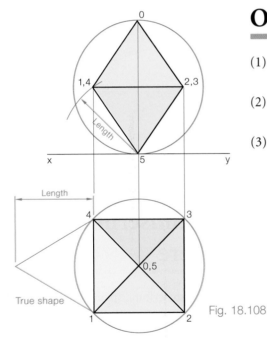

Fig. 18.108

Octahedron

(1) The plan of the octahedron appears as a square with the diagonals joined.

(2) The height for the elevation is found by drawing the true shape of one of the faces and using its length as shown to locate points 1 and 4.

(3) The circumscribing sphere is drawn in elevation and then in plan.

Icosahedron

(1) The plan of the top five triangles of an icosahedron having its apex facing straight up, will form a perfect pentagon. The sides of the pentagon equal the true length of each edge of the icosahedron and the edges leading up to the apex appear as spokes of this pentagon leading into the centre.

(2) Construct the pentagon in plan.

(3)   Draw lines from each of the vertices of the
pentagon to its centre to form the spokes.

(4)   Find a starting point for the lower pentagon by
extending one of these spokes, e.g. 3,0 to
intersect a circumscribing circle about the
pentagon. The vertices for the second pentagon
will lie on the same circle.

(5)   Complete the plan.

(6)   Two heights are needed to draw the elevation.
Find the true shape of one of the faces. Consider
this as a rebatment of the face.

(7)   Draw auxiliary views to show face 0,1,2 as an
edge view by viewing along true length 2,1. By
using length L from the true shape height A can
be found.

(8)   Similarly, an edge view of surface 1,2,3 will find
height B.

(9)   Construct elevation.

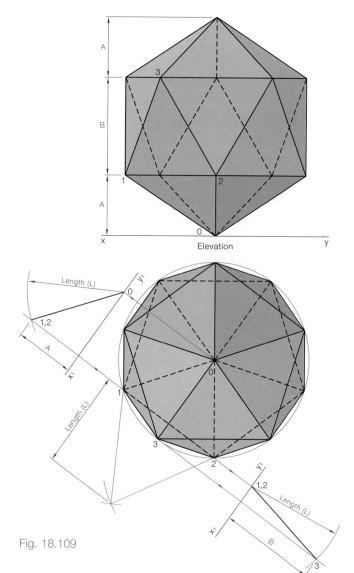

Fig. 18.109

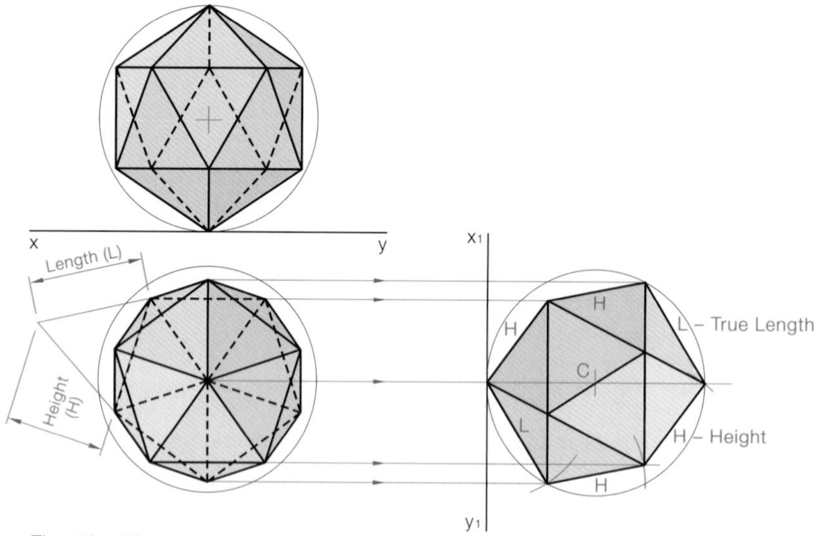

Circumscribing Sphere

The circumscribing sphere can easily be
found in elevation. If only a partial
elevation is to be drawn, centre C can be
found by projecting a view showing one
face edge on and one edge as a true length.
By bisecting the true length and extending
to cross the axis centre, C is located.

Fig. 18.110

3-Frequency Geodesic Dome (Octahedral)

In this example the construction for one of the four faces is shown. The other three faces may be found subsequently by symmetry or rotation about point O.

(1) Draw a semi-octahedron in plan.

(2) Project the end view which shows two of the faces as edge views. Draw in the circumscribing sphere.

(3) In the plan view, subdivide each edge of the face Oc_1c_4 into three equal spaces. Connect all the resultant points with straight lines as shown to form a triangular grid that should divide triangle Oc_1c_4 into nine smaller triangles.

(4) Index all the points as shown.

(5) Project points b_1, b_2 and b_3 to the end view.

(6) Point b_2, in plan, lies on line Ob_2 which is parallel to the x_1y_1. Radiate a line from c in end view, through b_2 to locate b_2, a point on the circumscribing sphere.

(7) Project back to plan.

(8) The radial projection lines from O to most points in the triangular grid of triangle Oc_1c_4 in the plan view, however, are not parallel to the x_1y_1 line. These must be rotated.

(9) A radial line is drawn from O through b_1 in plan, for example.

(10) Rotate Ob_1 about point O until it is parallel to x_1y_1.

(11) As Ob_1 rotates in plan point b_1 moves horizontally in end view.

(12) The rotated radial is extended to hit the circumscribed sphere at point s.

(13) By projecting point s back onto the original radial cb_1 extended we find point b_1 in end view.

(14) Points b_1 and b_3 can be projected from end view, back onto the radials in plan.

(15) Repeat this process for points a_1 and a_2.

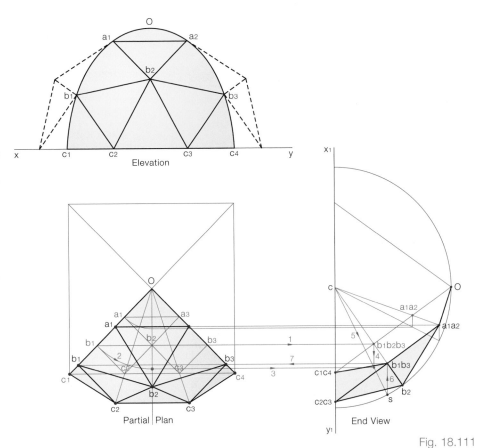

Fig. 18.111

3-Frequency Geodesic Dome (3/8 Icosahedral)

Only the top five equilateral triangles of the icosahedron are used to produce this dome.

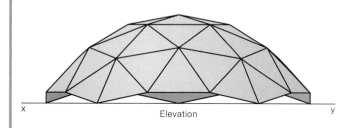

Elevation

(1) Draw the plan of the top five equilateral triangles. They form a pentagon in plan.
(2) Project an auxiliary view or an end view that will show one face as an edge view OAB and one edge as a true length OD.
(3) Construct the circumscribing sphere.
(4) Subdivide each edge of OAB into three equal parts and join up to form a triangular grid.
(5) Each of the points are projected radially to the circumscribing sphere.

HIGHER LEVEL

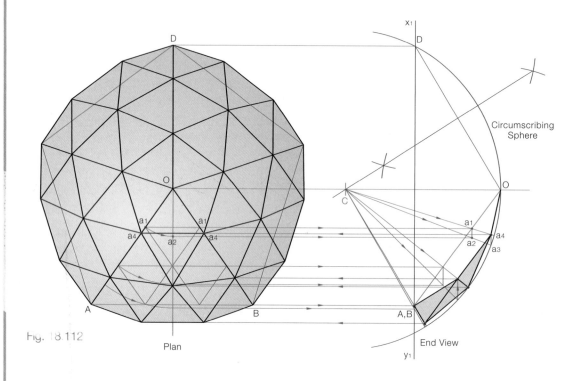

Fig. 18.112

Plan

End View

Method

Point a_1 on the grid in plan is projected to end view. Radial Oa_1 is rotated in plan to give Oa_2. Point a_2 is found in end view. Radiate a line from the centre of the circumscribing sphere C through a_2 in end view to intersect the sphere surface at a_3. This radial Ca_2a_3 is rotated back into position giving Ca_1a_4. Point a_4 is the new position of a_1 on the geodesic surface and is projected back to plan onto the radial Oa_1 extended.

Note: In elevation the bottom edges of the dome do not lie on the horizontal plane. In practice these irregularities at the bottom of the dome are easily accommodated by using dwarf walls.

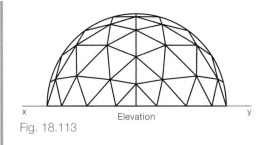

x — Elevation — y

Fig. 18.113

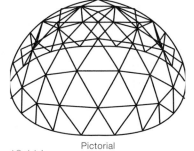

Fig. 18.114 — Pictorial

One advantage of using an octahedron as opposed to an icosahedron is that geodesic spheres constructed using an octahedron as a base can be divided neatly in half or in quarters producing planar divisions that do not cut through the geodesic faces.

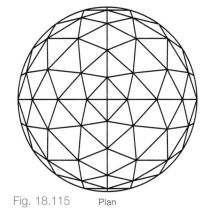

Fig. 18.115 — Plan

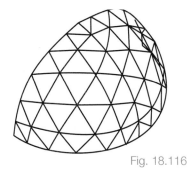

Fig. 18.116

HIGHER LEVEL

Structural Forms as They Occur in the Environment

The structures in nature hold great lessons for human study, having been under development for millions of years. Only the most successful structural forms have survived. Forms found in nature are shaped for maximum efficiency, transferring the required amount of force with the least amount of material. Furthermore, structures found in nature show a resourcefulness of material use and a capacity to respond to climactic and environmental forces. These are all worthwhile objectives for man-made structures to aspire to.

All natural structures must resist the physical forces of tension and compression. To increase efficiency, natural forms prefer tension members because compression members need a certain amount of bulk or they have a tendency to buckle. A spider's web comprises a network of tension strands and has been the source of inspiration for many well-known buildings:
- Olympic Stadium in Munich, Germany.
- Ganter Bridge in Eisten, Switzerland.
- Clouds of the Great Arch of La Defense in Paris, France.
- Great Belt East Suspension Bridge in Copenhagen, Denmark.
- Schlumberger Research Centre in Cambridge, England.

The honeycomb has been another inspirational, naturally occurring form because of its stackability and inherent strength. Some examples would be:
- Stansted Airport Terminal in Stansted, England.
- DG Bank Building in Munich, Germany.
- Green House in Dusseldorf, Germany.

- Papal Audience Hall in Rome, Italy.
- The skeleton form of mammals, particularly the rib cage, produces an efficient, strong structural form. This framework of strong members can be covered over with a light surface membrane:
  - Paddington Station Roof in London, England.
  - Gaudi Musical Theatre in Cologne, Germany.
  - Stazione Termini in Rome, Italy.
  - Stadelhofen Station in Zurich, Switzerland.

The study of soap films and bubbles has produced very aesthetically pleasing minimally surfaced shells and organic curves. Some examples would be:

- The Zarzeula Hippodrome roof in Madrid, Spain.
- Bordeaux Law Courts in Bordeaux, France.
- Wyss Garden Centre in Bern, Switzerland.
- Corporation Street Footbridge in Manchester, England.

Virus protein, when examined under huge magnification, shows very interesting domed formations. Such virus protein has been the inspiration for:

- Comptoir Wallon des Materiaux Forestiers de Reproduction in Marche-en-Famenne in Belgium.
- Aquatoll Dome in Neckarsulm, Germany.
- The Eden Project in Bodelva, England.
- IMAX Theatre in Paris, France.

Some other buildings of particular interest are:

- Auditorium Parco della Musica in Rome was inspired by the Scarab beetle.
- M and G Ricerche Research Lab in Venafro, Italy, was inspired by a caterpillar, as was the Waterloo International Terminal in London.
- Mercedes Benz Design Centre in Stuttgart, Germany, was inspired by fish fins.
- Ludwig Erhard Haus Building in Munich, Germany, was inspired by an armadillo, as was the Scottish Exhibition Conference Centre in Glasgow.
- Crystal Palace, London, was inspired by a water lily.
- Swiss Re Headquarters was inspired by a sea sponge.
- Royal Albert Bridge in Plymouth was inspired by a brontosaurus.

From dinosaurs to iron molecules, from sea sponges to soap films, from honeycombs to trees. All these naturally occurring structural forms have helped our understanding of form, shape, aesthetics, efficiency and economy. These are all desirable attributes of structural design. Using these ideas inspired from nature structural designers can become structural artists.

Students should do some research in this area.

Activities

Q1. Explain the difference between a beam and a column. Examine the types of load that each must support.

Q2. Stone was one of the few building materials available to builders in ancient times. Describe the properties of stone as a building material and then discuss how these properties affected building design during this period.

Q3. Make a neat freehand sketch of a pair of well-proportioned columns supporting a beam. The head and base of each column is to be widened in a decorative fashion.

Q4. Make a neat diagram of a cut, stone, semi-circular arch and name its parts.

Q5. Describe how the development of the arch made more 'open' building design possible.

Q6. Produce line drawings of the arches in Figures 18.7a to 18.7i.

Q7. It can be said that vaults are three-dimensional arches. Explain.

Q8. Using notes and sketches explain the difference between a barrel vault and a groined vault.

Q9. Describe how a masonry dome and a geodesic dome differ under each of the following headings:
- (i)   shape,
- (ii) design principle,
- (iii) possible size,
- (iv) forces exerted on its supports.

Q10. 'Most light frame constructions depend on triangulation for their strength.' Discuss this statement and support your answer with examples.

Q11. Make neat pictorial sketches of:
- (i)   a conoid,
- (ii) a hyperbolic paraboloid,
- (iii) a hyperboloid of revolution.

Q12. Using notes and diagrams, describe the stresses on a loaded beam.

Q13. Why is stone suitable for the building of columns and yet not ideal for the construction of long beams?

Q14. For each of the following structures explain why columns are not the usual form of support:
(i)   arch,
(ii)   barrel vault,
(iii) dome.

Q15. Explain why reinforced concrete is an ideal material for the construction of shell structures.

Q16. Fig. 18.117 shows the outline plan and elevation of a cooling tower. It is in the form of a hyperboloid of revolution.
(i)   Draw the given views.
(ii) Find the true shape of section S–S.

Scale 1:50

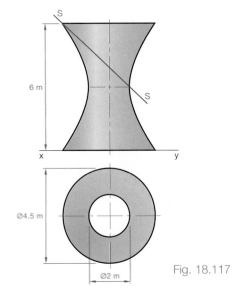

Fig. 18.117

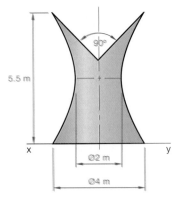

Fig. 18.118

Q17. The diagram Fig. 18.118 shows a hyperboloid of revolution which has been shaped at the top.
(i)   Draw the plan and elevation of the hyperboloid.
(ii) Project an end elevation.

Scale 1:50

Q18. Fig. 18.119 shows the plan and elevation of a hyperboloid of revolution with four rib lines along its surface. Draw the given plan and elevation.

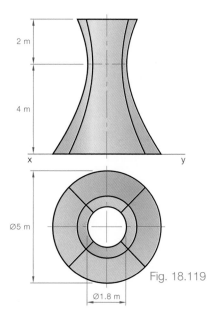

Fig. 18.119

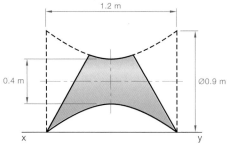

Fig. 18.120

Q19. A garden sculpture in the form of a cut hyperboloid of revolution is shown in Fig. 18.120. Draw the plan, elevation and end view of the sculpture.

Scale 1:10

Q20. Fig. 18.121 shows the outline plan of a hyperbolic paraboloid roof **ABCD**. The corners **B** and **D** are at ground level. Corner **A** is 2 m above ground level and corner **C** is 6 m above ground level.

(i)   Draw the given plan and project an elevation.
(ii)   Project an end view of the roof.
(iii) Find the curvature of the roof along the line joining **A** to **C**.

Scale 1:50

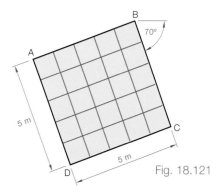

Fig. 18.121

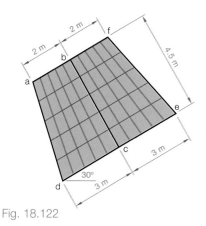

Fig. 18.122

Q21. Fig. 18.122 shows the outline plan of a hyperbolic paraboloid roof made up of two surfaces, **abcd** and **bcef**. The corners **a**, **d**, **e** and **f** are at ground level, corner **c** is 1 m above the ground and corner **b** is 5 m above the ground.

(i)   Draw the given plan and project an elevation.
(ii)   Project an end view of the roof.
(iii) Find the curvature of the roof along a line joining **d** and **f**.
(iv)   Draw a new elevation of the roof which shows the true length of edge **dc**.

Scale 1:50

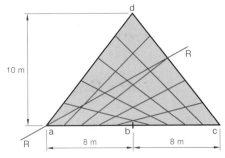

Fig. 18.123

Q22. Fig. 18.123 shows the outline plan of a hyperbolic paraboloid roof **abcd**. The corners **a** and **c** are 1 m above ground level. Corner **b** is 4 m above ground level and corner **d** is 12 m above ground level.

(i)   Draw the given plan and project an elevation.
(ii) Project an end view of the roof.
(iii) Show the true shape of section **R–R** through the roof.

Scale 1:100

Q23. Fig. 18.124 shows the outline plan of two adjoining hyperbolic roof surfaces **abcd** and **abef**. The corner **a** is at ground level and corner **b** is 1 m above ground level. Corners **d** and **e** are 4 m above ground level and corners **c** and **f** are 11 m above ground level.

(i)   Draw the given plan and project an elevation.
(ii) Project an end view.
(iii) Find the curvature of the roof along a line joining **c** to **f**.

Scale 1:100

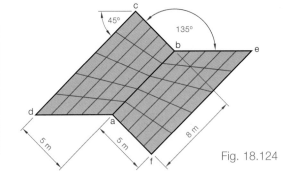

Fig. 18.124

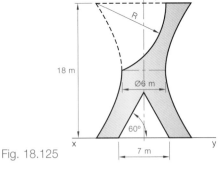

Fig. 18.125

Q24. The elevation of a hyperboloid of revolution is shown in Fig. 18.125. An equilateral triangular hole is cut through the bottom section and the top has been cut as shown.

(i)   Draw the plan and elevation of the building.
(ii) Project an end view.

Scale 1:100

Q25. The elevation of a hyperboloid of revolution which has been cut is shown in Fig. 18.126. Draw the elevation, end view and plan of the cut solid.

Scale 1:100

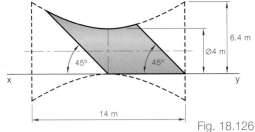

Fig. 18.126

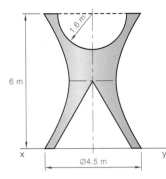

Fig. 18.127

Q26. Fig. 18.127 shows the elevation of a hyperboloid of revolution. The sides of the V-cut are elements of the hyperboloid. The true length of full length elements is 7 m.

(i)   Draw the plan and elevation of the solid.
(ii) Project an end view.

Scale 1:50

HIGHER LEVEL

Q27. Given two skew line directrices of a hyperbolic paraboloid ab and cd. Also, given the traces of the plane director, determine five elements on the surface of the hyperbolic paraboloid.

a = 40, 30, 40
b = 120, 10, 10
c = 60, 10, 50
d = 130, 60, 60

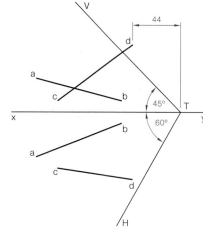

Fig. 18.128

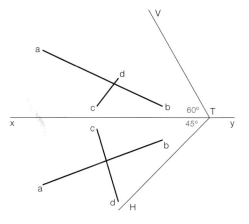

Fig. 18.129

Q28. Given two skew line directrices of a hyperbolic paraboloid ab and cd. Also, given the traces of the plane director VTH, determine five elements on the surface of the hyperbolic paraboloid.

a = 30, 60, 60
b = 140, 10, 20
c = 80, 10, 10
d = 100, 35, 75

Q29. Two skew lines ab and cd form the directrices of a hyperbolic paraboloid. The traces of the plane director for one set of elements is also given.

(i) Find the projections of five elements on the hyperbolic paraboloid.

(ii) Determine the traces of the plane director for the elements ab and cd.

a = 40, 15, 10
b = 105, 90, 100
c = 70, 70, 20
d = 130, 10, 40

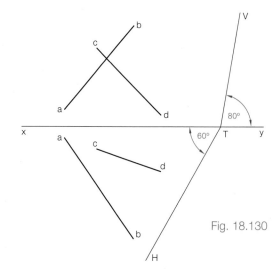

Fig. 18.130

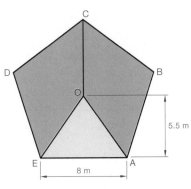

Fig. 18.131

Q30. Fig. 18.131 shows the regular pentagonal plan of two adjoining hyperbolic paraboloid roof surfaces ABCO and EDCO. The surface AEO is a plane surface. Points A and E are at ground level, D and B are 3 m above ground level, C is 5 m above the ground level and O is 10 m above ground level.

(i)   Draw the given plan and project an elevation.

(ii)   Show the curvature of the roof along the line CE and DO.

(iii)   Determine the plane director for the edges EO and DC on the surface DCOE. Show the traces of the plane director containing the element EO.

Scale 1:100

Q31. Fig. 18.132 shows the outline plan of a roof. The semi-circular plan is an extension of the hyperbolic paraboloid surface ABCD. Lines EAB and FCB are elements of the roof with E and F at ground level. Corner B is 12 m above ground level and corner D is 15 m above ground level.

(i)   Draw the plan and project the elevation.

(ii)   Determine the plane director for the elements AB and CD. Show the traces of the plane director containing the element AB.

(iii)   Show the curvature of the roof along the line joining D and B.

Scale 1:200

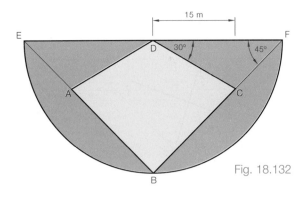

Fig. 18.132

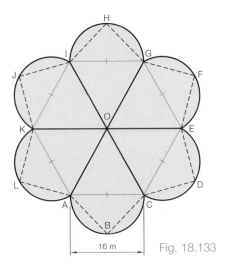

Fig. 18.133

Q32. Fig. 18.133 shows the plan of a roof which is made up from six adjoining hyperbolic paraboloid surfaces. The semicircles in plan are extensions of these surfaces.

ACEGIK forms a regular hexagon in plan.

Points **A, C, E, G, I** and **K** are 2 m above ground level. Points **B, D, F, H, J** and **L** are 10 m above ground level.

Point **O** is 16 m above ground level.

(i)   Draw the plan and elevation of the surfaces **ABCO** and **CDEO**.

(ii)   Show the curvature of the roof along a line joining **A** to **E**.

(iii)   Determine the plane director for the edges **OC** and **AB**. Show the traces of the plane director containing the element **AB**.

Scale 1:200

Q33. Fig. 18.134 shows the outline plan of four adjoining hyperbolic paraboloid roof surfaces **ABCO**, **CDEO**, **EFGO** and **GHAO**. The full roof perimeter is a square in plan. The four surfaces have been cut as shown, to form a circle in plan. The corners **A**, **C**, **E** and **G** are at ground level, corners **B**, **D**, **F** and **H** are 10 m above ground level and corner **O** is 22 m above ground level.

(i)   Draw the plan and project an elevation.

(ii) Determine the traces of the plane director for the edges **AB** and **OC** of the hyperbolic paraboloid surface **ABCO** and having its horizontal trace passing through **C**.

(iii) Find the curvature of the roof along a line joining **F** to **C**.

Scale 1:200

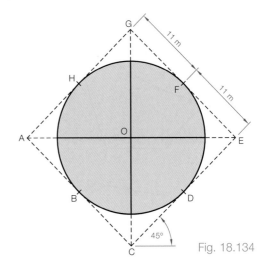

Fig. 18.134

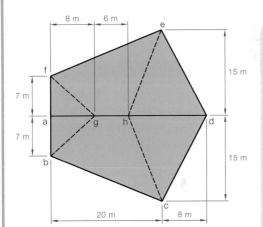

Fig. 18.135

Q34. Fig. 18.135 shows the outline plan of a roof. The roof surfaces **adef** and **adcb** are extensions of the hyperbolic paraboloid surfaces **efgh** and **bchg**. Corners **b**, **c**, **e** and **f** are at ground level, corner **a** is 18 m above ground level and corner **d** is 6 m above ground level.

(i)   Draw the given plan and project a front elevation and an end elevation.

(ii) Determine the traces of the plane director for the edges **bg** and **ch** and having its horizontal trace passing through **b**.

(iii) Determine the curvature of the roof along a line from **g** to **c**.

Scale 1:200

Q35. Fig. 18.136 shows the plan and elevation of a structure which is in the form of a hyperbolic paraboloid shell. The curve DE is a parabola whose vertex is at E. The surface of the unit is generated by translating the parabola ABC in a vertical position along the parabola DE.

(i)   Draw the given plan and elevation.

(ii) Project an end view.

Scale 1:500

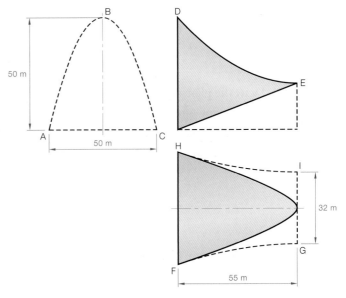

Fig. 18.136

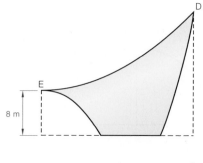

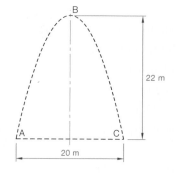

22 m

20 m

8 m

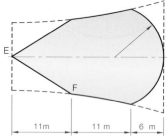

11m   11 m   6 m

Fig. 18.137

Q36. The outline plan and elevation of a structure are shown in Fig. 18.137. The structure is generated by translating the parabola ABC in a vertical position along the parabola DE whose vertex is at E.
(i)   Draw the given plan and elevation.
(ii) Project an end view.
(iii) Find the true shape of the curve EF.

GEODESIC DOMES

Q37. Explain the terms:
- geodesic, • great circle, • lesser circle,
- regular polyhedron.

Q38. Explain why there are only five possible regular polyhedra.

Q39. Construct a tetrahedron of 90 mm side and draw its circumscribing sphere.

Q40. Draw the plan and elevation of an octahedron having one vertex on the horizontal plane and one axis vertical. The sides of the octahedron are to be 70 mm long.

Q41. Draw the plan and elevation of an octahedron having one face resting on the horizontal plane. The true length of each edge is to be 70 mm.

Q42. Draw the plan, elevation and end view of an icosahedron of 60 mm side having one vertex resting on the horizontal plane and one vertical axis.

Q43. Explain the term 'frequency' in relation to geodesic structures.

Q44. Draw the plan and elevation of a 3-frequency geodesic dome based on an octahedron of 90 mm side.

Q45. Draw the plan and elevation of a 6-frequency geodesic dome based on a tetrahedron of 120 mm side.

Q46. Draw a 6-frequency, 3/8 icosahedra, geodesic dome based on an icosahedron of 90 mm side.

STRUCTURAL FORMS AND NATURE

Q47. 'Structural engineers should become structural artists by adding an aesthetic component to their work.' Discuss. Support your answer with examples.

Q48. 'An efficient design is not necessarily an aesthetically pleasing one. Numerous structures exist that are efficient but lack aesthetic value. Connecting design to natural forms can avoid this pitfall.' Discuss. Support your answer with examples.

Q49. Make a comparison between Robert Stephenson's 1850 Britannia Bridge in Wales and Brunel's 1859 Royal Albert Bridge in Plymouth under the following headings:

(i)   inspirational source,

(ii)   form,

(iii) efficiency,

(iv) aesthetic quality.

Q50. Find the link between the designs of the following buildings:
- BMW Pavilion in Frankfurt, Germany.
- Roof of the Gottlieb Daimler Stadium in Stuttgart, Germany.
- Oresund Bridge in Copenhagen, Denmark.

Make simple diagrams of two of these structures to help illustrate your answer.

Q51. Find the link from nature between the designs of the following structures:
- The Garabit Viaduct in Loubaresse, France.
- Montjuic Communications Tower in Barcelona, Spain.
- The Tavanasa Bridge in Tavanasa, Switzerland.

Make a simple diagram of one of these structures to illustrate your answer.

19 Geologic Geometry

Our studies to date have concerned us with drawings of man-made objects, be they machine parts or houses. This chapter will investigate the natural geological features of the earth, mapping of the earth's surface, mining, and finally the excavation works necessary for road building. Maps and map data are used throughout the course of the chapter. The accuracy of these maps and this data is extremely important in this type of work because of the scale of these earthworks projects.

Like all subjects, geologic geometry has its own subject-specific terminology. A good starting point is to define and explain some of these terms with notes and diagrams.

Contours

A contour is a line on a map to locate all points of equal elevation. This elevation/height can be relative to sea level or a chosen datum height. Contours may measure elevations above or below this datum level. On a single contour all points have the same elevation.

Contour Interval

This is the vertical distance between horizontal planes passing through successive contours. In Fig. 19.1 the contour interval is 10 m. On any given map the contour interval should not change.

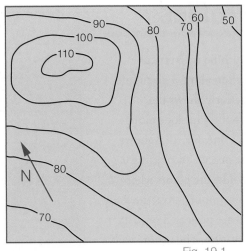

Fig. 19.1

Magnetic North

All maps should have the direction of north marked on them to allow for the correct orientation of the map. Magnetic north is found by using a compass. The direction of other lines or features on the map can be determined by reference to the north direction. On-site compass readings, however, are not to be taken as highly accurate indications of north. There are two reasons for this, (1) local magnetism may affect the position of the compass needle and (2) magnetic north and true north are not exactly the same.

Magnetic north can change due to the shifting of the earth's magnetic field.

True North

For accurate orientation of lines on a map, the angle of a line relative to true north is often needed. Sightings on a star (usually Polaris, the North Star) or the sun can give accurate readings from which true north can be calculated. A map will often indicate by how much magnetic north varies from true north.

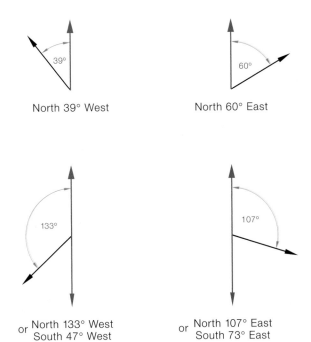

Bearing

The bearing of a line is the angle between the line and magnetic north. The bearing of a line may be established by using a directional compass. The correct method of recording bearings is by reference to the north or the south. Fig. 19.2 shows some examples. If a bearing is N 39° W, it could be also described as S 141° W. Similarly N 133° W could be described as S 47° W.

Fig. 19.2

Profiles

A profile is a vertical section along a given line. It clearly shows the variation in slope along that line. Fig. 19.3 shows the process of plotting a profile, the points where the contours cross the line AB are projected onto an elevation. The profile will not be completely accurate as the profile path between the plotted points is only guessed.

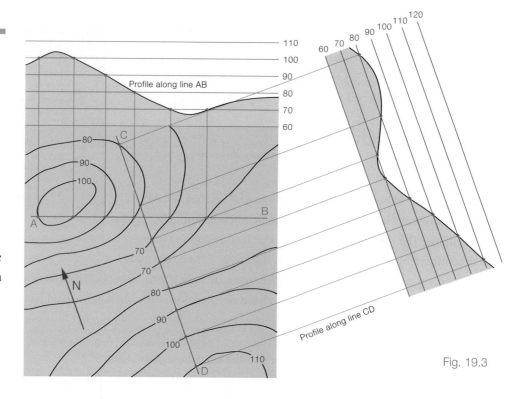

Fig. 19.3

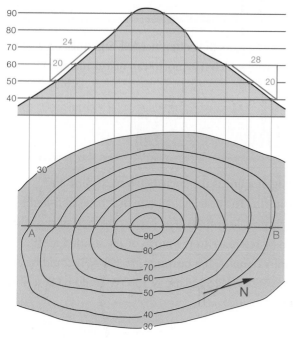

Fig. 19.4

Gradient

The gradient is the slope of the ground at a particular place. By examining the contours on a map an approximate gradient can be given. When the contours are close together the gradient is very steep. As the gap between contours widens on the map the slope decreases. Very widely spaced contours indicate land that is almost flat and/or land that is actually flat in places. A more accurate measurement of gradient is found by drawing a profile. At any point on the profile a slope can be found. Gradient can be given as a ratio or represented by a proportional triangle.

Fig. 19.4 shows how the gradient can be found along line AB. Written as a ratio it compares the vertical gain by the horizontal travel. 20:24 = 10:12 = 1:1.2, 1 in 1.2 m. The triangle graphically represents the same ratio.

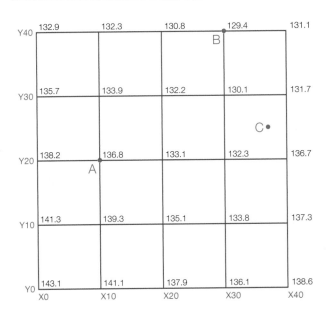

Fig. 19.5

Grid Layout

When surveying a site to determine contours and gradients one of the most practical approaches is to use a grid layout. The size of the grid squares affects the accuracy of the survey. Elevations/levels are taken at the corners of the squares and the ground is assumed to slope uniformly between adjacent level points. It is now possible to find fairly accurate contours by using **interpolation**. Fig. 19.5 shows a portion of a grid layout using 10 m squares. By using xy coordinates each corner can easily be identified. For example, corner A is x10,y20, corner B is x30,y40 and point C, which is not on a corner, may also be specified x37,y25.

Interpolation of Contours

The interpolation of contours is the finding of contours from grid levels. In Fig. 19.6 the position of 2 m contours are needed.

Edge AB of the grid will contain a point on contour 142 m. The difference in levels between A and B is 1.8 m. Divide AB into 18 equal parts and thus locate level 142 m as shown. In a similar way a point on the 142 m contour can be located on edge AC of the grid. The difference in levels here is 2 m. Divide AC into 20 equal parts and locate the 142 m level. Further points can be found using this method. Interpolation can be very slow and tedious. Fig. 19.7 shows the grid levels converted into contours.

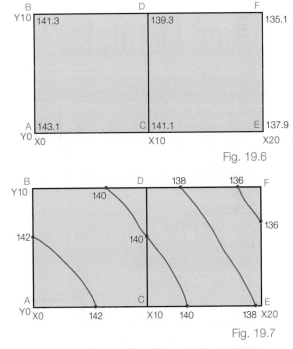

Fig. 19.6

Fig. 19.7

Using a Template to Help

Interpolation is based on the division of the sides of the grid boxes into differing numbers of equal parts. A template to speed up the division process would help a great deal.

(1)   On tracing paper draw a line AB of any length and at one end draw a perpendicular CD.

(2)   Step a number of equal spaces up and down from B on the line CD.

(3)   Join all these points back to A.

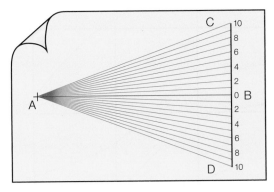

Fig. 19.8

Once measurements are taken perpendicular to line AB, it will be seen that the spacing between the lines remain equal all the way from B to A. The line CD should be longer than the sides of the squares of the grid and the number of divisions should be enough to cope with the largest difference in levels between two adjacent corners of the grid.

There is a difference of 17.1 − 15.7 = 1.4 m between the two ends of the grid square in Fig. 19.9. Slide the template across the grid until the grid side is divided into 14 divisions. Use a pin to mark the contour positions. The line CD must be kept parallel to the grid sides.

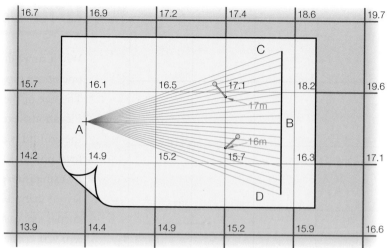

Fig. 19.9

Worked Examples

A portion of a grid layout is shown in Fig. 19.10. A 10 m square grid has been used. To a scale of 1:200 draw out the grid and plot the contour lines at 1 m vertical intervals using interpolation.

(1) If using a template it should be constructed to have at least 26 spaces and the CD line should be longer than 50 mm.

(2) By proportional division of the sides of the grids the contours may also be found. Contour 22 is shown in Fig. 19.11.

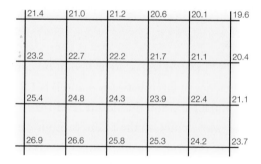

Fig 19.10

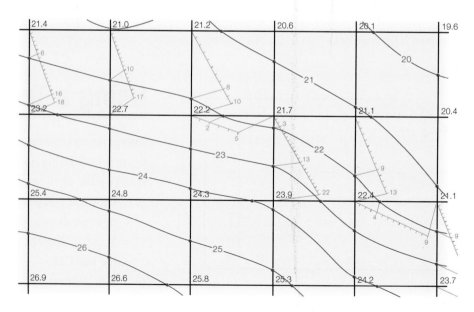

Fig. 19.11

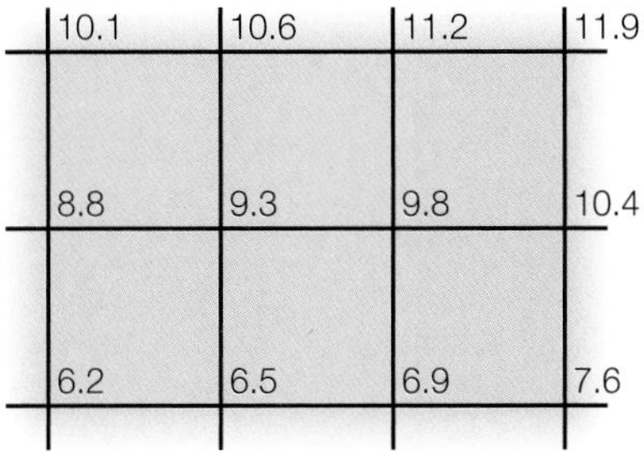

10.1	10.6	11.2	11.9
8.8	9.3	9.8	10.4
6.2	6.5	6.9	7.6

Fig. 19.12

A portion of a 10 m grid with levels is shown in Fig. 19.12. To a scale of 1:200 draw out the grid and plot the contour lines at 1 m intervals using profiles.

When the grid is small the use of profiles may be a quicker method of finding points on the contour lines.

(1) A profile of each line of the survey is constructed using the levels from the grid.

(2) Horizontal and vertical lines are drawn on the profiles at the levels where the contours are found.

(3) The points at which the profiles cross these lines indicate where the contour lines cross the grid.

(4) In Fig. 19.13 the profiles are superimposed on each other.

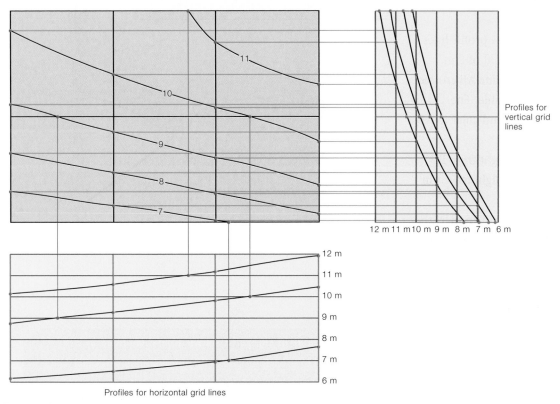

Profiles for vertical grid lines

12 m 11 m 10 m 9 m 8 m 7 m 6 m

12 m
11 m
10 m
9 m
8 m
7 m
6 m

Profiles for horizontal grid lines

Fig. 19.13

The map in Fig. 19.14 shows ground contours at 5 m intervals. An object stands vertically on the ground at A. Determine the minimum height of the object if it is to be visible from the ground at B.

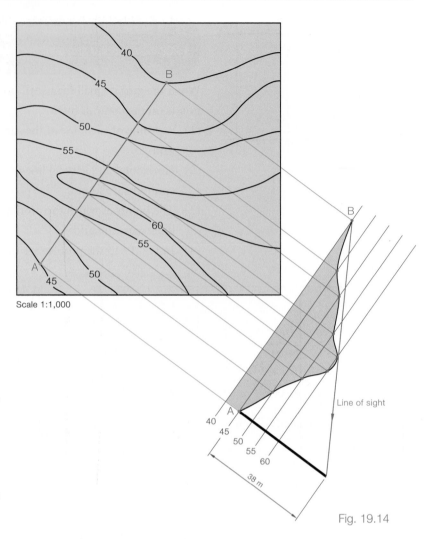

Scale 1:1,000

Fig. 19.14

To solve this problem a profile is found along the line AB.

(1)   Join A to B.

(2)   The lowest point on the profile will be 40 m. Set up the profile lines parallel to line AB.

(3)   The spacing between these profile lines will be the scaled equivalent of 5 m.

(4)   Project the points where line AB crosses the contours onto the profile. The projection lines are perpendicular to AB.

(5)   Draw the profile.

(6)   Draw the lowest line of sight from B tangential to the profile (light travels in straight lines).

(7)   Draw the vertical object at A to meet the line of sight. If the object is above 38 m tall it will be seen from the ground at point B.

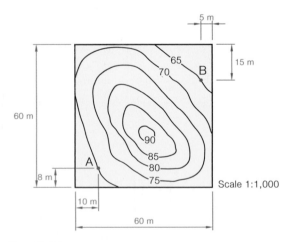

Fig. 19.15

The map in Fig. 19.15 shows ground contours at 5 m vertical intervals. An object 40 m tall stands vertically at A. Reproduce this map to a scale of 1:500 and determine if the object at A is visible from the ground at B.

The given map is to a scale of 1:1,000. The new map is to be reproduced to a scale of 1:500, i.e. doubled in size.

(1)   Divide the original map into smaller boxes.

(2)   Draw the new grid layout to the larger scale. The contours are now drawn carefully in the bigger grid. If care is taken a reasonably accurate enlargement can be produced.

(3)   Locate points A and B and join.

(4)   Draw a profile along the line AB.

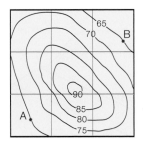

(5)   Draw the object at A to a height of 40 m. Also draw the line of sight from B tangential to the profile line.

(6)   It can be seen that the object at A is not visible from B

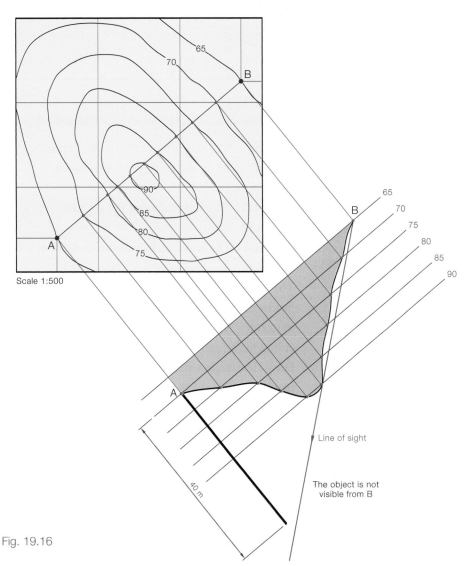

Scale 1:500

Line of sight

The object is not visible from B

40 m

Fig. 19.16

The Geometry of Mining

Mining concerns the removal of useless material and useful material both on the surface (opencast mining) and beneath the surface. Mining companies like to minimise the mining of useless material and maximise the mining of useful material. To this end, surveying, testing and planning is involved.

For the duration of this chapter we deal with mineral deposits with definite limits and boundaries. These are known as **veins** or **strata**. The strata is made up of rock or **ore** and is assumed to be of uniform thickness and be planar on top and bottom surfaces. Obviously in real geographic situations the stratum may undulate and vary in thickness.

The stratum of ore may come to the surface as in Fig. 19.17. This is an outcrop point. Outcrop points may facilitate open mining and thus minimise expense. The vein, however, may not intersect the surface of the earth. In cases like this the vein's theoretical outcrop point may serve as a starting point for mining.

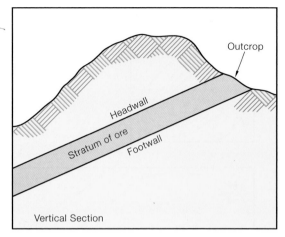

Fig. 19.17

Terminology

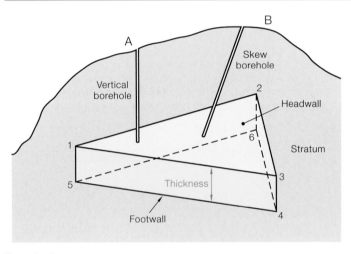

Fig. 19.18

Stratum – A layer, seam or vein of ore, generally assumed to be an inclined plane of uniform thickness.

Headwall – The top surface of the stratum, 1, 2, 3, Fig. 19.18.

Footwall – The lower surface of the stratum, 4, 5, 6, Fig. 19.18.

Thickness – The perpendicular distance between the headwall and the footwall.

Outcrop – A point at which a section of the stratum comes to the earth's surface.

Dip – The angle a stratum makes with the horizontal plane (the slope of the stratum).

Strike – The bearing of a level line on the surface of the stratum. It is usually related to the compass north. It is shown in plan.

Borehole – Hole drilled from the surface of the earth through a stratum of ore in order to determine its position and thickness.

> The map shown in Fig. 19.19 shows ground contours at 10 m vertical intervals. Also shown are points A, B and C which are outcrop points on a stratum of ore. Determine the strike of the stratum.

(1)   Since A, B and C are outcrop points they are all on the stratum. Join the points giving a triangular plane of ore.

(2)   Project an elevation of this plane using the heights of the contours.

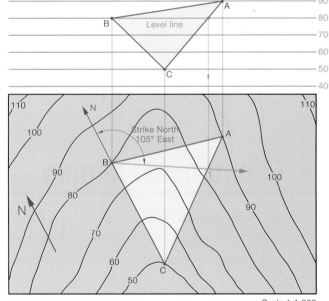

Fig. 19.19

Scale 1:1,000

(3) In elevation draw a level line across the plane ABC. Usually the starting point for this level line is the mid-height vertex. In this example the line is drawn from B to intersect edge AC at point 1.

(4) Find line B1 in plan by projecting point 1 down to edge AC in plan. Joint point 1 to vertex B.

(5) The angle the line B1 makes with the given north is the strike. It is written as North 122° East.

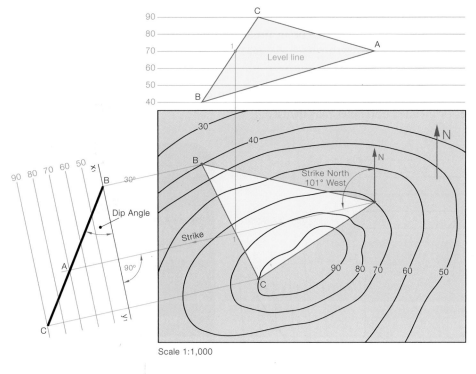

Scale 1:1,000

Fig. 19.20

The map shown in Fig. 19.20 shows ground contours at 10 m intervals. Also shown are points A, B and C which are outcrop points on a stratum of ore. Determine the dip and strike of the stratum.

(1) Construct the plan and elevation of the stratum as explained in the previous example.

(2) A level line is drawn in elevation and is projected to plan. The angle line A1 makes with the given north is the strike.

(3) By projecting an auxiliary view of the stratum viewing in the direction of the strike an edge view of the stratum is found. Points A, B and C line up.

(4) The angle the edge view of the stratum makes with the horizontal is the dip.

Fig. 19.21 shows ground contours at 10 m vertical intervals on a map. A, B and C are outcrop points on a stratum of ore.

(i) Determine the dip and strike of the stratum.

(ii) Find the outline of the outcrop between points A and C, and between points C and B.

(1) Find the dip and strike as outlined previously.

(2) The outcrop line is where the stratum comes to the surface. In the auxiliary the stratum is seen as an edge view.

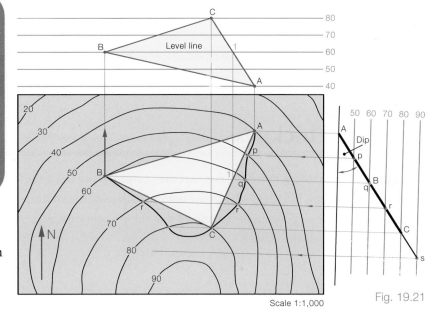

Scale 1:1,000

Fig. 19.21

Where this edge view crosses the levels lines they are projected back to give points on the contours in plan. For example, the edge view crosses the 50 m level at point p. Point p is projected back to the map and is found on the 50 m contour line. Similarly for point q. Point r when projected back crosses the 70 m contour twice and thus gives two points on the outcrop.

(3)   Join the points with a line remembering to include points A, B and C.

(4)   It should be noted that the 90 m contour definitely does not include outcrop points. This is proved by extending the edge view in the auxiliary to the 90 m level at point s. This point projected back does not intersect the 90 m contour in plan.

Up to now the examples given have all used outcrop points to locate the stratum. Boreholes may also be used to locate points on the stratum. Vertical boreholes or inclined boreholes may be used.

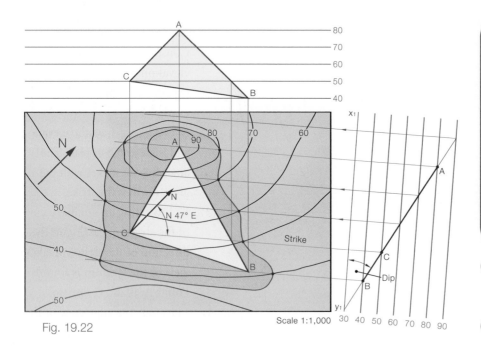

Fig. 19.22

The map shown in Fig. 19.22 shows ground contours at 10 m vertical intervals. Vertical boreholes at A, B and C strike a stratum of ore at altitudes of 80 m, 40 m and 50 m respectively.

(i)   Determine the dip and strike of the stratum.

(ii)   Find the complete outline of the outcrop.

(1)   Points A, B and C are found by using the altitudes from the question.

(2)   Find the strike and dip of the stratum in the usual way.

(3)   The outcrop is found as explained in the previous example. It should be noted that A, B and C are not part of the outcrop.

(4)   There are two outcrop points on the 80 m contour and none on the 90 m contour. When drawing the outcrop line, care must be taken to join the two points without crossing a contour line. In a similar way there are two outcrop points on the 40 m contour. These points must be joined without crossing the 50 m contour line.

Stratum Thickness

Up to this point we have ignored the fact that the stratum of ore has a thickness. The problems have dealt with the top surface of the stratum (the headwall) or the bottom surface of the stratum (the footwall). As has been mentioned earlier in the solving of these problems, it is assumed that the stratum thickness remains constant throughout, i.e. that the headwall and footwall are parallel.

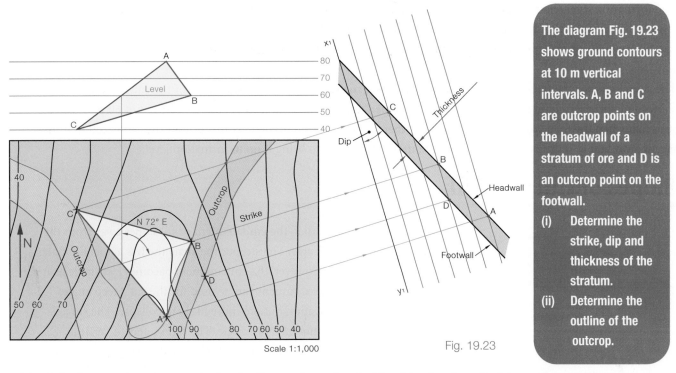

The diagram Fig. 19.23 shows ground contours at 10 m vertical intervals. A, B and C are outcrop points on the headwall of a stratum of ore and D is an outcrop point on the footwall.

(i)   Determine the strike, dip and thickness of the stratum.

(ii) Determine the outline of the outcrop.

Fig. 19.23

(1)   Join the outcrop points on the headwall to make a triangle. Use this triangle to find the strike and dip of the stratum in the usual way.

(2)   Project D which is on the footwall onto the auxiliary view.

(3)   Draw the footwall in the auxiliary parallel to the headwall.

(4)   Mark in the thickness of the stratum as the **perpendicular** distance between the two lines.

(5)   Find the outcrop as before using the headwall and the footwall.

Earthworks

When constructing roads, car parks, railroads etc., extensive use is made of contour maps to determine how much filling is needed in the hollows and how much cutting away of soil is needed in the high areas. Particularly if a road or railway is to be built on irregular terrain, then for the comfort of the drivers, the land must be levelled or at least reduced to an acceptable gradient. A profile along the proposed road will show what the road looks like and what the topography of the land is along the length of the road.

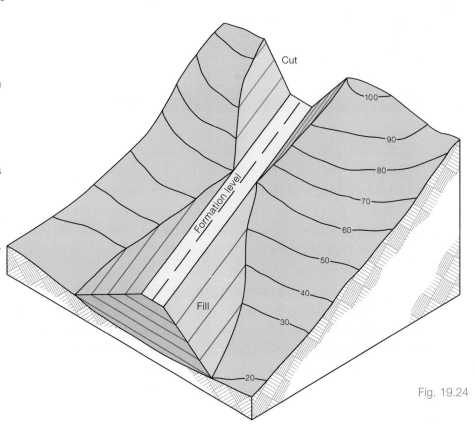

Fig. 19.24

The **formation** level refers to the level of the proposed road or car park. The **cut** is the amount of land that has to be cut away to bring the level of land down to the formation level. The **fill** is the amount of fill of material that needs to be put in a hollow to bring the level up to the formation level. In the construction of most roads there will be both cut and fill.

The side slopes for the fill are kept the same for the whole road and similarly for the slope of the cutting. Fig. 19.24 shows a pictorial of a level road passing through a sloped terrain. The road is level and has a height of 60 m. It can be seen that when the road crosses the 60 m contour there is no cut or fill needed. As the ground rises above 60 m it must be cut away and as it drops below 60 m the area needs to be filled to bring it up to formation level.

Slopes of Cut and Fill

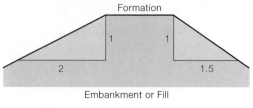

Fig. 19.25

As mentioned earlier, the embankment or fill slopes away from the road at an even angle. The steeper the angle the less actual fill material will be needed. However, the embankment becomes less stable as it gets steeper. A similar argument can be used for the cut. Steep angles involve less excavation but are more likely to collapse. The slope is expressed as a ratio 1:2 or an angle. The ratio refers to vertical height:width. The left side of Fig. 19.25 has a slope of 1:2 and the right side of 1:1.5.

Fig. 19.26 shows ground contours at 5 m vertical intervals. AB is the line of a proposed roadway. The road is to have the following specifications:

(i)   Formation width 16 m.

(ii)   Formation level 75 m.

(iii)   Side slopes for cuttings 1:1.

(iv)   Side slopes for embankments 1:1.5.

Show the earthworks needed to accommodate the roadway.

(1)   Draw the sides of the formation parallel to the line AB.

(2)   The formation level is at 75 m so therefore the 75 m contour will have neither cut nor fill.

(3)   The slope for cutting is 1:1. For every 1 m rise in the cut one moves 1 m from the road. The contours are at 5 m intervals, so to get a 5 m rise in the cut a move 5 m away from the road is needed. The road side is at 75 m level. A line 5 m away and parallel represents 80 m on the cut, 10 m away and parallel to the side of the road represents 85 m on the cut. Draw in the cut lines as shown. Where they intersect the contour lines, locate points on the cut outline. Draw in the cut.

(4)   The fill is constructed in the same way. The slope for fill is 1:1.5. For a 5 m fall in the embankment level, a distance of 1.5 × 5 m = 7.5 m must be travelled away from the road. Draw in the embankment lines parallel to the roadside and 7.5 m apart as shown. As you move out from the road you move down the bank, the level drops. Where the fill lines and the contour lines cross give points on the embankment line.

(5)   Draw in the symbols for cut and fill as shown.

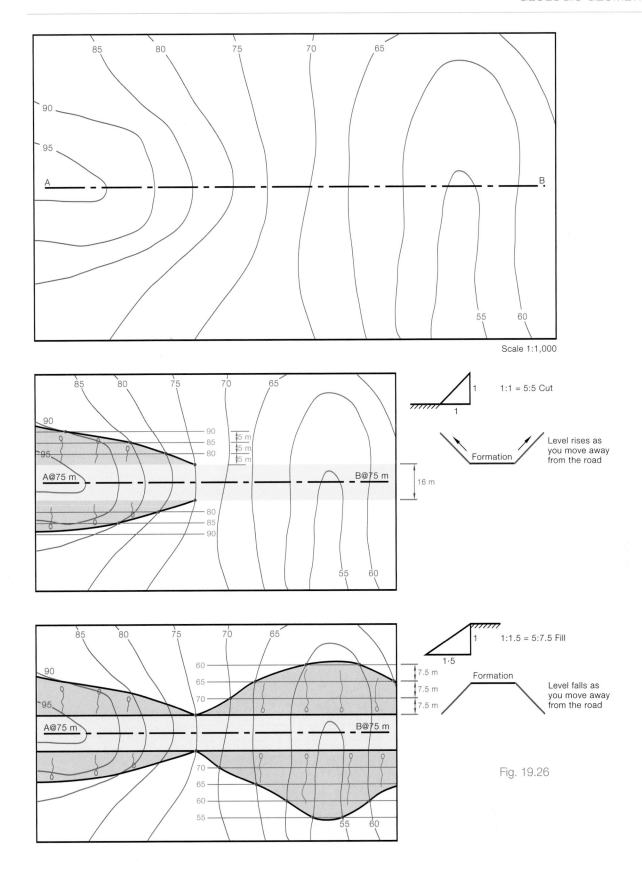

Scale 1:1,000

1:1 = 5:5 Cut

Level rises as you move away from the road

Formation

16 m

1:1.5 = 5:7.5 Fill

Level falls as you move away from the road

Formation

Fig. 19.26

Figures 19.27a and 19.27b show ground contours at 4 m vertical intervals. ABCD is the centre line of a proposed roadway with the centre for the curve at O. The road is to have the following specification.

(i)   Formation width 14 m.

(ii) Formation level 52 m.

(iii) Side slopes for cutting 1:1.5.

(iv) Side slopes for embankment 1:2.

Show the earthworks needed to accommodate the roadway.

(1) Draw in the formation.

(2) Mark the 52 m contour as it crosses the side of the formation.

(3) Cutting slope 1:1.5. With the difference between contours at 4 m this will mean a spacing between the cutting contours of 6 m (4 × 1.5). Draw in the cuttings.

(4) Embankment slope of 1:2. With the contours at 4 m intervals this will mean a spacing between the fill contours of 8 m (4 × 2). These cutting contours remain parallel to the formation even around the curve.

(5) Complete the outline of the earthworks as shown in Fig. 19.27b.

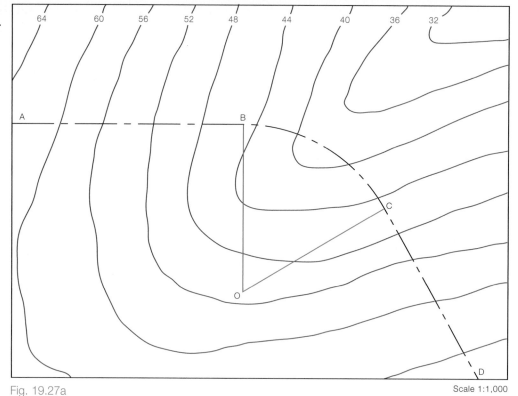

Fig. 19.27a

Scale 1:1,000

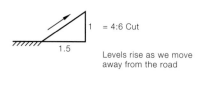

1 = 4:6 Cut

Levels rise as we move away from the road

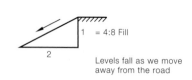

1 = 4:8 Fill

Levels fall as we move away from the road

Fig. 19.27b

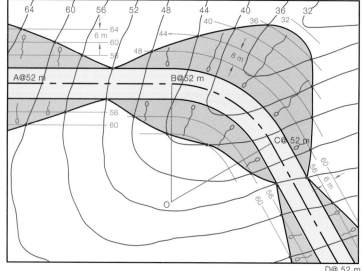

Figures 19.28a and 19.28b show ground contours at 2 m vertical intervals. AB shows a proposed roadway with CDEF being a car park. The car park is level and at the same level as the road. The road and car park are to have the following specifications:

    (i)   Formation width 12 m.

    (ii)   Formation level 110 m.

    (iii) Side slopes for cutting 1:2.

    (iv) Side slopes for embankment 1:2.5.

Show the earthworks necessary to accommodate the road and car park.

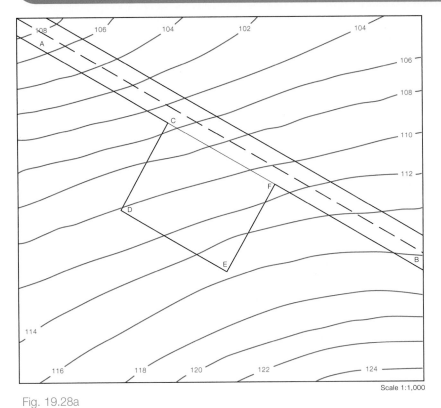

Fig. 19.28a

(1) Ignore the car park initially and find the cut and fill for the road. The slopes for cutting are 1:2 and the contours are at 2 m vertical intervals. The cutting contours are at (2 × 2 m) 4 m spacings from the side of the road. Draw the cut outline.

(2) The slopes for embankment are 1:2.5 and the contours are at 2 m vertical intervals. The fill lines are at (2 × 2.5 m) 5 m spacing from the side of the road. Draw the cut outline.

(3) Each side of the car park is treated like the side of a road. The cut and fill are plotted slightly beyond the sides.

(4) The earthworks for each side intersect each other.

(5) It should be noted that at corner, C, E and F where embankments intersect, and cuts intersect, a valley or ridge will be formed. These are indicated in Fig. 19.28b.

(6) Draw in the symbols.

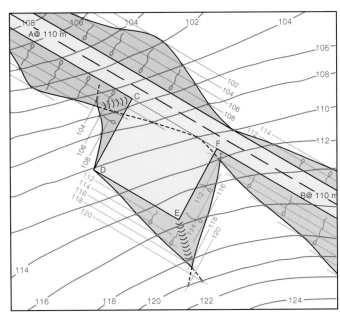

Fig. 19.28b

Skew Boreholes

It is possible to determine the strike, dip and thickness of a stratum of ore using only two non-parallel boreholes. The pictorial diagram, Fig. 19.29, shows two skew boreholes (skew means non-parallel, non-intersecting lines) intersecting a vein of ore. Borehole A intersects the top surface, the headwall, at A_H and exits the stratum through the footwall at A_F. Similarly borehole B enters the headwall at B_H and exits through the footwall at B_F. A straight line joining A_H and B_H will run along the headwall for its entire length. The line $A_F B_F$ lies on the footwall. By finding a view that shows $A_H B_H$ and $A_F B_F$ appearing parallel, an edge view of the stratum can be seen.

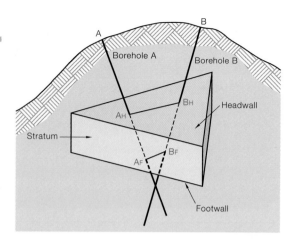

Fig. 19.29

On a contour map, A and B are two points whose altitudes are 80 m and 100 m respectively. On the map, B is located 80 m east of A. A skew borehole at A is drilled in a southerly direction in plan and has an actual inclination of 45° to the horizontal plane. It reveals the top and bottom surfaces of the stratum at altitudes of 65 m and 25 m respectively.

A skew borehole at B is drilled in a north-westerly direction in plan and has an actual inclination of 65° to the horizontal plane. It reveals the top and bottom surfaces of the stratum at altitudes of 80 m and 45 m.

Find the strike, dip and thickness of the stratum.

Scale 1:1,000

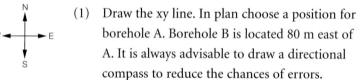

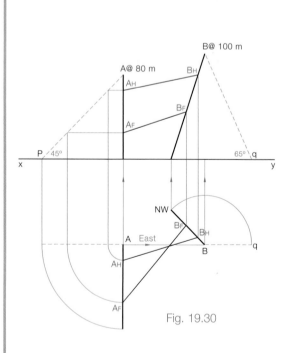

Fig. 19.30

(1) Draw the xy line. In plan choose a position for borehole A. Borehole B is located 80 m east of A. It is always advisable to draw a directional compass to reduce the chances of errors.

(2) Project points A and B to elevation and measure vertically to the specified altitudes of 80 m and 100 m.

(3) Borehole A is bored at an angle of 45° to the HP and in a southerly direction. The borehole is constructed first in a westerly or easterly direction and then rotated to a southerly direction. Draw a line from A at 45° to the xy line. Where this line meets the xy line at p, project down to a horizontal from A in plan. This 'constructed' borehole can now be swung around into a southerly direction. The borehole is drawn in bold in both views.

(4) This borehole reveals the top and bottom of the stratum at altitudes of 65 m and 25 m. An altitude is a vertical measurement. Vertical distances of 65 m and 25 m above the xy line are found on the borehole giving A_H and A_F.

(5) A_H and A_F are found in plan by projecting the two points onto the constructional borehole, projecting to plan and rotating onto the actual borehole.

(6) The construction of borehole B is the same. It is bored at an angle of 65° in a north-westerly direction. Draw a line from B at an angle of 65° to the xy line. Where this line meets the xy line at q, project down to a horizontal from B in plan. The constructional borehole is rotated about B into a north-westerly direction and drawn in bold. Find this borehole in elevation.

(7) B_H and B_F have altitudes of 80 m and 45 m respectively. Project these heights onto borehole B in elevation and project to plan.

(8) Join A_H to B_H and also A_F to B_F. The first of these skew lines lies on the headwall and the second on the footwall.

(1) Fig. 19.31 shows that by getting a view showing $A_H B_H$ and $A_F B_F$ appearing as parallel, the strike, dip and thickness of the stratum can be found.
Draw a level line in elevation from one of the points, e.g. A_H. From B_H in elevation draw a line parallel to $A_F B_F$ to intersect the level line at O.

(2) From B_H in plan draw a line parallel to $A_F B_F$. This line intersects the projection line from O in elevation to find point O in plan.

(3) Join O back to A_H. View along $A_H O$ which is the strike. An auxiliary projected in this direction shows the skew lines appearing parallel and thus reveals the thickness and dip of the stratum.

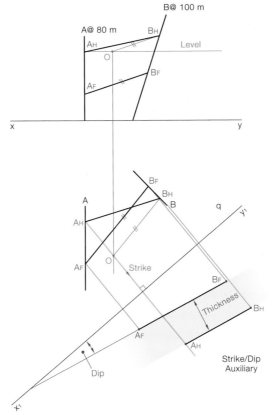

Fig. 19.31

On a contour map A and B are two points whose altitudes are 70 m and 90 m respectively. On a map, B is located 90 m south-east of A. A skew borehole at A is drilled in a north-westerly direction in plan and has an actual inclination of 50° to the horizontal plane. It reveals the top and bottom surfaces of the stratum at distances of 35 m and 65 m respectively from A.

A skew borehole at B is drilled in a north-easterly direction in plan and has an actual inclination of 60° to the horizontal plane. It reveals the top and bottom surfaces of the stratum at altitudes of 70 m and 35 m respectively.

(i)   Determine the strike, dip and thickness of the stratum.

(ii) A second skew borehole from A is drilled in a southerly direction and has an actual inclination of 60° to the horizontal plane. Determine the altitude at which this borehole touches the bottom surface of the stratum and also the inclination of the borehole to the stratum.

Scale 1:1,000

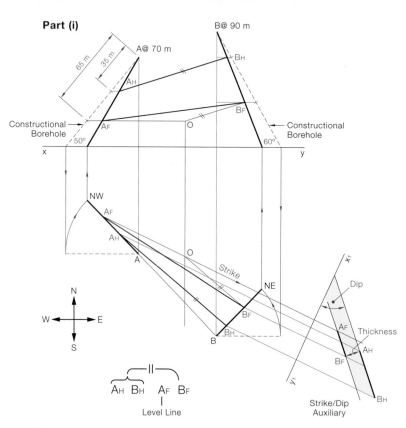

Fig. 19.32

(1)   Set up the problem as explained in the previous example. Points A and B are first found in plan. B is 90 m away from A and at a 45° angle in a south-easterly direction.

(2)   Project the two points to elevation and at the required elevation.

(3)   Draw the borehole A at a 50° angle in elevation, drop it to plan and rotate to a north-westerly direction. Project the rotated borehole to elevation.

(4)   This borehole reveals the top and bottom surfaces of the stratum at distances of 35 m and 65 m respectively from A.

These two distances must be measured down from A, along the constructional borehole. This constructional borehole shows true angles and true lengths. As this borehole is rotated into position the points move horizontally thus locating A_H and A_F on the actual borehole. These may be projected down to plan.

(5)   Borehole B is found in a similar fashion. The points on the headwall and footwall are given as altitudes. These vertical heights are projected horizontally onto the actual borehole and then down to plan.

(6) A_HB_H and A_FB_F are treated as skew lines. The strike dip and thickness are found as explained in Fig. 19.30.

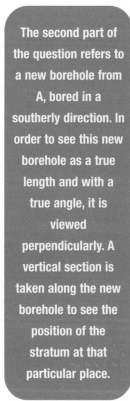

The second part of the question refers to a new borehole from A, bored in a southerly direction. In order to see this new borehole as a true length and with a true angle, it is viewed perpendicularly. A vertical section is taken along the new borehole to see the position of the stratum at that particular place.

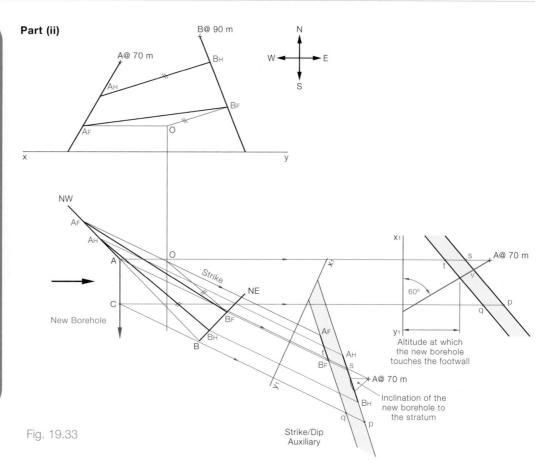

Part (ii)

Fig. 19.33

(1) Draw the new borehole from A in plan in a southerly direction.

(2) View perpendicular to this to get the auxiliary view. Point A is projected onto this view to an altitude of 70 m. The borehole is now drawn in the auxiliary making an angle of 60° to the horizontal plane (from question).

(3) The stratum is found by taking a vertical section along the new borehole and projecting it onto the new auxiliary. A vertical borehole is drilled from point A in plan and a second vertical borehole is drilled from a point C anywhere along the new borehole.

(4) **Vertical boreholes will appear perpendicular to the horizontal plane in all elevations.** Draw these vertical boreholes in the new elevation. These two vertical boreholes will hit the stratum at points s, t, p and q (Fig. 19.33). The heights of these four points are found by projecting the same vertical boreholes, A and C, onto the strike/dip auxiliary.

(5) When the points s, t, p and q have been located the vertical section through the stratum can be drawn. The required altitude and inclination can then be clearly seen.

(6) To find the true inclination of the borehole to the stratum, the length Av (which is a true length) is taken on a compass. Use this, as a radius, in the strike/dip auxiliary. With A as centre, scribe an arc to hit the headwall in two places. The inclination of the borehole can then be seen.

On a contour map A and B are two points whose altitudes are 120 m and 100 m respectively. On the map. B is located 95 m north-east of A. A skew borehole at A is drilled in a north-easterly direction in plan and has an actual inclination of 60° to the horizontal plane. It reveals the top and bottom surfaces of a stratum at distances of 45 m and 100 m respectively from A.

A skew borehole at B is drilled in a southerly direction in plan and has an actual inclination of 50° to the horizontal plane. It reveals the top and bottom surfaces of the stratum at altitudes of 60 m and 45 m respectively.

(i)   Determine the strike, dip and thickness of the stratum.

(ii)   Another skew borehole at B is drilled in a south-westerly direction in plan and meets the top surface of the stratum at a distance of 55 m from B. Determine the altitude at which this borehole hits the bottom surface of the stratum and the length of the borehole as it passes through the stratum.

Scale 1:1,000

HIGHER LEVEL

(1) Set up A and B in plan and elevation.

(2) Draw the constructional borehole for each point and rotate them into their proper positions.

(3) Locate A_H and A_F noting that the **distances** from A are given. These must be measured **down** from A along the constructional borehole which shows the borehole as a true length.

(4) Locate B_H and B_F by measuring vertical heights above the xy line. Borehole B is in a southerly direction and therefore is only seen as a vertical line in elevation. To find B_H and B_F in plan they must be projected across to the constructional borehole, dropped vertically to plan and rotated into place.

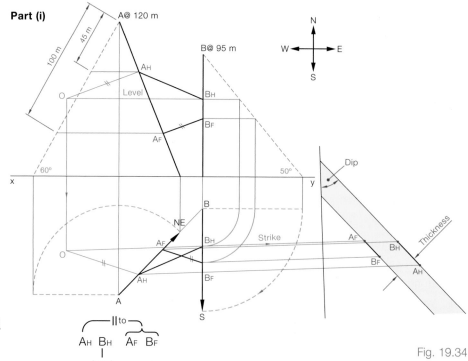

Fig. 19.34

(5) To find the strike, a level line is drawn from one of the points, e.g. B_H. From the other end of this line on the headwall a line is drawn parallel to A_FB_F to intersect the level line at O. Point O is projected to plan and is found exactly by drawing a line from A_H in plan, parallel to A_FB_F in plan. The level line in elevation B_HO, when found in plan, is the strike.

(6) Project the auxiliary and show the dip and thickness of the stratum.

The new borehole is in a south-westerly direction. A vertical section is taken along this borehole and a sectional elevation projected.

(1) Draw xy parallel to the new borehole.

(2) Project point B onto the new elevation.

(3) The stratum is found. Both A_H and A_F are along the new borehole and can therefore be projected to the new elevation. A further point on the headwall and on the footwall are needed. A vertical borehole is bored at B. Vertical boreholes project perpendicular to the horizontal plane in all elevations. Projected to the strike/dip auxiliary it passes through the stratum at s and t. These two points can now be found in the new auxiliary. Points A_F and s are on the footwall. Points A_H and t are on the headwall.

(4) The new borehole is located by swinging an arc of 55 m length from point B.

(5) The length of the borehole as it passes through the stratum and the altitude at which it hits the bottom surface of the stratum are clearly seen, see Fig. 19.35.

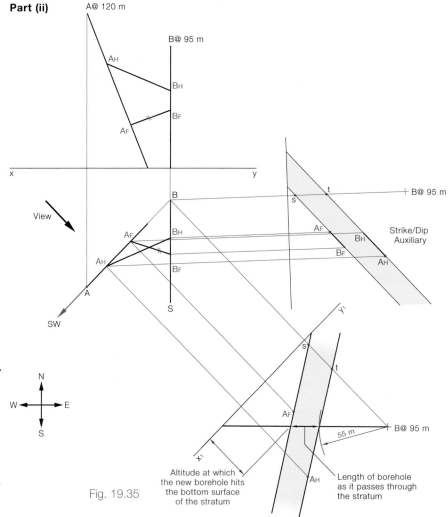

Fig. 19.35

True Dip and Apparent Dip

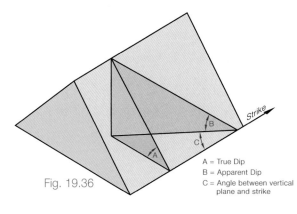

Fig. 19.36

A = True Dip
B = Apparent Dip
C = Angle between vertical plane and strike

The true dip of a stratum, which is what we have been finding up to this stage, is taken perpendicular to the strike. It can be taken from an edge view of the stratum plane(s) or as a vertical section taken perpendicular to the strike direction. Consider a vertical section taken at a different angle. This will show the layer(s) apparently at a lesser dip. This angle is the apparent dip.

Consider the practical example of a pitched roof. If you walk directly down the roof, taking the shortest route from ridge to eaves, then that is the steepest slope down the roof. By walking at an angle, the journey will be longer but not as steep. This is the essence of apparent dip. Any plane surface can have only one true dip angle but can have multiple apparent dip angles depending at which angle the section plane is taken.

If a vertical sectional plane is taken perpendicular to the strike of a stratum, then the dip is at its maximum, the true dip of the stratum is found. When the angle between the cross-section and the strike is anything less than 90° then the apparent dip is some value less than the true dip.

The apparent dip of a bed in any desired direction may be calculated from the true dip by the equation:
tan (apparent dip) = tan (true dip) × sin (angle between the strike of the stratum and the direction of the apparent dip)
Referring back to Fig. 19.36.

tan B = tan A × sin C

The apparent dip can also be easily established by graphical means.

On a contour map A and B are two points whose altitudes are 85 m and 110 m respectively. On the map, B is located 70 m north of A. A skew borehole at A is drilled in a south-westerly direction in plan and has an actual inclination of 55° to the horizontal plane. It reveals the top and bottom surfaces of a stratum at altitudes of 60 m and 40 m respectively. A skew borehole at B is drilled in a south-easterly direction in plan and has an actual inclination of 60° to the horizontal plane. It reveals the top and bottom surfaces of the stratum at altitudes of 90 m and 10 m respectively.

(i)   Determine the strike, dip and thickness of the stratum.
(ii)   Determine the apparent dip of the stratum on a vertical section through A that trends in a southerly direction.

Scale 1:1,000

(1)   Set up the problem and find the strike, dip and thickness of the stratum in the usual way.
(2)   To find the apparent dip, a vertical section is taken in a southerly direction from A. Two vertical boreholes are introduced on this southerly plane, one at A and another at C.

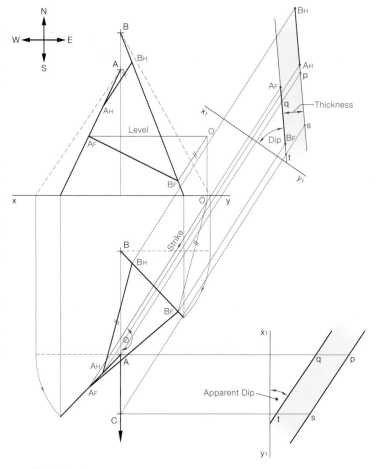

Fig. 19.37

HIGHER LEVEL

(3) Draw a new auxiliary to show the sectional view. The vertical boreholes are projected to the strike/dip auxiliary and to this new auxiliary. Heights p, q, s and t are found from the strike/dip auxiliary and transferred to the new auxiliary. The apparent dip can be measured from the new auxiliary.

(4) The apparent dip can be calculated once the strike and dip are known.

$$\tan \text{(apparent dip)} = \tan \text{(true dip)} \times \sin \text{(angle between strike and direction of apparent dip)}$$

$$\tan \text{(apparent dip)} = \tan 47° \times \sin \Theta$$

$$\tan \text{(apparent dip)} = \tan 47° \times \sin 149°$$

$$\tan \text{(apparent dip)} = 1.07 \times 0.52$$

$$\tan \text{(apparent dip)} = 0.56$$

$$\text{Apparent dip} = 29°$$

Earthworks for Inclined Roads

The earthwork problems that we have dealt with so far have involved level stretches of road and level, car parking sites. On a variable height site it is often more practical to design a sloping road because it can often reduce the amount of earth to be moved. By closely balancing the amount of cut and fill it can mean that the material removed in the cut can be used to build up the fill.

Plotting of Fill for a Sloping Road

Fig. 19.38 shows a road rising at a steep gradient. The road is to be built on a level plane. It can be seen that the amount of fill needed increases as the road rises. It can also be seen that the level lines along the embankment are parallel to each other but are not parallel to the side of the formation. They splay away from the road as it rises. The slope of the fill remains constant, so for a straight stretch of road it may be considered as a plane. This plane leans against the fill cone at the high end of the road and is tangential to it.

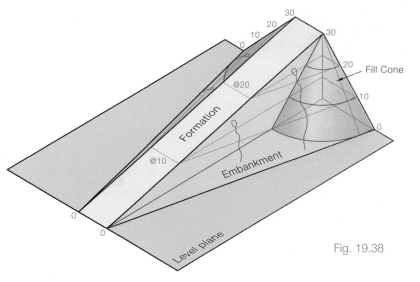

Fig. 19.38

Plotting of Cut for a Sloping Road

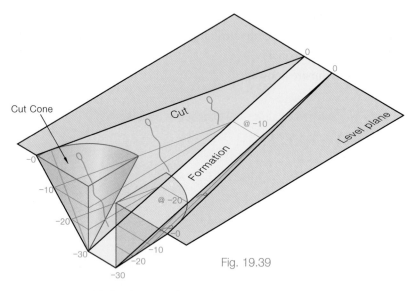

Fig. 19.39

The diagram Fig. 19.39 shows a road sloping downwards into a level plane. The cutting needed increases as the road level drops. Level lines along the cutting are parallel to each other but are not parallel to the sides of the formation. They splay away from the road as it falls. The cut can be considered to be a plane when the road is straight. This plane is tangential to the cut cone. The cut cone is an inverted cone as shown.

Fig. 19.40a shows ground contours at 5 m vertical intervals. AB is the line of a proposed roadway. The road has the following specifications.

    (i)   Formation width is 12 m.

    (ii)   Formation level at A is 70 m.

    (iii)   Gradient A to B is 1 in 15 rising.

    (iv)   Side slopes for cuttings 1 in 2.

    (v)   Side slopes for embankments 1 in 1.5.

On the drawing supplied, show the earthworks necessary to accommodate the roadway.

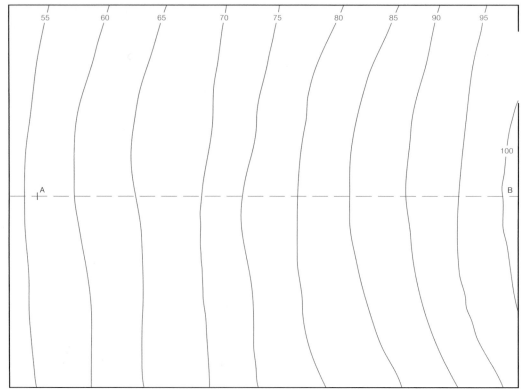

Fig. 19.40a

Scale 1:1,000

(1) Draw in the formation sides 6 m each side of the centre line.

(2) The road is level from side to side so the 70 m level from A is projected to the sides of the formation.

(3) The road rises at 1:15. Travelling from A to B the road rises by 1 m for every 15 m travelled on the map. For the purpose of solving these problems we are only interested in altitudes that correspond to contour levels.

Locate a point C along the road that produces a rise of 5 m or 10 m or 15 m (a multiple of 5 m). By measuring 150 m from point A, a point C is found that has an altitude 10 m greater than A.

(4) Project C to the sides of the formation. The fill cones are drawn. These appear as semicircles on the map. The radius in this example will be 15 m. **Fill cones are drawn at the high end of the formation.**

The 15 m is calculated by looking at the change in altitude and relating it to the embankment ratio. For a rise of 1 m a horizontal distance of 1.5 m is travelled away from the formation side. For a rise of 1 m a horizontal distance of 1.5 m is travelled away from the formation side.

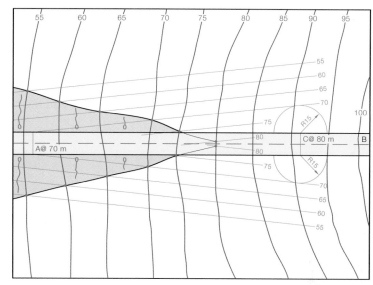

Fig. 19.40b

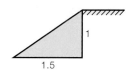
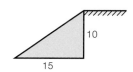

Fig. 19.41

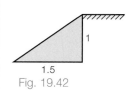
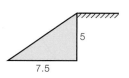

Fig. 19.42

(5) Join the 70 m level on the side of the road as a tangent to the fill cone circle. This is a 70 m contour line along the embankment.

(6) Subsequent contour lines on the embankment will be parallel to this and 7.5 m apart on the map. Again, the figure of 7.5 m has been calculated from the fill ratio. The contours on the map are at 5 m intervals. To match these, the fill contours must be at 5 m intervals. A 5 m rise produces a 7.5 m horizontal spacing.

(7) Where the corresponding fill contours and map contours intersect gives points on the embankment edge.

(8) Note how the embankment point on the 80 m contour line was found to help locate the exact point where the fill edge hit the road.

Moving out from the side of the road, we move down the bank and the fill contours must drop.

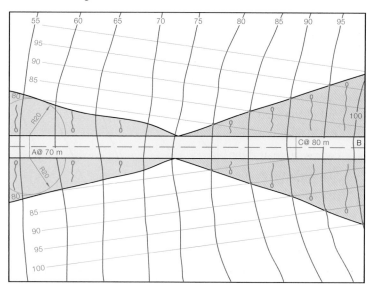

Fig. 19.43

Cuttings

(9)   The cutting cone is drawn at the low end of the formation. This cone will have a 20 m radius in plan. The 20 m is calculated by slotting the fall from C to A into the cutting ratio. 1:2 = 10:20

(10) Join the 80 m level at C as a tangent to the cut cone. This line forms the 80 m contour line on the cutting.

(11) Draw subsequent contour lines on the cutting parallel to this first line and 10 m apart.

$$1:2 \;\; = \;\; 5:10$$

Height between ╱ ╲ Width between
contours on map.   cutting contours.

(12) Moving out from the road we move up the cutting and the cut contours must rise.

(13) Complete the outline of the earthworks.

> Fig. 19.44a, shows ground contours at 5 m vertical intervals. ABC is the line of a proposed roadway. The road has the following specifications:
>
> (i)   Formation width is 12 m.
>
> (ii)   Formation level at A is 50 m.
>
> (iii) Gradient A to B to C is 1 in 15 falling.
>
> (iv)   Side slopes for cutting 1 in 1.5.
>
> (v)   Side slopes for fill 1 in 1.
>
> On the drawing, show the earthworks necessary to accommodate the road.

(1)   Draw in the formation sides 6 m each side of the centre line.

(2)   The road is falling 1:15 from A to B to C. We ignore the bend in the road and treat the straight stretch A to B. If we travel from A, a distance of 150 m, we will locate point D and will have fallen in altitude by 10 m.

(3)   The fill cone is drawn at the high end of the road at A. The radius of the cone is 10 m and the spacing between the embankment contours will be 5 m.

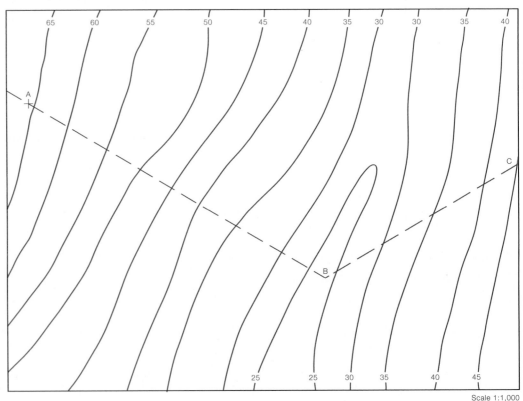

Scale 1:1,000

Fig. 19.44a

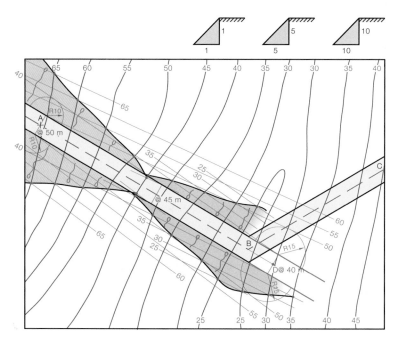

Fig. 19.44b

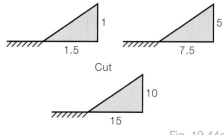

Cut

Fig. 19.44c

(4) The cut cone is always drawn at the lower end of the road. The cut cone will have a radius of 15 m and the spacing between the cutting contours will be 7.5 m.

(5) Draw in the cut and fill for the first section of road A to D.

(6) Rotate point D about the corner O onto the other section of road. D is at an altitude of 40 m.

H I G H E R   L E V E L

(7) Locate point E at an altitude of 45 m. D and E will be 75 m apart.

(8) Set up the cut and fill cones. The fill cone will be at the high end of the road, at E, and will have a radius of 5 m. The cutting cone will be at the lower end of the road and will have a radius of 7.5 m. Both of these are calculated from the cut and fill ratios.

Altitude difference between D + E = 5 m

Fill 1:1 = 5:5

Cut 1:1.5 = 5:7.5

(9) Complete the earthworks.

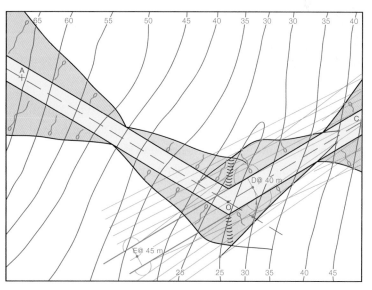

Fig. 19.45

Fig. 19.46a shows ground contours at 5 m vertical intervals. ABC is a roadway which widens onto a car parking area on one side. The road has the following specifications:

(i) Formation width 12 m.

(ii) Formation level at A is 100 m.

(iii) A to B is level, B to C is 1 in 10 rising.

(iv) Side slopes for cutting 1 in 1.5.

(v) Side slopes for embankments 1 in 1.

On the drawing show the earthworks necessary to accommodate the road and car park.

HIGHER LEVEL

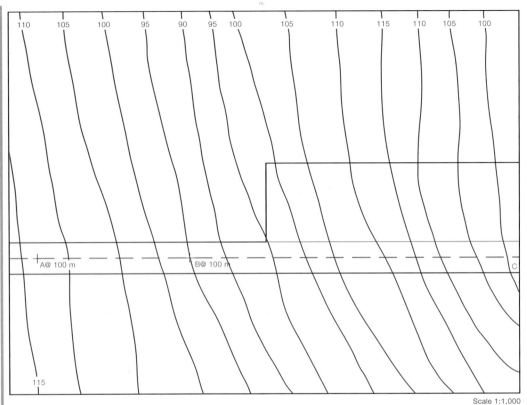

Fig. 19.46a

Scale 1:1,000

(1) A to B is level at 100 m. For level roads the cut and fill contours are parallel to the road. The contour spacing for the cut is 7.5 m. Cut 1:1.5 = 5:7.5. The contour spacing for the embankment is 5 m. Fill 1:1 = 5:5.

(2) The side of the car park, st, will also be level. By looking at the levels it can be seen that fill will be required. The difficulty is that since B to C is rising 1:10, the level of edge st is not known.

(3) Measure 100 m from point B to locate D@110 m. A profile of the road and car park are taken between B and D. The gradient is drawn in and points s and t are projected onto the sloping line.

(4) An embankment triangle is drawn to show the slope of the fill. A line is drawn from st in the profile, parallel to the embankment slope. This line strikes the 100 m level lines. This is projected back to give the 100 m level on the fill.

(5) Other fill contour lines will be parallel to this and at 5 m spacings.

(6) All remaining sides of the formation are sloping. Set up the cut and fill cones at B and D. Fill cone at high end of formation and of radius 10 m. Cut cone at low end of formation and of radius 15 m. Spacing of contours 5 m for fill and 7.5 m for cut.

(7) Complete the earthworks as shown.

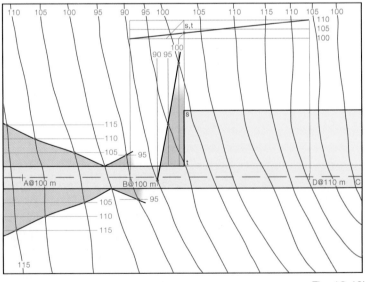

Fig. 19.46b

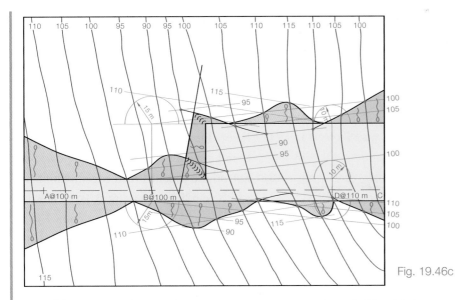

Fig. 19.46c

Fig. 19.47 shows ground contours at 5 m vertical intervals. ABCD is a proposed roadway that widens from C to D. The road has the following specification:

(i)   A to C formation width of 12 m.

(ii) Formation level at B is 205 m.

(iii) A to B is 1 in 10 rising, B to D is 1 in 15 rising.

(iv) Side slopes for cutting 1 in 2.

(v)   Side slopes for embankment 1 in 1.5.

On the drawing show the earthworks necessary to accommodate the road.

(1) A to B is 1 in 10 rising. B is at 205 m. Measure toward A for 50 m to point E which will be at 200 m.

(2) Draw the cut and fill cones at B and E and deal only with this section of road. The difference in altitude between B and E is 5 m, therefore the cut cone has a radius of 10 m and the fill cone has a radius of 7.5 m.

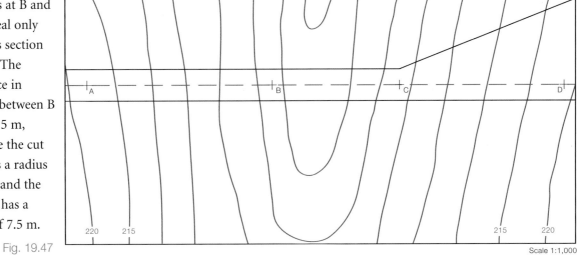

Fig. 19.47

Scale 1:1,000

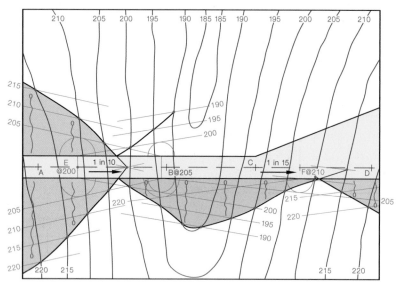

Fig. 19.48

(3) the slope of the road changes at B to 1 in 15 rising. Measure from B to F for 75 m. Point F will be at a 210 m level. Set up the cut and fill cones at B and F. The cut cone has a 10 m radius. The fill cone has a 7.5 m radius.

(4) Ignore the fact that the road widens at C and draw the fill.

(5) Extend the widened road edge to point G which is in line with point B. Point G will be at 205 m level. Also project point F to the side of the widened road at H. H is at 210 m level. Treat GH as a separate road and find the outline of the earthworks.

(6) The cut cone at G will be 10 m radius, the fill cone at H will be at 7.5 m radius. The spacing between the cut contours is 10 m and the spacing between the fill contours is 7.5 m.

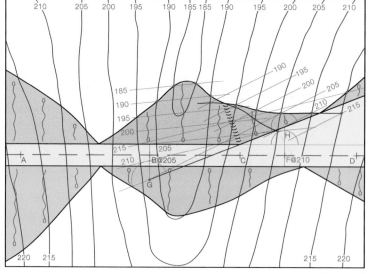

Fig. 19.49

Activities

DEFINITIONS

Q1. Explain the following terms:
(i)   contour,
(ii) contour interval,
(iii) bearing,
(iv) profile,
(v)   gradient.

Q2. Explain the difference between magnetic north and true north.

PROFILES

Q3. To a scale of 1:1,000 redraw the portion of the map shown in Fig. 19.50.

(i)   Draw a profile of the line AB.

(ii) Determine the gradient of the slope at C in an easterly direction.

(iii) If a vertical mast 20 m high stands at point A, is it visible from point B on the ground?

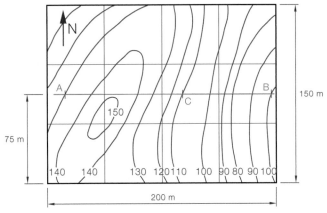

Fig. 19.50

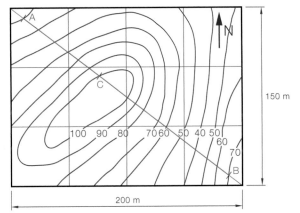

Fig. 19.51

Q4. To a scale of 1:1,000 redraw the portion of the map shown in Fig. 19.51.

(i)   Find the profile of the line AB.

(ii) Determine the gradient at point C in the AB direction.

(iii) How tall does a vertical object at C need to stand in order to be seen from point B?

Q5. To a scale of 1:1,000 redraw the portion of the map shown in Fig. 19.52.

(i)   Draw a profile along the line AB.

(ii) Determine if a building, standing at C, and having a vertical height of 30 m, is visible from the ground from point D.

(iii) Determine the gradient at E in a westerly direction.

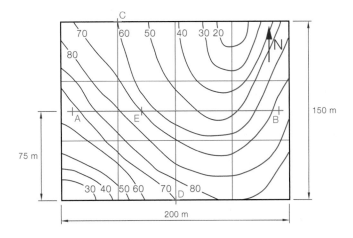

Fig. 19.52

INTERPOLATION OF CONTOURS

Q6. Using the division of lines method plot the contours for the grid levels shown in Figures 19.53a and 19.53b. Scale 1:1,000.

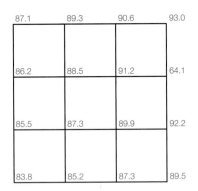

50 m grid squares
Contour interval required = 2 m

Fig. 19.53a

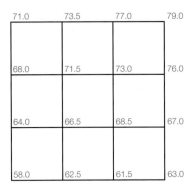

50 m grid squares
Contour interval required = 5 m

Fig. 19.53b

Q7. Using an interpolation template, plot the contours for the grid layouts shown in Figures 19.54a and 19.54b. Scale 1:1,000.

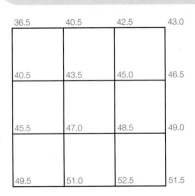

50 m grid squares
Contour interval required = 2 m

Fig. 19.54a

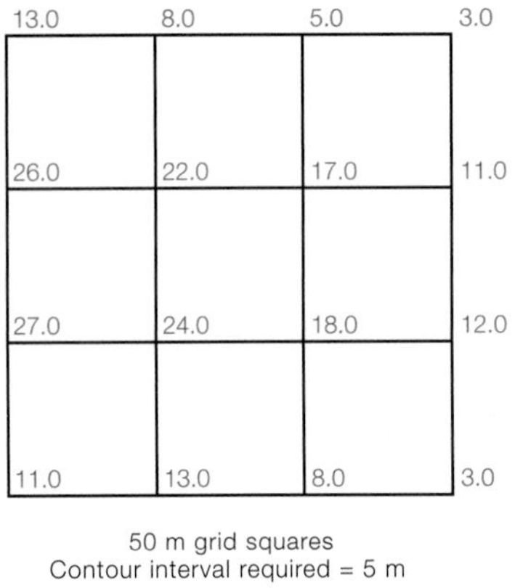

50 m grid squares
Contour interval required = 5 m

Fig. 19.54b

Q8. Using profiles determine the contours for the grid layout shown in Fig. 19.55. Scale 1:1,000.

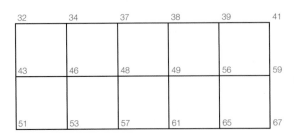

50 m grid squares
Contour interval required = 5 m

Fig. 19.55

MINING STRIKE AND DIP

Q9. Explain the following mining terms:

(i) strike,   (iii) stratum,   (v) footwall,   (vii) thickness.

(ii) dip,   (iv) headwall,   (vi) outcrop,

Q10. The maps shown in Figures 19.56a, 19.56b, 19.56c and 19.56d show ground contours at 10 m vertical intervals. Also shown are outcrop points A, B and C on a stratum of ore. Redraw the maps to a scale of 1:1,000 and find the strike and dip of the stratum.

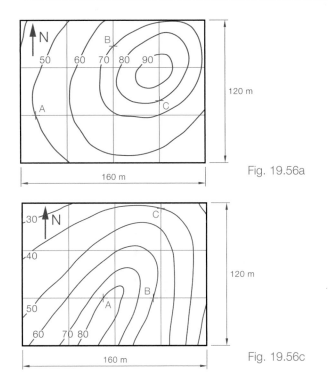

Fig. 19.56a

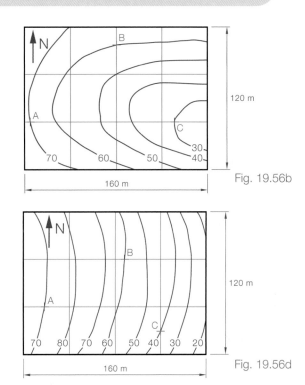

Fig. 19.56b

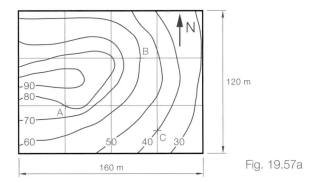

Fig. 19.56c

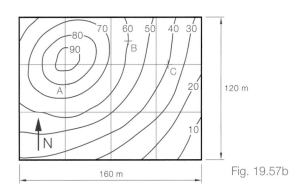

Fig. 19.56d

Q11. Figures 19.57a and 19.57b show ground contours at 10 m vertical intervals. Points A, B and C are outcrop points on a stratum of ore. Redraw the maps to a scale of 1:1,000.

(i) Find the strike and dip of the stratum.

(ii) Determine the outline of the outcrop between A and C and between C and B.

Fig. 19.57a

Fig. 19.57b

Q12. The maps shown in Figures 19.58a and 19.58b show ground contours at 10 m vertical intervals. Vertical boreholes at A, B and C strike a stratum at altitudes of 90, 60 and 50 m respectively. Redraw the maps to a scale of 1:1,000.

(i) Determine the strike and dip of the stratum.

(ii) Find the complete outline of the outcrop.

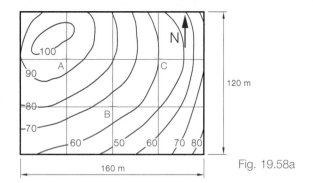

Fig. 19.58a

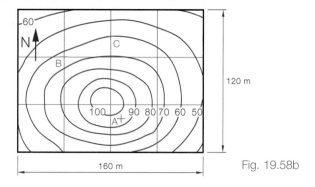

Fig. 19.58b

Q13. Figures 19.59a and 19.59b show ground contours at 10 m vertical intervals. Points A, B and C are outcrop points on the headwall of a stratum of ore and D is an outcrop point on the footwall. Redraw the diagrams to a scale of 1:1,000.

(i) Determine the strike, dip and thickness of the stratum.

(ii) Find the outline of the outcrop.

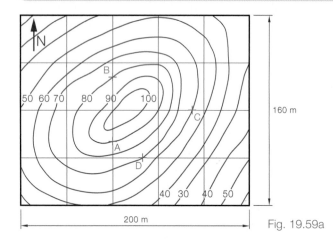

Fig. 19.59a

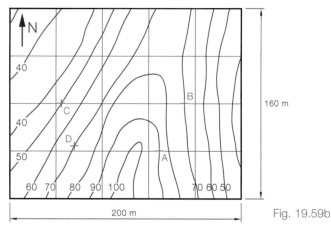

Fig. 19.59b

EARTHWORKS

Q14. Figures 19.60a and 19.60b, show ground contours at 5 m vertical intervals. AB is the line of a proposed roadway. The road is to have the following specifications. Redraw the maps to a scale of 1:1,000.

    (i)   Formation width 14 m.

    (ii) Formation level 85 m.

    (iii) Side slopes for cutting 1:1.5, side slopes for embankment 1:2.

         Show the earthworks necessary to accommodate the roadway.

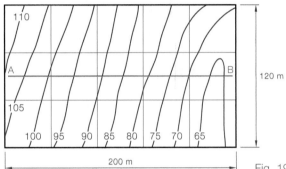

Fig. 19.60a

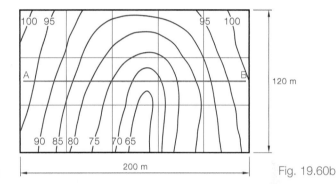

Fig. 19.60b

Q15. Figures 19.61a and 19.61b, show ground contours at 2 m vertical intervals. ABCD is the centre line of a proposed roadway with the centre for the curve at point O. The road is to have the following specifications:

    (i)   Formation width 14 m.

    (ii) Formation level 40 m.

    (iii) Side slopes for cutting 1:2, side slopes for embankment 1:2.5.

Redraw the given maps to a scale of 1:1,000 and show the earthworks necessary to accommodate the roadway.

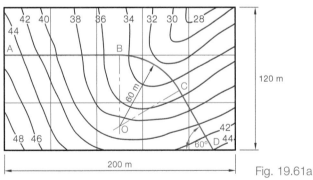

Fig. 19.61a

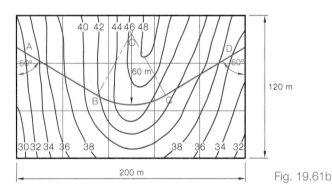

Fig. 19.61b

Q16. The maps shown in Figures 19.62a and 19.62b show ground contours at 4 m vertical intervals. AB shows a proposed roadway with CDEF being a car park. The car park and road are at the same level. The road and car park are to have the following specification:

(i)   Formation width 12 m.

(ii)   Formation level 100 m.

(iii) Side slopes for cutting 1:1.5, side slopes for embankment 1:1.

Redraw the maps to a scale of 1:1,000 and show the earthworks necessary to accommodate the road and car park.

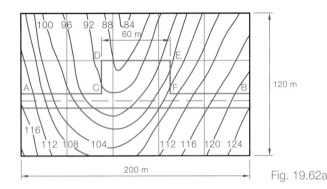

Fig. 19.62a

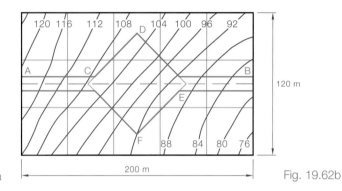

Fig. 19.62b

MINING: SKEW BOREHOLES

Q17. On a contour map A and B are two points whose altitudes are 105 m and 80 m respectively. On the map B is located 120 m north-east of A. A skew borehole at A is drilled in a south-westerly direction in plan and has an actual inclination of 60° to the horizontal plane. It reveals the top and bottom surfaces of the stratum at distances of 30 m and 65 m respectively from A.

A skew borehole at B is drilled in a southerly direction in plan and has an actual inclination of 50° to the horizontal plane. It reveals the top and bottom surfaces of the stratum at altitudes of 50 m and 35 m respectively.

(i)   Determine the dip, strike and thickness of the stratum.

(ii)   Another skew borehole at B is drilled in a south-westerly direction in plan and meets the bottom surface of the stratum at a distance of 110 m from B. Determine the inclination of this borehole to the horizontal plane.

Scale 1:1,000.

Q18. On a contour map, A and B are two points whose altitudes are 115 m and 120 m respectively. On the map, B is located 125 m north-east of A. A skew borehole at A is drilled in a northerly direction in plan and has an actual inclination of 60° to the horizontal plane. It reveals the top and bottom surfaces of the stratum at altitudes of 105 m and 40 m respectively.

A skew borehole at B is drilled in a south-westerly direction in plan and has a true inclination of 50° to the horizontal plane. It reveals the top and bottom surfaces of the stratum at altitudes of 85 m and 65 m respectively.

(i)   Determine the strike, dip and thickness of the stratum.

(ii)   Another skew borehole at B is drilled in a southerly direction in plan. The length of the borehole as it goes through the stratum is 20 m. Determine the altitude at which this borehole hits the bottom surface of the stratum.

Scale 1:1,000.

HIGHER LEVEL

Q19. On a contour map, A and B are two points whose altitudes are 80 m and 95 m respectively. On the map, A is located 100 m south-east of B. A skew borehole at A is drilled in a northerly direction in plan and has an actual inclination of 45° to the horizontal plane. It reveals the top and bottom surfaces of the stratum at altitudes of 20 m and 90 m respectively.

A skew borehole at B is drilled in a south-westerly direction in plan and has a true inclination of 60° to the horizontal plane. It reveals the top and bottom surfaces of the stratum at altitudes of 60 m and 45 m respectively.

(i) Determine the strike, dip and thickness of the stratum.

(ii) Another skew borehole from B is drilled in a southerly direction in plan and has an actual inclination of 60° to the top surface of the stratum. Determine the altitude at which this borehole reaches the bottom surface of the stratum.

Scale 1:1,000.

APPARENT DIP

Q20. On a contour map, A and B are two points whose altitudes are 95 m and 105 m respectively. On the map, A is located 65 m north of B. A skew borehole at A is drilled in a north-easterly direction in plan and has an actual inclination of 60° to the horizontal plane. It reveals the top and bottom surfaces of the stratum at altitudes of 65 m and 35 m respectively.

A skew borehole at B is drilled in a north-westerly direction in plan and has a true inclination of 40° to the horizontal plane. It reveals the top and bottom surfaces of the stratum at altitudes of 85 m and 15 m respectively.

(i) Determine the strike, dip and thickness of the stratum.

(ii) Determine the apparent dip of the stratum in a westerly direction.

Scale 1:1,000.

Q21. On a contour map, A and B are two points whose altitudes are 110 m and 115 m respectively. On the map, A is located 120 m west of B. A skew borehole at A is drilled in a north-easterly direction in plan and has an actual inclination of 65° to the horizontal plane. It reveals the top and bottom surfaces of a stratum at altitudes of 90 m and 25 m respectively.

A skew borehole at B is drilled in a south-westerly direction in plan and has an actual inclination of 50° to the horizontal plane. It reveals the top and bottom surfaces of the stratum at altitudes of 70 m and 55 m respectively.

(i) Determine the strike, dip and thickness of the stratum.

(ii) Determine the apparent dip of the stratum in a south-easterly direction.

Scale 1:1,000

Q22. On a contour map, A and B are two points whose altitudes are 100 m and 80 m respectively. On the map, B is located 120 m north-west of A. A skew borehole at A is drilled in a north-easterly direction in plan and has an actual inclination of 60° to the horizontal plane. It reveals the top and bottom surfaces of the stratum at altitudes of 80 m and 35 m respectively.

A skew borehole at B is drilled in a southerly direction in plan and has a true inclination of 50° to the horizontal plane. It reveals the top and bottom surfaces of the stratum at altitudes of 55 m and 30 m respectively.

(i) Determine the strike, dip and thickness of the stratum.

(ii) Determine the apparent dip of the stratum along a south-easterly section.

Scale 1:1,000.

HIGHER LEVEL

Q23. Figures 19.63a and 19.63b, show ground contours at 5 m vertical intervals. AB is the line of a proposed roadway. To a scale of 1:1,000, redraw the maps and show the earthworks necessary to accommodate the roadway.

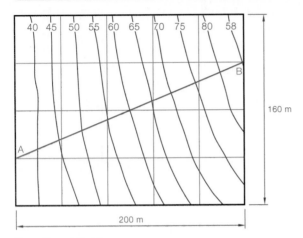

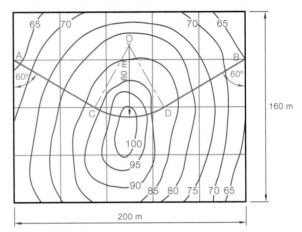

Formation width 12 m
Formation level at A 70 m
Gradient A to B is 1 in 15 falling
Side slopes for cutting 1 in 1.5
Side slopes for embankment 1 in 1

Fig. 19.63a

Formation width 12 m
Formation level at A 85 m
C to D level
Gradient A to C 1 in 10 rising
Gradient D to B 1 in 15 falling
Side slopes for cutting 1 in 1.5
Side slopes for embankment 1 in 2

Fig. 19.63b

Q24. Figures 19.64a and 19.64b, show ground contours at 5 m vertical intervals. ABC is the line of a proposed roadway. To a scale of 1:1,000, redraw each map and show the earthworks necessary to accommodate the roadway.

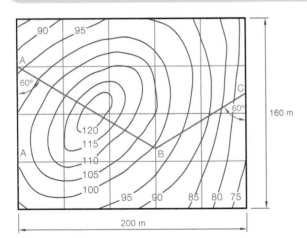

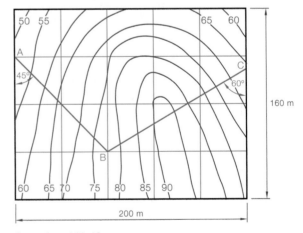

Formation width 12 m
Formation level at A 100 m
Gradient A to B to C 1 in 15 falling
Side slopes for cutting 1 in 1.5
Side slopes for embankment 1 in 2

Fig. 19.64a

Formation width 12 m
Formation level at A 70 m
Gradient A to B to C 1 in 15 rising
Side slopes for cutting 1 in 1.5
Side slopes for embankment 1 in 2

Fig. 19.64b

Q25. Figures 19.65a, 19.65b, 19.65c and 19.65d, show ground contours at 5 m vertical intervals. ABC is a roadway which widens into a car parking area. Redraw each map to a scale of 1:1,000 and show the earthworks necessary to accommodate the road and car park.

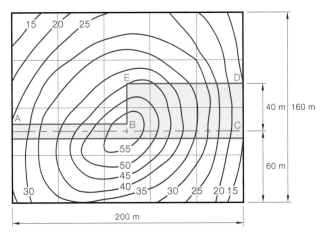

Formation width A to B 12 m
Formation level at A 40 m
Gradient from A to C 1 in 20 rising
From B to C the road widens as shown
Side slopes for cutting 1 in 1.5
Side slopes for embankment 1 in 2

Fig. 19.65a

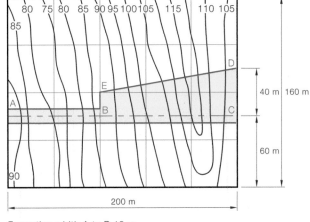

Formation width A to B 12 m
Formation level at B 100 m
Gradient from A to C 1 in 15 rising
From B to C the road widens as shown
Side slopes for cutting 1 in 1.5
Side slopes for embankment 1 in 2

Fig. 19.65b

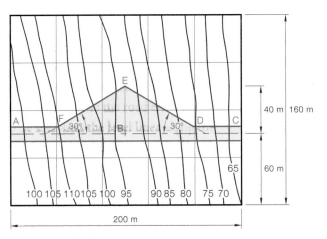

Formation width 12 m
Formation level at A 90 m
Gradient from A to C 1 in 20 falling
Road widens at DEF as shown
Side slopes for cutting 1 in 1.5
Side slopes for embankment 1 in 2

Fig. 19.65c

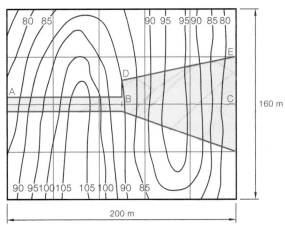

Formation width A to B 12 m
Formation level at A 100 m
Gradient from A to C 1 in 15 rising
Road widens at DEF as shown
Side slopes for cutting 1 in 1.5
Side slopes for embankment 1 in 1

Fig. 19.65d

20 Surface Geometry

SYLLABUS OUTLINE
Areas to be studied (in an applied context):

• Dihedral angles between surfaces. • Surface developments of containers and structures such as plane intersecting roof surfaces, sheet metal containers, hoppers and transition pieces. • Projections and developments of intersecting prismatic, right cylindrical transition and ducting details. • *Projections and developments of intersecting prismatic, oblique cylindrical, oblique conical transition and ducting details.* • Projection and developments of transition pieces connecting rectilinear to rectilinear and circular to circular cross-section. • *Projection and developments of transition pieces connecting circular to rectilinear cross-section.*

Learning outcomes
Students should be able to:

Higher and Ordinary levels
• Determine the dihedral angles between adjacent plane surfaces forming solid objects.
• Prepare surface developments of surface containers, intersecting roof surfaces, and sheet metal fabrications.
• Determine the lines and points of intersection between two intersecting surfaces or objects.
• Develop intersecting ductwork involving prismatic and right cylindrical surfaces.
• Determine the developments of transition pieces between ducts of circular/circular and rectilinear/rectilinear cross-section.

Higher level only
• *Develop intersecting ductwork involving oblique prismatic and oblique cylindrical surfaces.*
• *Determine the developments of transition pieces between ducts of circular/rectilinear cross-section.*

Dihedral Angle

The angle between two planes is a dihedral angle. We have already looked at the finding of dihedral angles in chapter 9, The Oblique Plane. The dihedral angle is the smallest angle that can be measured between the planes and is measured perpendicular to each plane and perpendicular to the line of intersection. The dihedral angle is often needed in roof construction, hopper construction and other fabrications involving plane surfaces.

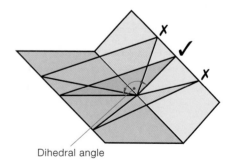

Dihedral angle

Fig. 20.1

Finding the Dihedral Angle

1. Point View Method

Draw a line on a plane, e.g. a sheet of paper, and view along the length of the line so that we see the line as a point. When the line is seen as a point, the plane that it is resting on appears as an edge view.

To get the edge view of a plane you must find the point view of any straight line on that plane.

When two planes intersect, the line of intersection will be a straight line and this straight line rests on both planes at the same time. A point view of the line of intersection will show both planes as edge views and will therefore show the dihedral angle between the two planes.

To get the dihedral angle between two planes, get the point view of the line of intersection of the planes.

> Fig. 20.2 shows the plan and elevation of a solid with an equilateral triangular base. Find the dihedral angle between surfaces P and Q.

Using the theory outlined above we need to get a point view of line bO.

(1) Identify the line of intersection between the planes, line bO.

(2) Find the true length of bO. This is done by projecting an auxiliary viewing perpendicular to bO in plan. x_1y_1 will therefore be parallel to the line of intersection in plan. The view projected from the plan will be an auxiliary elevation and as such will have heights equal to the front elevation.

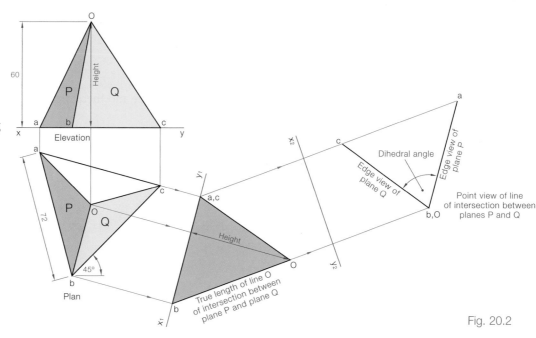

Fig. 20.2

(3) The final stage is to view along the true length found in step (2). Extend on line bO and project the other points in this direction. Draw x_2y_2 perpendicular to this line of sight, i.e. perpendicular to the true length. Being a second auxiliary plan the distances are taken from x_1y_1 back to the plan. The line of intersection appears as a point, the planes appear as lines and the dihedral angle is displayed clearly.

2. Rebatment Method

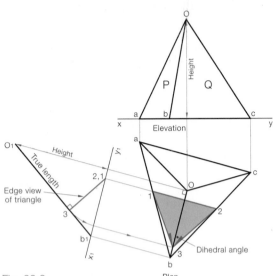

Fig. 20.3

This method is perhaps more difficult to understand but is much neater. If we introduce a cutting plane to cut through the line of intersection, bO, perpendicularly, the triangle that it produces underneath the planes contains the dihedral angle. If we can rebat this plane onto the horizontal plane we will see its true shape and angles in plan.

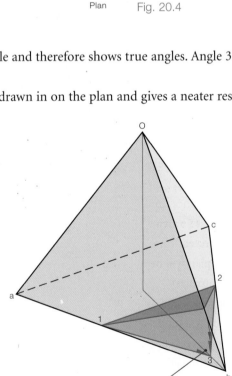

Fig. 20.4

(1)   Ob is the plan of the line of intersection. Find the true length of this line by using an auxiliary elevation. Draw x_1y_1 parallel to the line of intersection in plan. In the auxiliary, point b rests on x_1y_1 and point O_1 is the 'height' above x_1y_1.

(2)   In the auxiliary, draw the edge view of the triangle 1,2,3 perpendicular to the true length.

(3)   Rebat or hinge the triangle about edge 1,2 so that it rests on the x_1y_1 and project back to the line of intersection in plan.

(4)   Join up the triangle 1,2,3 in plan. This is the true shape of the triangle and therefore shows true angles. Angle 3 is the dihedral angle between planes P and Q.

(5)   Fig. 20.4 shows exactly the same method except that the auxiliary is drawn in on the plan and gives a neater result.

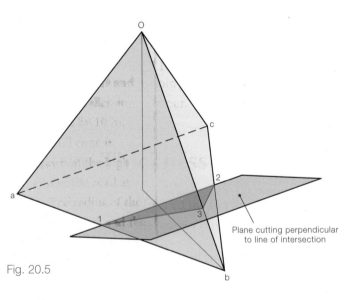

Fig. 20.5

Plane cutting perpendicular to line of intersection

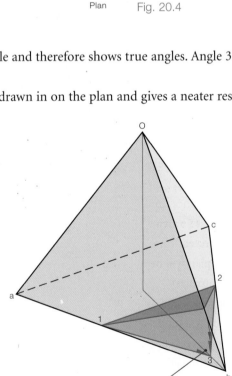

Fig. 20.6   Dihedral angle is seen when triangle 1,2,3 is rebatted horizontally

Roof Geometry

Roof geometry provides a very practical application of plane geometry, development of surfaces and dihedral angles. There is nothing new in this section, rather it is the application of what has already been learned.

Fig. 20.7 shows the outline plan of a roof. Surfaces A and B have a pitch of 45°. Surface C has a pitch of 40° and surface D has a pitch of 60°.

(i)   Draw the plan and elevation.

(ii) Develop surfaces B, C and D.

(iii) Find the dihedral angle between surfaces B and D.

Scale 1:100

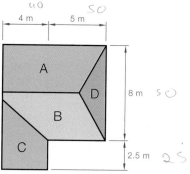

Fig. 20.7

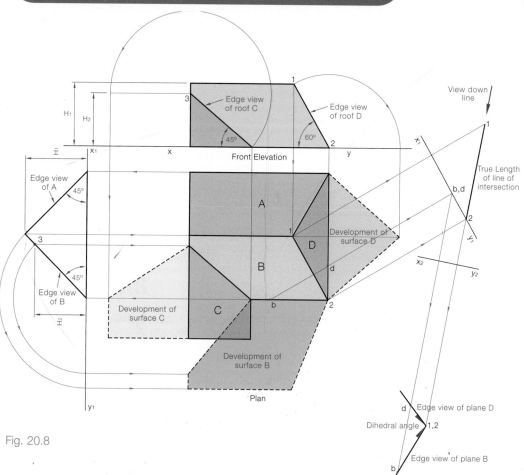

Fig. 20.8

(1) Auxiliary views are used extensively in solving roof geometry questions. Edge views of planes A and B are found by using an auxiliary elevation. The auxiliary shows the true pitch of these planes, 45° (from the question). The height, H_1, for the elevation is found here.

(2) Draw the elevation which will show planes C and D as edge views and again their true pitch will be seen, 40° and 60° respectively. H_2, the height of roof C, is found here. Point 1 is projected to plan and surface D is drawn in plan.

(3) H$_2$, the height of roof C, is stepped up on the auxiliary which shows roof A and B as edge views. Point 3 is found and projected to plan.

(4) Develop the surfaces by rebatting the planes where they are seen as edge views. Planes C and D are rebatted in the front elevation and surface B is rebatted in the auxiliary elevation. The planes in each case are folded until they are horizontal and the developments are found in plan.

(5) The dihedral angle is constructed using the point view method and is found as explained earlier.

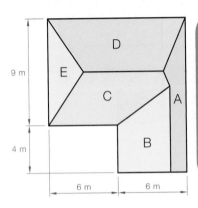

Fig. 20.9 shows the plan of a roof. Surfaces C and D have a pitch of 50°. Surface A has a pitch of 70°, surface B has a pitch of 40° and surface E has a pitch of 60°.

(i) Draw the plan and elevation of the roof.
(ii) Develop the surfaces A and C.
(iii) Find the dihedral angle between surfaces A and D.
(iv) Find the dihedral angle between surfaces B and C.

Scale 1:100

Fig. 20.9

The problem is solved using edge views of the roof surfaces, either using auxiliary views or the front elevation. As we have learned earlier, **an edge view of a plane is found by viewing along a line which is seen as a true length on the plane.** In most cases we use a horizontal line and view along its length in plan. When we see the planes as edge views we can use the pitch angle given in the question. The two dihedral angles are found using the two methods outlined earlier, point view method and rebatted triangle method.

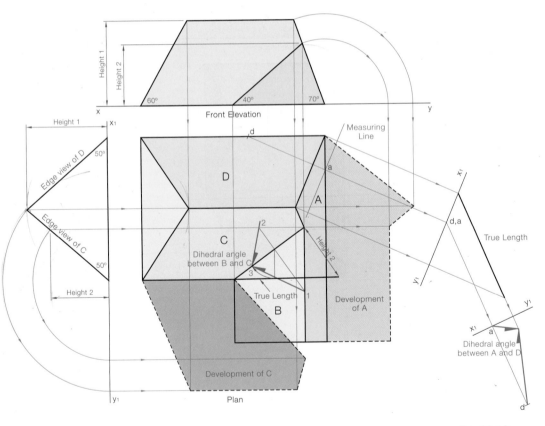

Fig. 20.10

The surfaces C and B form a valley. When forming the triangle that will define the dihedral angle, triangle 1,2,3, it is essential that corners 1 and 2 are level with each other.

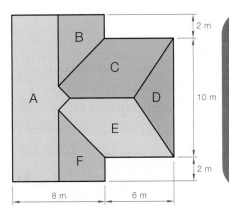

Fig. 20.11

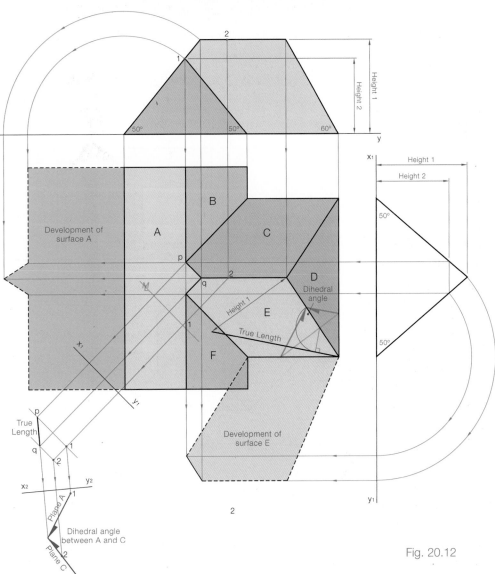

Fig. 20.11 shows the plan of a roof. Surfaces A, B, C, D, E and F have a pitch of 50° and surface D has a pitch of 60°.

(i)   Draw the plan and elevation.

(ii) Develop surfaces A and E.

(iii) Find the dihedral angle between surfaces D and E.

(iv) Find the dihedral angle between surfaces A and C.

Scale 1:100

When two roof surfaces of equal pitch intersect, the line of intersection will bisect the angle formed by the roof surfaces. The line of intersection between surfaces B and C will therefore be a 45° line, as will the line of intersection between surfaces E and F. The dihedral angle between A and C is best found using the point view method. Line pq is the line of intersection between them.

Project an auxiliary to show the true length of pq. Select a point on plane A, point 1, and project to the auxiliary. The height of point 1 is found in the elevation. Similarly, select a point on plane C, point 2, and project to the auxiliary. The height of point 2 is also found in elevation. View along the true length to get the dihedral angle. A measuring line is used to shorten distances in the second auxiliary.

Fig. 20.12

Intersecting Ductwork and Pipework

This section deals with the intersecting of ductwork and the subsequent development of the surfaces. We also look at the intersection of pipework. This work is used extensively in the sheet metalwork industry where unusual jointing pieces and connectors would be made up as one-offs. The material in this section is very closely linked to chapter 11, Developments and Envelopments.

> A rectangular section duct is to intersect a square section duct at an angle of 45° as shown in Fig. 20.13. Find the surface development of each ducting piece.

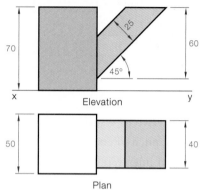

Fig. 20.13

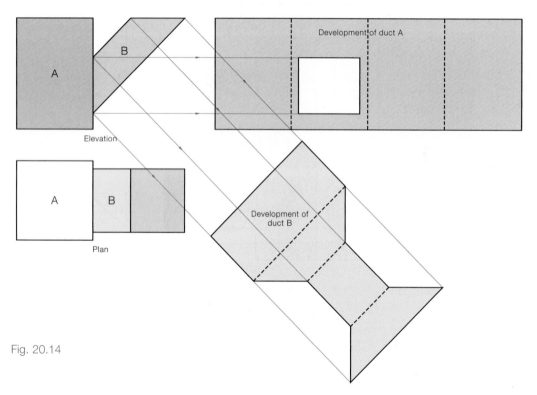

Fig. 20.14

A square sectioned duct of 50 mm side is being intersected by a rectangular sectioned duct of sides 32 mm × 50 mm. The ducts meet at an angle of 60°. Find the complete surface development of both ducting pieces in Fig. 20.15.

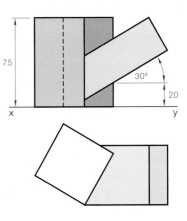

(1)   The line of intersection is found first. The points where duct B joins into duct A can be seen in plan and are projected up to elevation. The line of intersection will be made up of straight lines as the intersecting ducts are planar.

(2)   The development of each duct piece is obvious from Fig. 20.16.

Fig. 20.15

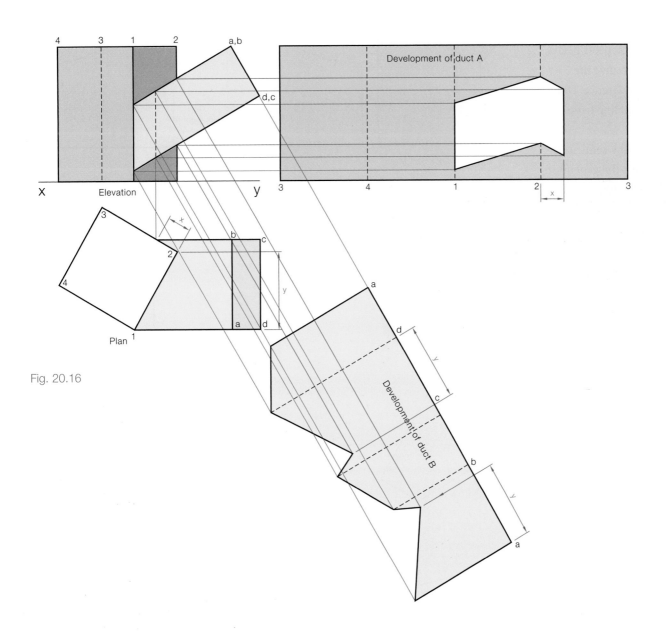

Fig. 20.16

Joining Pipes and Ducts of Equal Diameter

The elevation of an elbow joint for a circular duct is shown in Fig. 20.17. Find the development of the part of the duct marked A.

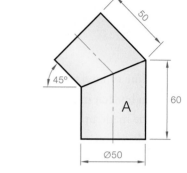

Fig. 20.17

(1) Set up the elevation. There is no need to draw a plan.
(2) Draw the half-duct as shown and divide into six equal parts. Index the points.
(3) Project the base of the front elevation to the right. Step-off twelve steps to give the circumference. Draw a vertical line from each step.
(4) From the semicircle, project the generators. The length of each generator is projected across to the development.

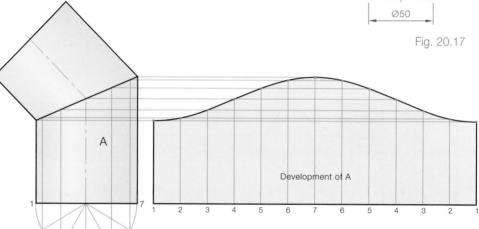

Fig. 20.18

The elevation of a double elbow joint for a circular duct is shown. Develop the surface of the section marked A, as in Fig. 20.19.

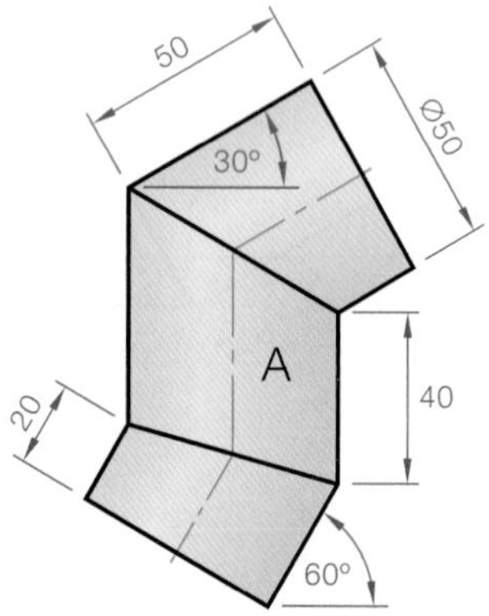

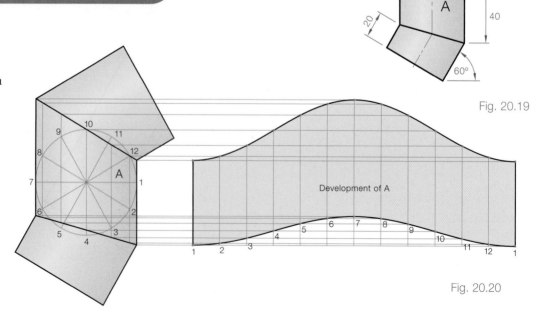

Fig. 20.19

(1) In this case the circular section of the duct is drawn in the elevation. It is divided into twelve equal parts and the generators drawn through the divisions.
(2) The construction is as shown in the previous example.

Fig. 20.20

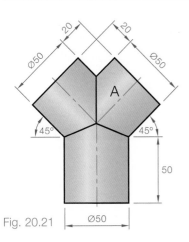

Fig. 20.21

The diagram shows a 'Y' joint between three 50 mm diameter pipes. Develop the surface of the section marked A, see Fig. 20.21.

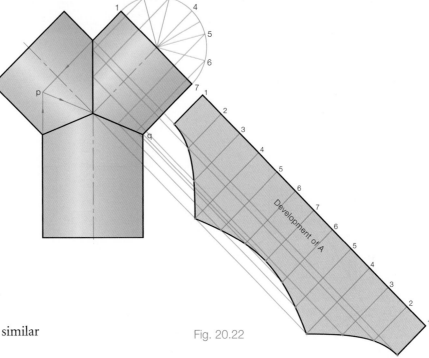

Fig. 20.22

(1) The joint lines are found by either halving the angles or by finding the intersection of the centre lines. Alternatively the sides of two of the pipes are extended to cross at p and q, giving one of the joint lines as shown. This is then repeated to find the other joint lines.

(2) The development is carried out in a similar way to the previous examples.

A pipe P intersects a larger pipe at right angles. Draw the given end view and complete the front elevation. Develop the surface of pipe P.

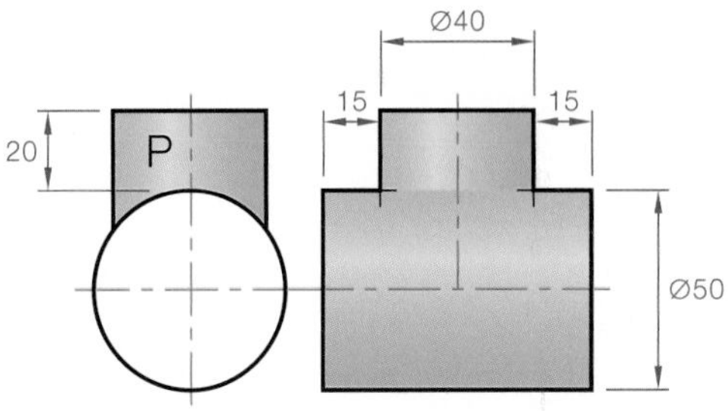

(1) The line of intersection between the two pipes must be found. It will not appear as a straight line as it did in the previous three examples because the pipes are of different diameters. Where the generators in end view meet the circle they are projected across to find points on the generators in the front elevation.

(2) The development is done in the usual way.

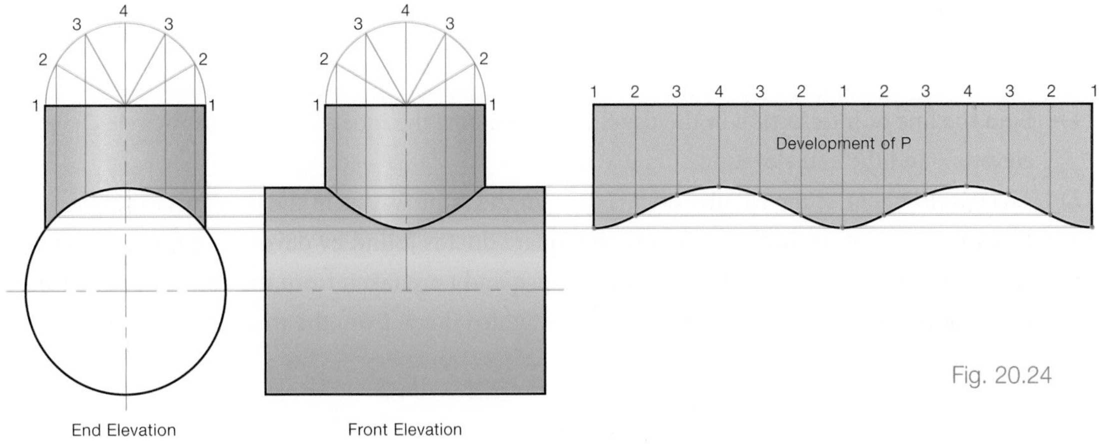

Fig. 20.23

End Elevation   Front Elevation

Development of P

Fig. 20.24

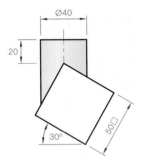

A circular duct pipe intersects a square duct pipe as shown.

(i) Draw a front elevation and end view showing the line of intersection.

(ii) Develop the surface of the cylindrical duct.

(iii) Show the true shape of the hole to be cut in the square duct, see Fig. 20.25.

Fig. 20.25

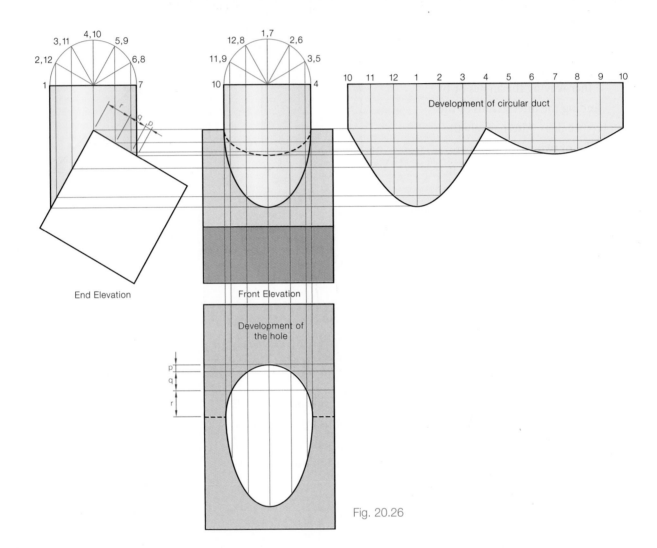

Fig. 20.26

(1) Find the line of intersection in the usual way. Note how the indexing of the semicircle changes between the front elevation and the end elevation.

(2) The development of the circular duct is done in the same way as in the previous example.

(3) The true shape of the hole to be cut in the square duct is found by developing the two surfaces that it straddles. The complete sides are developed first. Distances p, q and r are taken from the end view which shows the true length of the sides of the square duct. Generators are extended down from the front elevation. Similar construction for the other side of the square duct.

The diagram shows the end view of a T-junction joining a 40 mm diameter pipe and a 50 mm diameter pipe. One side of the smaller pipe is tangential to the larger pipe as shown, Fig. 20.27.

(i)   Draw the given view and find the front elevation showing the line of intersection.

(ii)   Develop the surface of the 40 mm diameter pipe.

(iii) Develop enough of the 50 mm diameter pipe to show the true shape of the hole to be cut in it.

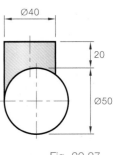

Fig. 20.27

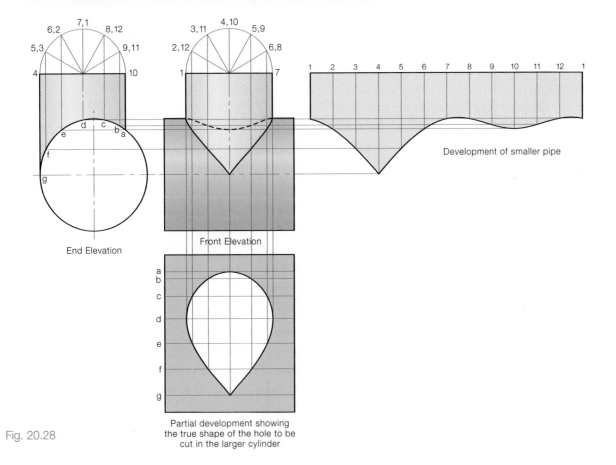

Fig. 20.28

(1)   Draw the given end view and project across the front elevation. The construction of the line of intersection is as in the previous problem.

(2)   When developing the larger cylinder we only develop enough of the surface to show the hole to be cut in it. Project down the sides of the cylinder from the front elevation. Choose a starting point and step-off distances a to b, b to c, c to d etc., as taken from the end view.

(3)   Extend the generators to intersect these lines to give the hole's shape.

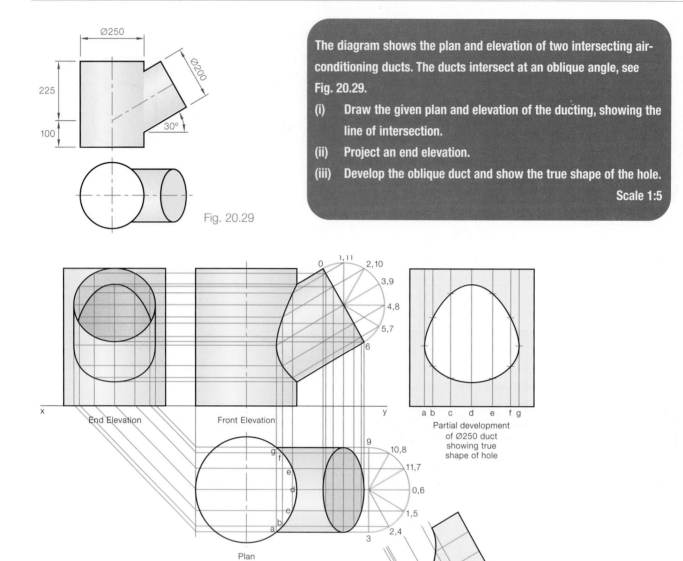

Ø250
225
100
Ø200
30°

The diagram shows the plan and elevation of two intersecting air-conditioning ducts. The ducts intersect at an oblique angle, see Fig. 20.29.

(i)   Draw the given plan and elevation of the ducting, showing the line of intersection.

(ii)   Project an end elevation.

(iii)   Develop the oblique duct and show the true shape of the hole.

Scale 1:5

Fig. 20.29

End Elevation

Front Elevation

Plan

Partial development of Ø250 duct showing true shape of hole

Development of Ø200 duct

Fig. 20.30

Construction of the solution should be obvious from the drawing and follows the same pattern as the previous examples.

The plan and incomplete elevation of two ducts intersecting is shown. One duct is circular in cross-section, while the other is square in cross-section, see Fig. 20.31.

(i) Find the line of intersection between the two ducts and project an end view.

(ii) Develop the surface of the square duct.

Scale 1:5.

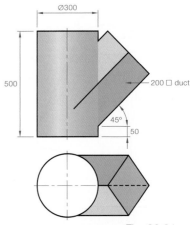

Fig. 20.31

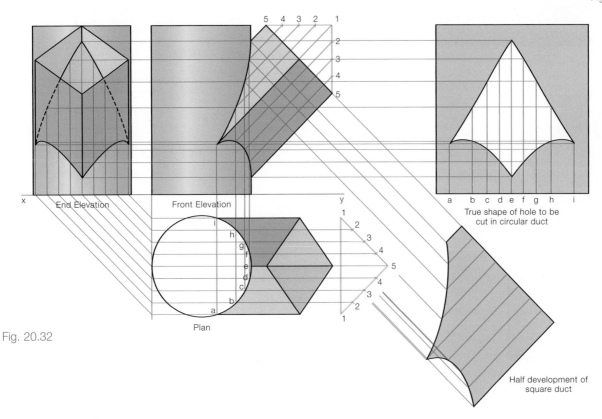

Fig. 20.32

Transition Pieces

A transition piece is one that connects differently shaped openings, differently sized openings and differently angled openings, or any combination of these. In most cases the transition piece is composed of plane surfaces and conical surfaces. Transition pieces are widely used in ducting systems used in ventilation, heating, air conditioning etc.

The development of transition pieces is done by triangulation. This is simply a method of dividing a surface into a number of triangles and using these triangles to build up the development. Triangles are used because if its sides are of a given length, it can only be one shape. A triangle can also be easily reproduced by using the compass.

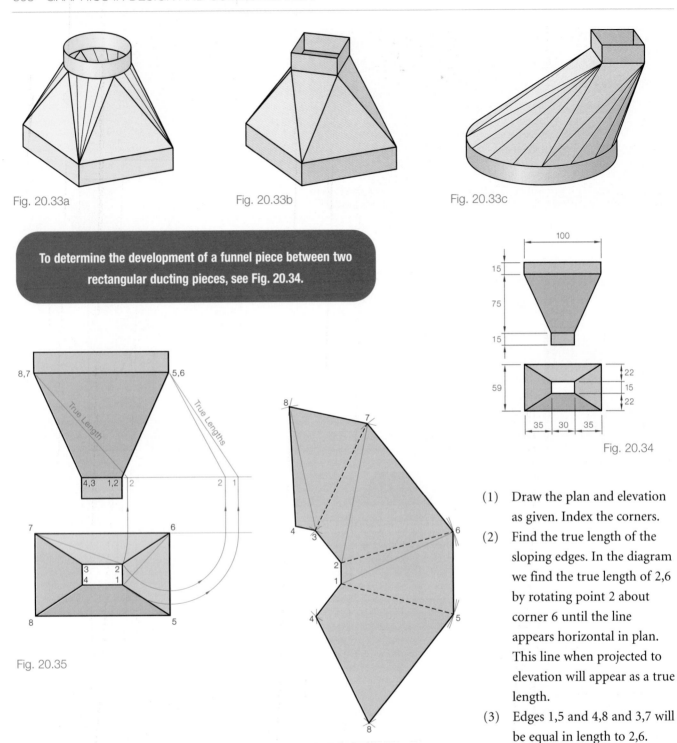

Fig. 20.33a

Fig. 20.33b

Fig. 20.33c

To determine the development of a funnel piece between two rectangular ducting pieces, see Fig. 20.34.

Fig. 20.34

Fig. 20.35

(1) Draw the plan and elevation as given. Index the corners.

(2) Find the true length of the sloping edges. In the diagram we find the true length of 2,6 by rotating point 2 about corner 6 until the line appears horizontal in plan. This line when projected to elevation will appear as a true length.

(3) Edges 1,5 and 4,8 and 3,7 will be equal in length to 2,6.

(4) Start the development with edge 1,2 which is a true length in plan.

(5) With the true length of 2,6 and centre 2 swing an arc.

(6) With true length of diagonal 1,6 and centre 1 swing another arc. The two arcs cross locating point 6.

(7) Point 5 is found using the true length of 5,6 (from plan) and the true length of 1,5 (equal to 2,6).

(8) The complete development is built up using triangulation in this way. As a check on the development, lines parallel on the surface must also be parallel on the development. Edge 1,2 must be parallel to edge 5,6 on the development.

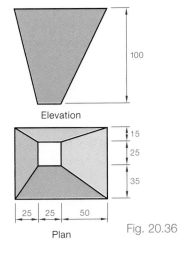

Elevation

Plan

Fig. 20.36

25 25 50

15
25
35

100

Given the plan and elevation of a sheet, metal hopper. Find the complete development of the surfaces. Fig. 36

(1) Draw the given plan and elevation. Index all corners.

(2) All horizontal edges appear as true lengths in plan. The true length of the sloping edges and the diagonals must be found.

(3) Start the development with one of the top edges of the hopper, e.g. 1,4.

(4) Find the corner 8 next by swinging the true length of diagonal 1,8 from point 1, and by swinging a second arc, the true length, of 4,8 from corner 4.

(5) All other points are found using triangulation and the true lengths found in elevation.

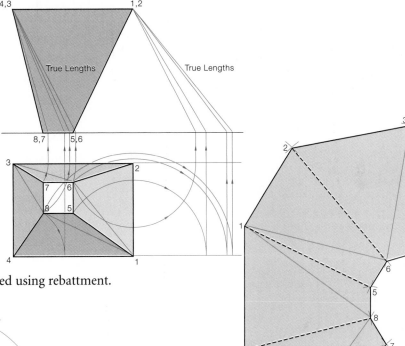

Alternative Method

The two previous examples can be developed using rebattment.

Fig. 20.37

Using the same measurements as in Fig. 20.36 find the development of the funnel piece using rebattment.

(1) The two sides 3,4,8,7 and 1,2,6,5 are folded down in elevation and projected to plan.

(2) The development of these two sides can be found in plan.

(3) The other two sides are found by using the information that the seam length must be equal for two adjoining edges.

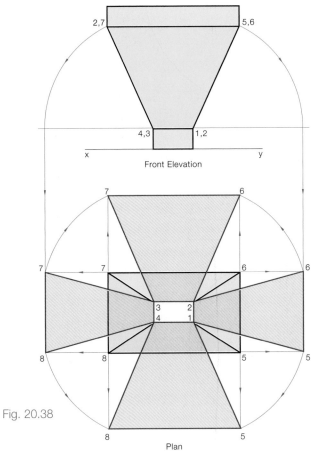

Front Elevation

Fig. 20.38

Plan

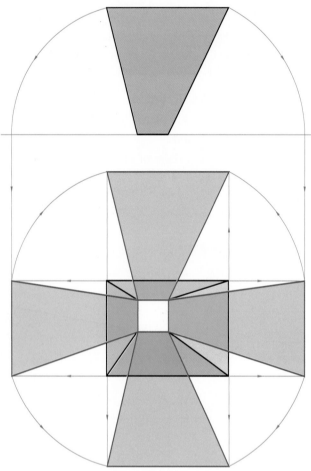

Fig. 20.39

Using the same measurements as in Fig. 20.36, find the development of the hopper using the rebattment method.

The construction of the solution is carried out in exactly the same way as in the previous example.

In these two examples the rebattment method is a simpler method than the triangulation method. This is because in both cases we already had edge views of two of the sides in elevation which made their rebattment extremely easy. The triangulation method may appear more complex but is much more versatile and also produces a development pattern having all sides connected in a continuous sheet. This, of course, would make the production of the object a matter of bending at seams rather than joining at seams.

To develop the surface of a transition piece connecting two circular pipes.

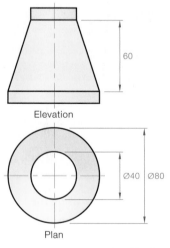

60

Ø40 Ø80

Elevation

Plan

Fig. 20.40

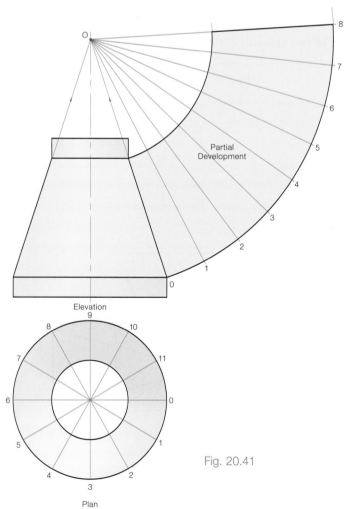

Partial Development

Elevation

Plan

Fig. 20.41

(1)   The centres of the inlet and outlet pipes lie on the same axis and therefore the transition piece will be conical. The sides of the elevation are extended to meet, giving the apex of this conical piece.

(2)   The development is now completed as for a truncated cone. Divide the plan into twelve equal divisions. In elevation, having centre at O, the apex, swing an arc from the top and bottom of the truncated cone.

(3)   Step-off the twelve equal divisions from plan around this arc. Join these points to the apex to complete the development.

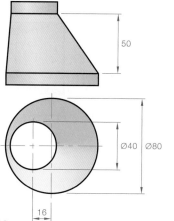

Fig. 20.42

> **To develop the surface of a transition piece connecting two circular pipes whose axes are not aligned, see Fig. 20.42.**

Even though the transition piece may look like an oblique cone it can be shown that generators on its surface do not meet at a single point when extended. The surface is warped and can only be developed approximately by triangulation.

(1)   Draw the plan and elevation and divide both circles into 12 equal parts.

(2)   Draw the generators in plan and elevation.

(3)   Draw the diagonals which will divide the surface into triangles.

(4)   The true lengths of the twelve generators and the twelve diagonals must now be found and are probably best found on a separate diagram.

(5)   The development may now be built up using the true lengths and the compass as explained before.

Note: The true lengths of the generators and the diagonals are found on separate diagrams for clarity. In each case the true length is found by using the apparent length of the line in plan and the height of the line in elevation to create a right-angled triangle. The hypotenuse of the triangle is the true length.

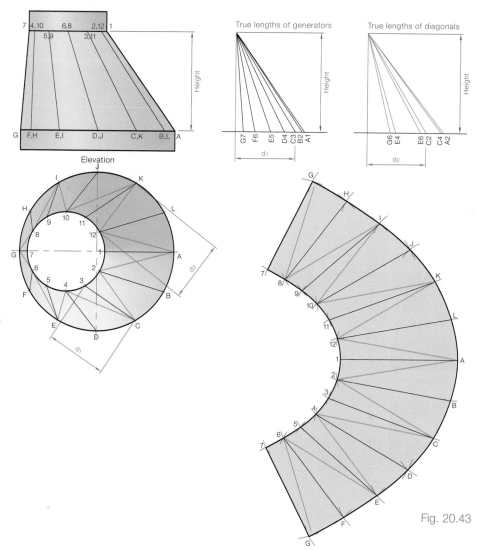

Fig. 20.43

To develop the surface of the transition piece connecting ducting of square section and rectangular section, see Fig. 20.44.

This development could be solved by rebattment or by triangulation. It will be solved by triangulation in this example.

When finding the true lengths, care must be taken that the correct heights are used.

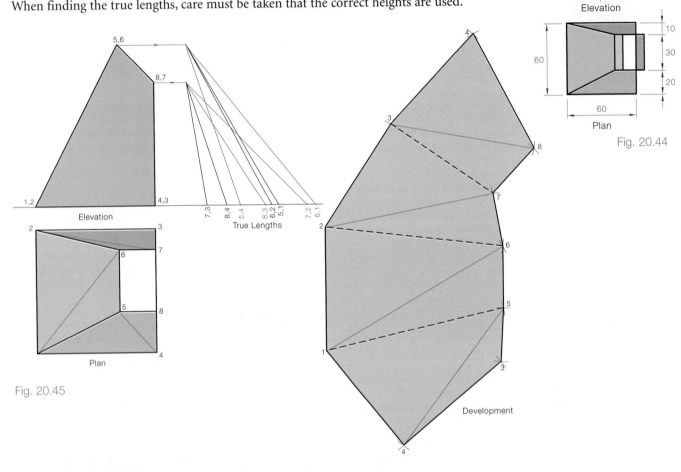

Fig. 20.45

Fig. 20.44

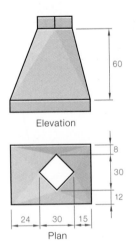

Fig. 20.46

To develop the transition piece connecting a square duct and a rectangular duct. The measurements are given in Fig. 20.46.

(1) Draw the given plan and elevation.

(2) Divide the surface into triangles.

(3) Index the corners.

(4) Find the true lengths of all edges of these triangles.

(5) Complete the development in the usual way.

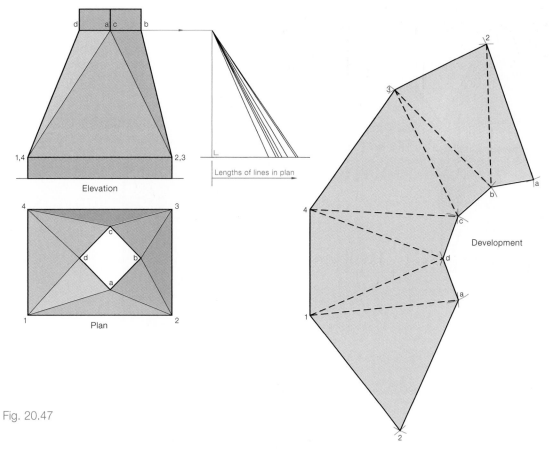

Fig. 20.47

Transition Pieces: Circular to Rectilinear

> **To find the development of a transition piece connecting a circular pipe and a rectangular pipe on the same axis, Fig. 20.48.**

The transition piece is composed of four isosceles triangles and four conical surfaces. The conical surfaces are subdivided into small triangular portions and the complete development is completed by triangulation.

(1)   Divide the circle into equal divisions.

(2)   Join the corners to the divisions thus forming the triangles that can be developed.

(3)   Find the true lengths of lines a1, a2, a3, a4 and a5 by rotation in plan.

(4)   The transition piece is symmetrical and therefore these true lengths can be used for the other three corners.

(5)   Start with the isosceles triangle a1d. The length of ad is seen in plan and the true length of a1 is used to form the triangle.

(6)   From point 1 on the development swing an arc equal in length to one of the divisions on the circle. From point 'a' on the development swing an arc equal to the length of a2. The two arcs cross, locating point 2 on the development.

(7)   Build up the development in this way.

(8)   The smaller the triangles are made on the transition piece the more accurate the development.

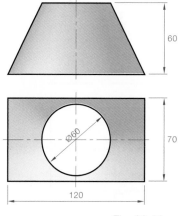

Fig. 20.48

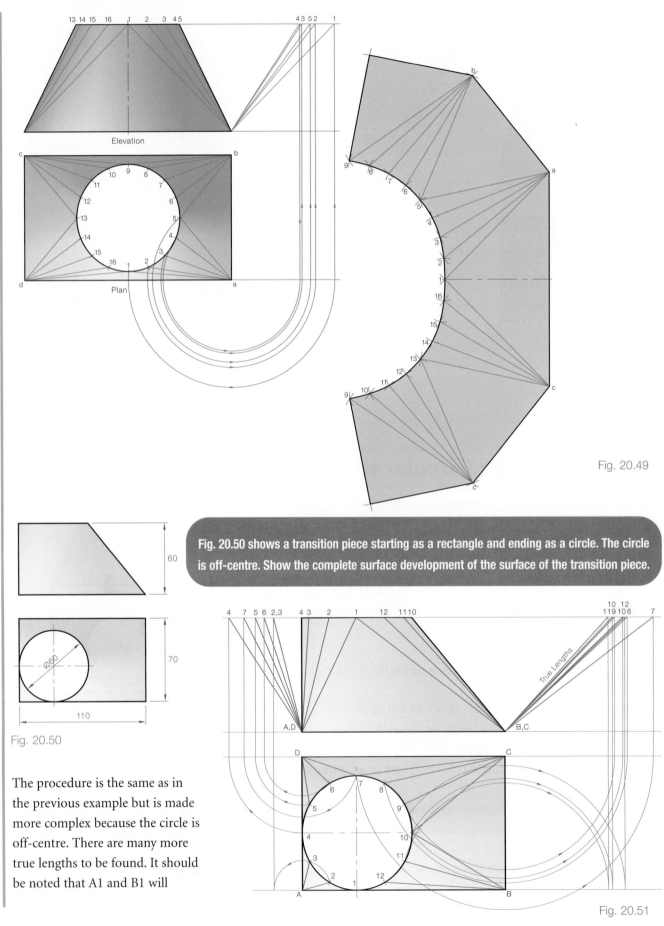

Elevation

Plan

Fig. 20.49

HIGHER LEVEL

Fig. 20.50 shows a transition piece starting as a rectangle and ending as a circle. The circle is off-centre. Show the complete surface development of the surface of the transition piece.

60

70

⌀60

110

Fig. 20.50

The procedure is the same as in the previous example but is made more complex because the circle is off-centre. There are many more true lengths to be found. It should be noted that A1 and B1 will

True Lengths

Fig. 20.51

appear as true lengths in the front elevation. Elements A1 and A4 will be the same length, as will elements A2 and A3. Proper indexing is important to help keep track of which distances need to be taken.

(1) Divide the circle into a number of divisions.
(2) Divide the surface into triangles.
(3) Start with one of the larger triangles, e.g. B,C,10.
(4) Using the divisions from the circle and the appropriate true length the development is built up as before.

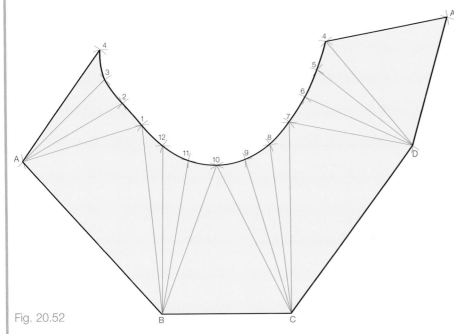

Fig. 20.52

(1) Divide the circle in plan into a number of equal parts. Project these points to elevation.
(2) Using the 'distances' from the elevation and the divisions on the circle in plan to find the true shape of the joint line.
(3) Divide the transition piece into triangles in the usual way.
(4) Find the true lengths of the elements on the drawing or using a separate diagram as shown here.
(5) The development is done in the usual way ensuring that the distances 1 to 2 and 2 to 3 etc., are taken from the true shape of the joint, the ellipse.

Fig. 20.52 shows a transition piece joining a square duct to a circular duct. The ducts lie on different axes. Make a development of the transition piece.

The true shape of the seam joining the transition piece and the cylindrical pipe must be found. It will be elliptical because the cylindrical pipe is cut at an angle.

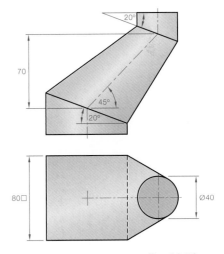

Fig. 20.53a

HIGHER LEVEL

HIGHER LEVEL

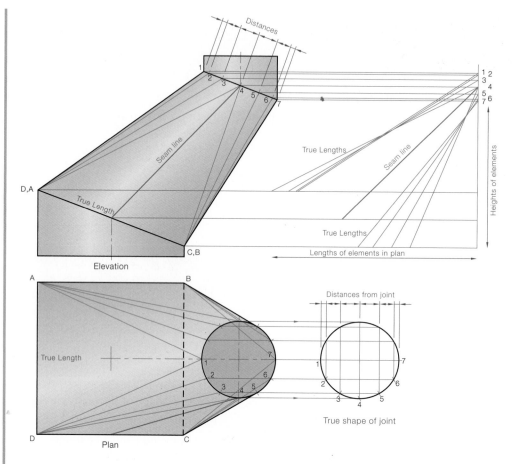

Fig. 20.53b

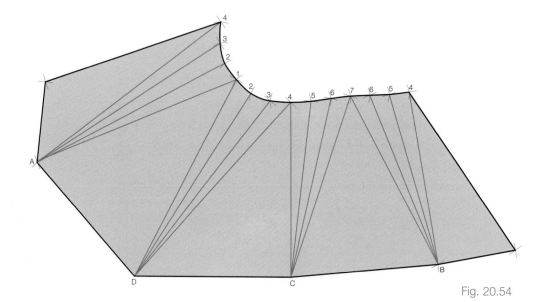

Fig. 20.54

Fig. 20.55 shows a transition piece connecting two cylindrical pipes of different diameters and on different axes. Find a half-development of this transition piece.

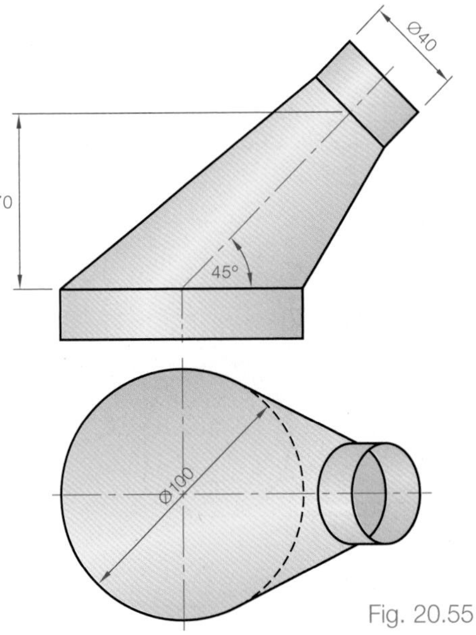

This transition piece looks like a frustum of an oblique cone but it is not and must be solved by triangulation. The large pipe is shown full-size in plan and an auxiliary is needed to show the true size of the inclined pipe.

(1) Draw the elevation and use the auxiliary of the small pipe to help draw the ellipse in plan.

(2) Divide up the circles and triangulate half of the transition piece.

(3) Index the sides of the triangles carefully. The true length of each of these lines must be found. Set up a right-angled triangle using the height of the element in elevation and the length of the element in plan. The hypotenuse of this triangle gives the true length.

(4) Construct the development as before.

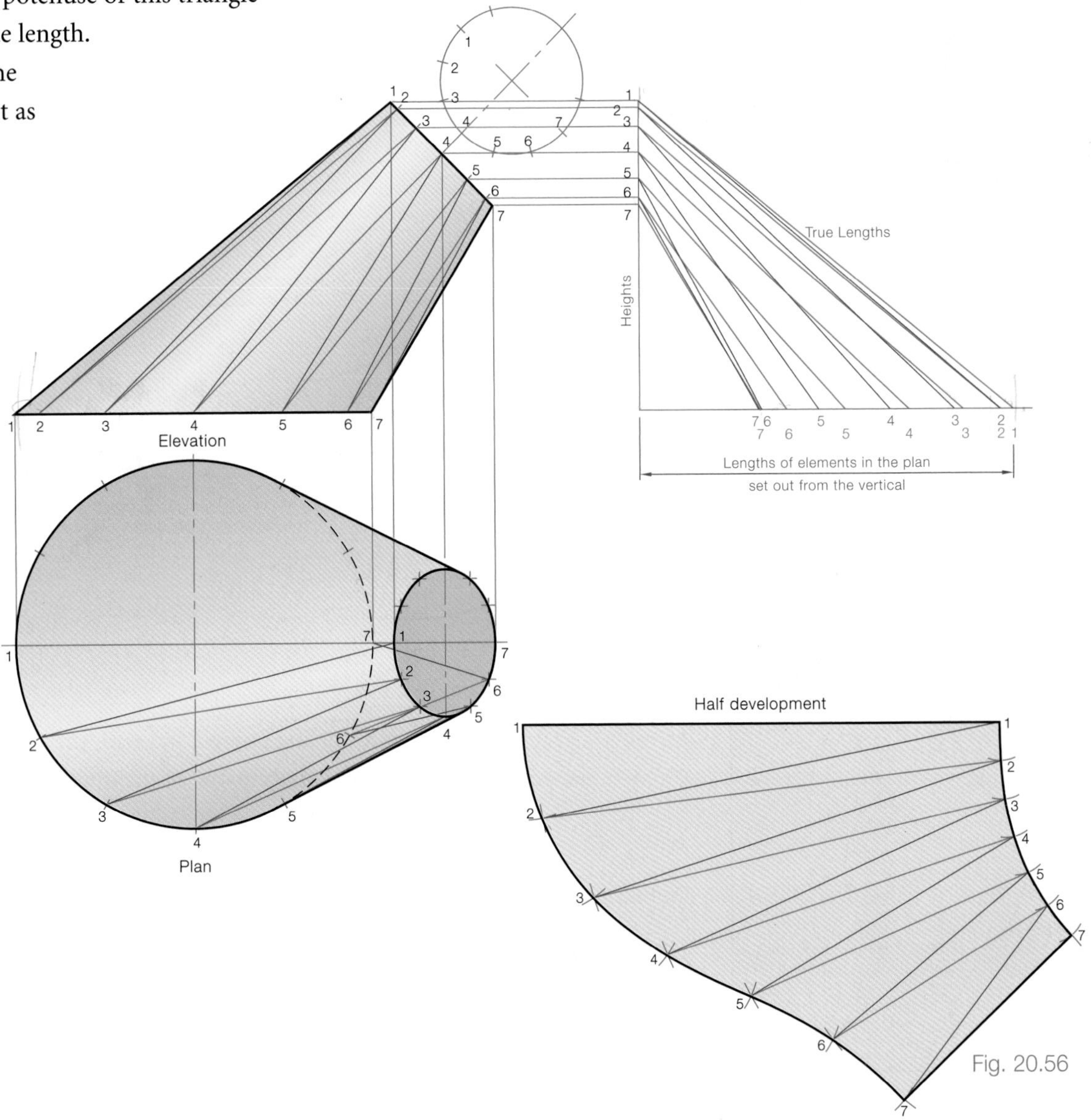

Fig. 20.55

Ø40

70

45°

Ø100

True Lengths

Heights

Lengths of elements in the plan
set out from the vertical

Elevation

Plan

Half development

Fig. 20.56

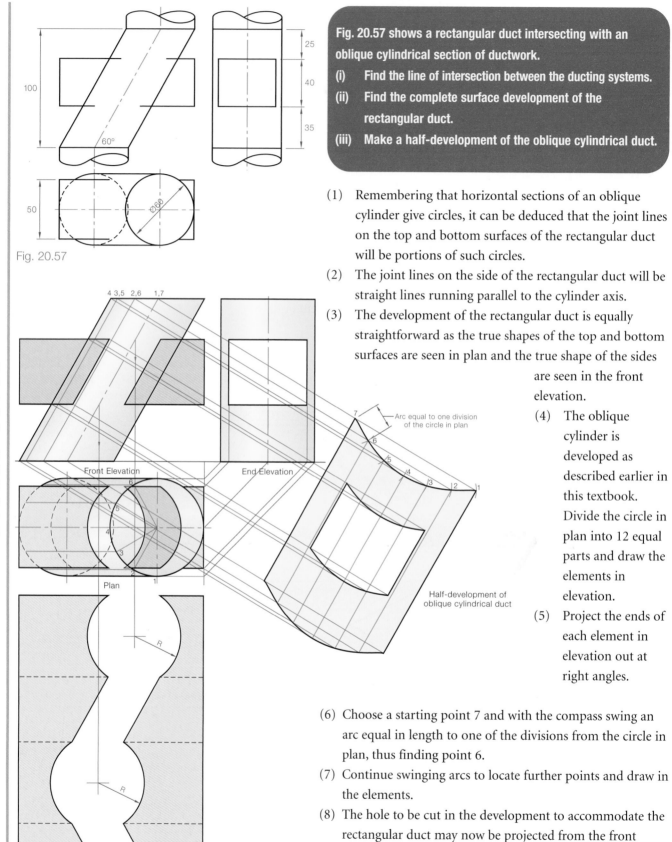

Fig. 20.57

Fig. 20.57 shows a rectangular duct intersecting with an oblique cylindrical section of ductwork.

(i)   Find the line of intersection between the ducting systems.

(ii)   Find the complete surface development of the rectangular duct.

(iii) Make a half-development of the oblique cylindrical duct.

(1)   Remembering that horizontal sections of an oblique cylinder give circles, it can be deduced that the joint lines on the top and bottom surfaces of the rectangular duct will be portions of such circles.

(2)   The joint lines on the side of the rectangular duct will be straight lines running parallel to the cylinder axis.

(3)   The development of the rectangular duct is equally straightforward as the true shapes of the top and bottom surfaces are seen in plan and the true shape of the sides are seen in the front elevation.

(4)   The oblique cylinder is developed as described earlier in this textbook. Divide the circle in plan into 12 equal parts and draw the elements in elevation.

(5)   Project the ends of each element in elevation out at right angles.

(6)   Choose a starting point 7 and with the compass swing an arc equal in length to one of the divisions from the circle in plan, thus finding point 6.

(7)   Continue swinging arcs to locate further points and draw in the elements.

(8)   The hole to be cut in the development to accommodate the rectangular duct may now be projected from the front elevation onto the development. It will follow the same curve as the top and bottom of the development.

Front Elevation

End Elevation

Plan

Arc equal to one division of the circle in plan

Half-development of oblique cylindrical duct

Fig. 20.58

Development of rectangular duct

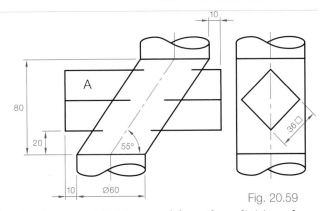

Fig. 20.59 shows a square duct intersecting with an oblique cylindrical section of ductwork.

(i)   Draw the given views and project a plan.

(ii)   Show the line of intersection in all views.

(iii) Develop the surface of the square ducting section A.

(iv)   Develop the surface of the oblique cylindrical duct.

Fig. 20.59

(1) The joint lines must be found first. Divide one circle in the plan into equal divisions, and from these divisions draw elements along the surface of the cylinder. Find these elements in all three views.

(2) Where the elements cross the square duct in end view locates points on the joint line.

(3) The corner 'c' can be located as shown. An element is drawn in the corner in plan to the top circle. This element is located in elevation and 'c' is projected up onto this line.

(4) The development of section A of the square duct is projected down from the front elevation. The distances between the lines in the development are taken from the end view.

(5) The oblique cylinder is developed as before with special attention being given to corner 'c'.

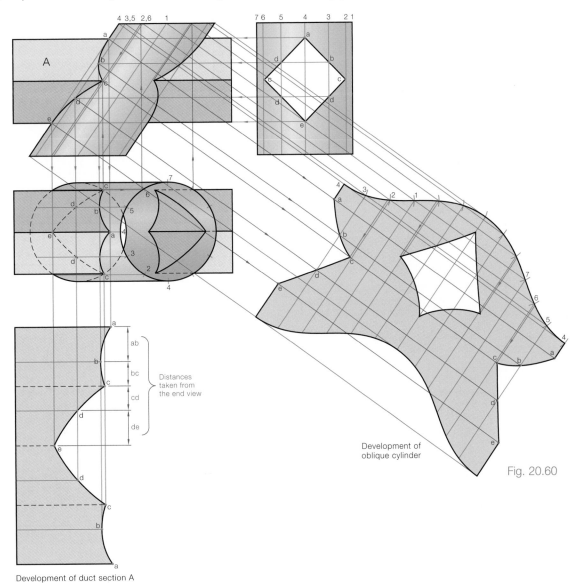

Fig. 20.60

Development of oblique cylinder

Distances taken from the end view

Development of duct section A

HIGHER LEVEL

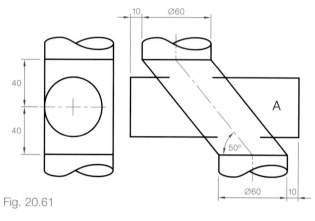

Fig. 20.61

Fig. 20.61 shows a cylindrical duct intersecting an oblique cylindrical duct. The cylindrical duct is off-centre.

(i)   Draw the given views and project a plan.

(ii) Find the joint line in all views.

(iii) Develop section A of the cylindrical duct.

(iv) Develop the oblique cylindrical duct.

The development of the oblique cylinder is carried out in the usual way. The distance 'x' is found in plan and helps to locate the extra element introduced to locate point f.

The spacing of the lines in the development of section A are found using the distances between the points on the circle in end view. The gaps will vary as we move around the circle.

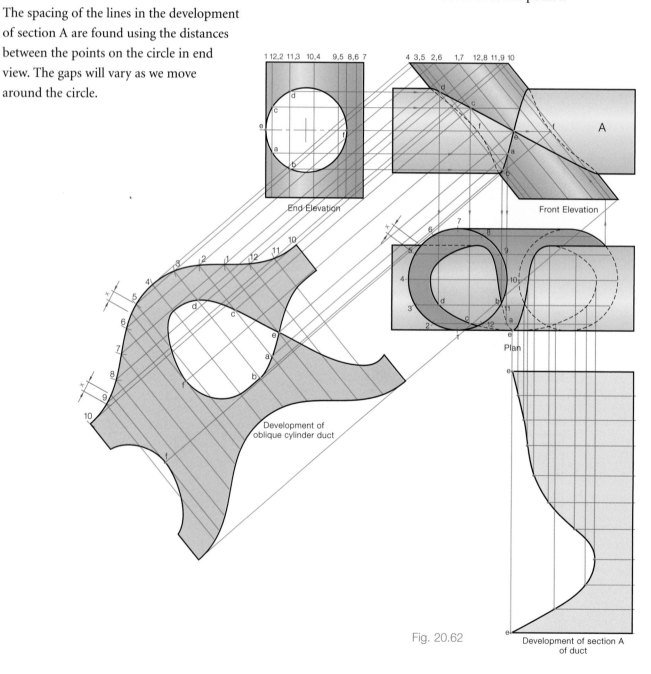

Fig. 20.62

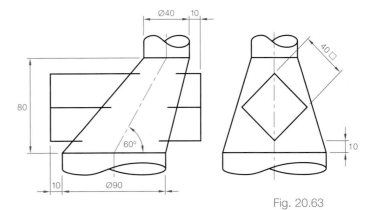

Fig. 20.63 shows a transition piece which is in the form of a truncated oblique cone. The transition piece is intersected by a square duct as shown.

(i) Draw the given views and project a plan.

(ii) Find the joint line in all views.

(iii) Develop the surface of the transition piece.

(iv) Develop the surface of the square duct.

Fig. 20.63

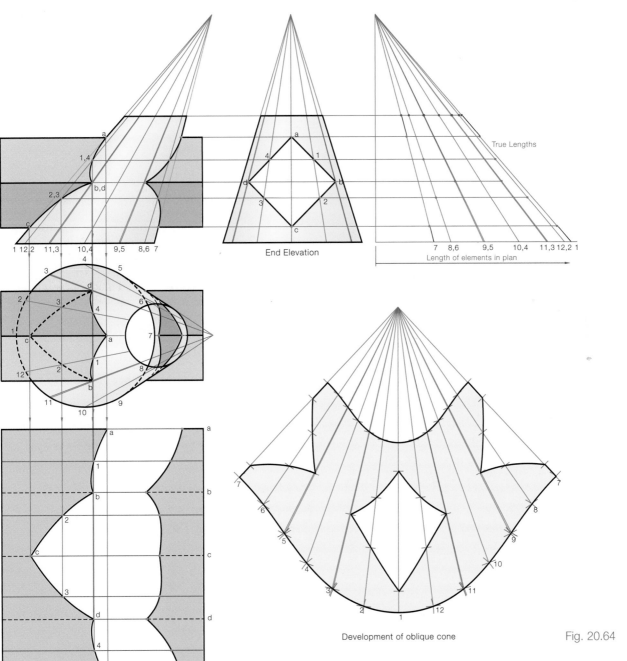

HIGHER LEVEL

True Lengths

End Elevation

Length of elements in plan

Development of square duct

Development of oblique cone

Fig. 20.64

HIGHER LEVEL

(1) The transition piece is an oblique cone. Generators along its surface will all meet at one point, the apex of the cone. Divide the large circular duct into 12 equal parts. Draw in the generators and extend them to meet at the cone apex. The generators are used, as before, to find the joint line between the square duct and the transition piece. Points are projected from the end view back to the other views.

(2) The development of the square duct is found in the same way as in the previous examples. The distances between the lines in the development are taken from the end view. The points on the seam are projected down from plan.

(3) The method of developing an oblique cone has been examined earlier. The true length of each generator must be found. A right angle is formed using the length of an element in plan and the height of the same element in elevation. The hypotenuse of this triangle equals the true length of the element.

(4) Choose a location for the apex and draw one of the elements, e.g. element 1. From the bottom of this element swing an arc having a radius equal in length to one of the divisions on the large circle. Using the true length of element 12 draw an arc from the apex to cut the first arc. This locates point 12 on the development. Find the complete development in this way.

(5) The cut-outs from this development are found by stepping true length distances on the generators as shown.

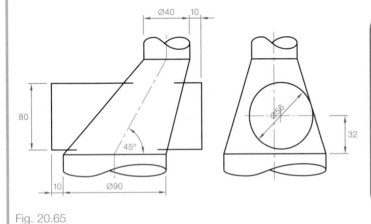

Fig. 20.65

Fig. 20.65 shows a transition which is in the form of a truncated oblique cone. The transition piece is intersected by a circular duct. The circular duct is off-centre.

(i) Draw the given views and project a plan.
(ii) Find the joint line in all views.
(iii) Develop the surface of the transition piece.
(iv) Develop the surface of the circular duct.

The construction of this solution is very similar to the previous example. There are a large number of points to be found and proper indexing of points is essential.

HIGHER LEVEL

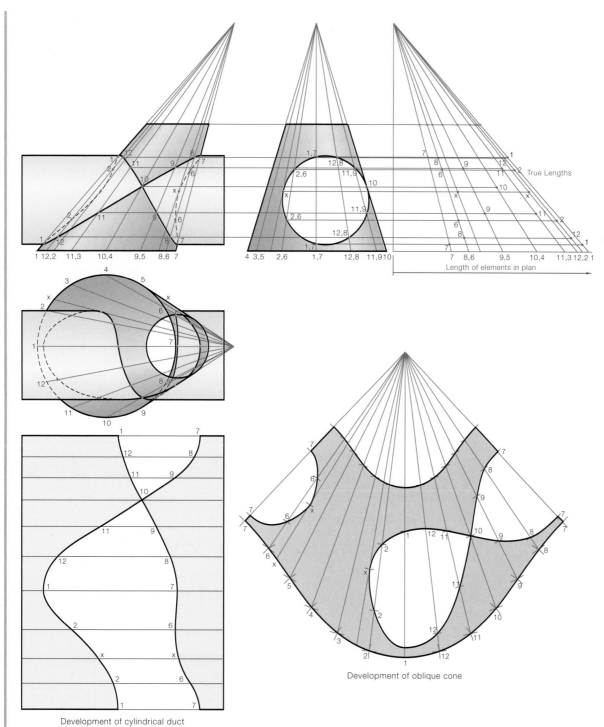

True Lengths

Length of elements in plan

Development of cylindrical duct

Development of oblique cone

Fig. 20.66

Activities

DIHEDRAL ANGLE

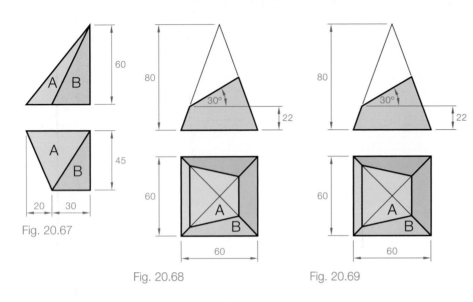

Fig. 20.67

Fig. 20.68

Fig. 20.69

Q1. to Q3.
For each of the following draw the given plan and elevation of the solids and determine the dihedral angle between surfaces A and B using the point view method.

Q4. to Q8.
For each of the following roof structures draw the given views. Determine the dihedral angle between surfaces A and B using the triangle method.
Scale 1:100

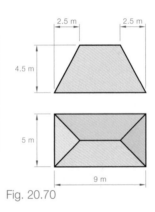

Fig. 20.70

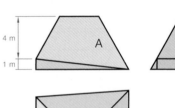

All roof surfaces have a pitch of 60°

Fig. 20.71

A = Pitch of 60°
B = Pitch of 45°

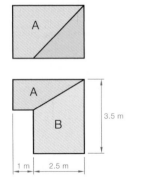

Fig. 20.72

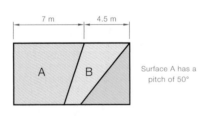

Surface A has a pitch of 50°

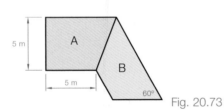

Fig. 20.73

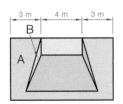

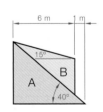

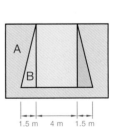

Fig. 20.74

ROOF GEOMETRY

Q9. Fig. 20.75 shows the plan and elevation of a lean-to roof. Surface A has a pitch of 30°, surface B has a pitch of 45° and surface C has a pitch of 60°.

(i)   Draw the plan and elevation of the roof.

(ii) Develop the surfaces A and B.

(iii) Find the dihedral angle between the surfaces A and B.

Scale 1:100

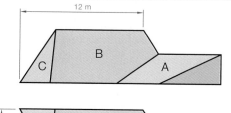

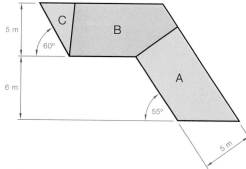

Fig. 20.75

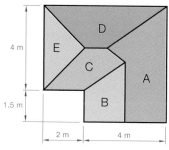

Fig. 20.76

Q10. Fig. 20.76 shows the outline plan of a pitch roof. The surfaces A and B have a pitch of 50°. Surfaces C, D and E have pitches of 50°.

(i)   Draw the given plan and project an elevation.

(ii) Develop the surfaces A and C.

(iii) Determine the dihedral angle between surfaces A and D and between surfaces B and C.

Scale 1:50

Q11. Fig. 20.77 shows the outline plan of a lean-to roof. Surfaces A and B have a pitch of 45°. Surface C has a pitch of 25°.

(i)   Draw the plan and elevation of the roof.

(ii) Find the dihedral angle between surfaces B and C.

(iii) Develop surfaces A and C.

Scale 1:100

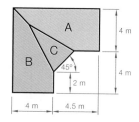

Fig. 20.77

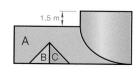

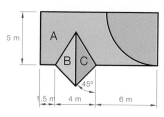

Fig. 20.78

Q12. Fig. 20.78 shows the plan and elevation of a lean-to roof with a dormer window and a quarter tower. Surface A has a pitch of 35°. Surfaces B and C have a pitch of 30°.

(i)   Draw the plan and elevation of the roof.

(ii) Find the dihedral angle between surfaces A and B.

(iii) Develop the surface of roof A.

Scale 1:100

INTERSECTING DUCTS AND PIPES

Q13. to Q15.

The diagrams show the projections of intersecting ducts/pipes. In each case draw the given views and find the joint line in all views. Make a complete surface development of each ducting piece.

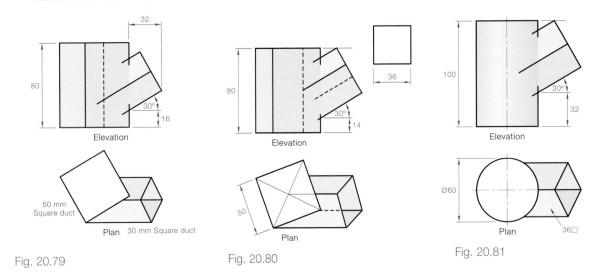

Fig. 20.79   Fig. 20.80   Fig. 20.81

Q16. to Q18.

The diagrams show end views of intersecting ducts/pipes. In each case draw the front elevation, end elevation and plan showing the joint line clearly. Develop the surface of part A and enough of the larger duct to show the true shape of the hole to be cut in it.

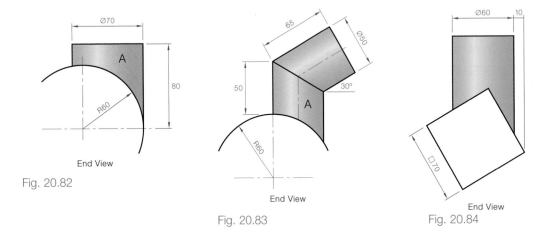

Fig. 20.82   Fig. 20.83   Fig. 20.84

Q19. to Q21.

The diagrams show pipe joints. Draw the given views and find the joint line.
Develop the surfaces of part A and part B.

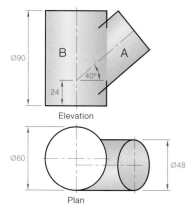

Ø90

B   A

40°

24

Elevation

Ø60

Ø48

Plan

Fig. 20.85

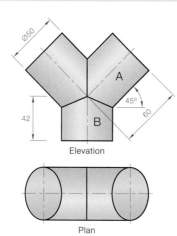

Ø50

A

42

45°

60

B

Elevation

Plan

Fig. 20.86

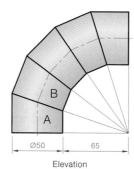

B

A

Ø50   65

Elevation

Fig. 20.87

Q22. to Q24.

Given the plan and elevation of a hopper/funnel. Draw the given views
and make a complete surface development of the object.

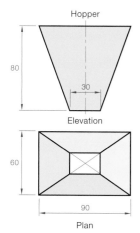

Hopper

80

30

Elevation

60

90

Plan

Fig. 20.88

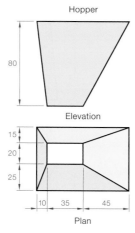

Hopper

80

Elevation

15

20

25

10   35   45

Plan

Fig. 20.89

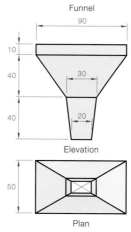

Funnel

90

10

40

30

40

20

Elevation

50

Plan

Fig. 20.90

Q25. to Q27.

Given the plan and elevation of transition pieces. In each case draw the given views and make a *one*-piece surface development of the object.

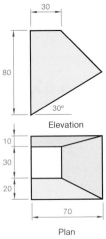

Fig. 20.91

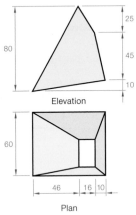

Fig. 20.92

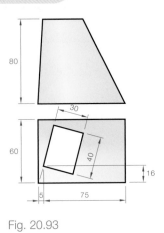

Fig. 20.93

Q28. to Q30.

Make a *one*-piece surface development of the following transition pieces.

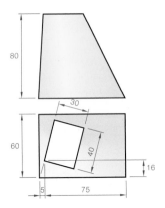

Fig. 20.94

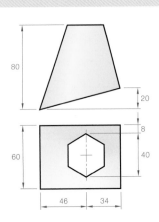

Fig. 20.95

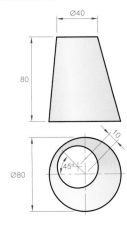

Fig. 20.96

Q31. to Q33.

Draw the given views and make a full surface development of the transition piece.

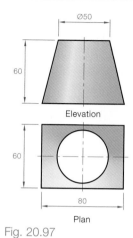

Fig. 20.97

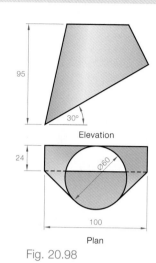

Fig. 20.98

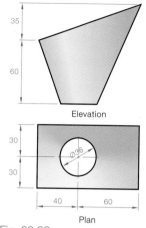

Fig. 20.99

Q34. to Q36.

The following drawings show projections of transition pieces. Draw the given views and produce a one-piece development of each transition piece.

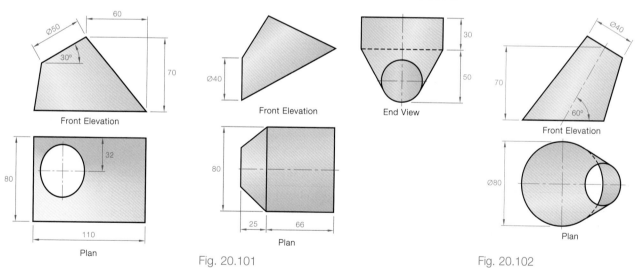

Fig. 20.100

Fig. 20.101

Fig. 20.102

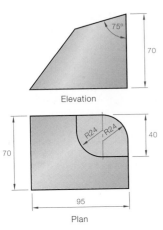

Elevation

Plan

Fig. 20.103

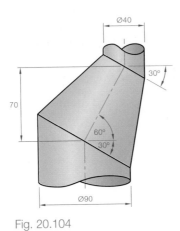

Fig. 20.104

Q37. and Q38.
Draw the given views and make a full one-piece development of each transition piece.

Q39. Fig. 20.105 shows a curved duct being joined by a straight, cylindrical duct.
(i) Draw the plan and complete the elevation.
(ii) Draw the complete surface development of the cylindrical duct.

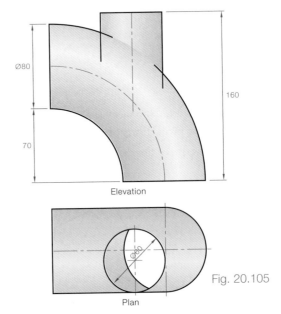

Elevation

Plan

Fig. 20.105

Q40. Fig. 20.106 shows an oblique cylindrical duct penetrated by a square duct.
(i) Draw the given views and project a plan.
(ii) Find the joint line in all views.
(iii) Make a complete surface development of the square duct.
(iv) Make a complete surface development of the oblique cylindrical duct.

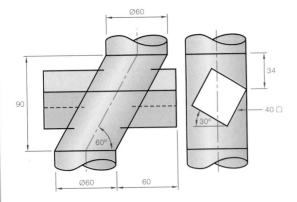

Fig. 20.106

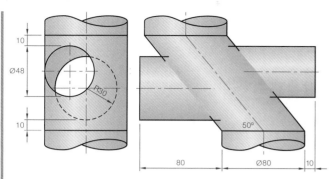

Fig. 20.107

Q41. Fig. 20.107 shows an oblique cylindrical duct penetrated by two different-sized cylindrical ducts.

(i)   Draw the given views and project a plan.
(ii) Find the joint line in all views.
(iii) Make a complete surface development of both cylindrical ducts.
(iv) Develop the oblique cylindrical duct.

Q42. Shown in Fig. 20.108 is a transition piece in the form of a truncated oblique cone. This transition piece is penetrated by a square-sectioned duct of 45 mm side.

(i)   Draw the given views and complete the plan.
(ii) Find the joint line in all views.
(iii) Develop the surface of the oblique cone.
(iv) Develop the surface of the square duct.

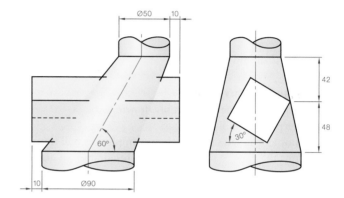

Fig. 20.108

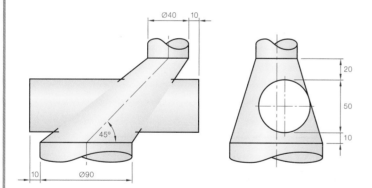

Fig. 20.109

Q43. A truncated oblique cone forms a transition piece. A cylindrical duct penetrates the transition piece as shown.

(i)   Draw the given views and project a plan.
(ii) Find the joint line in all views.
(iii) Develop the surface of the cylindrical duct.
(iv) Develop the surface of the transition piece.

HIGHER LEVEL

21 Assemblies

SYLLABUS OUTLINE

Areas to be studied (in an applied context):

• Interpretation of exploded and assembled drawings. • Drawings – layout and conventions. • System of projection. • Sectional views. • Hatching. • Dimensioning. • Joining methods. • Machine surface and texture symbols. • Modelling assemblies in 3-D CAD.

Learning outcomes
Students should be able to:

Higher and Ordinary levels
- Understand product assembly drawings.
- Interpret assembly drawings.
- Draw assembled views from drawings of a small number of single components.
- Draw the views essential to the representation of an assembly.
- Draw single-plane sectional views.
- Hatch sectioned parts in each view.
- Fully dimension drawings.
- Measure components to be drawn and relate the model/drawing to the artefact.
- Generate CAD models of assemblies.
- Apply balloon detailing.
- Use abbreviations and symbols.

Higher level only
- *Draw a number of sectional views.*
- *Draw views that have been sectioned.*
- *Indicate on the drawing a surface finish as appropriate.*
- *Indicate methods of assembly.*

The understanding of machine and flat-pack assembly drawings is a necessary skill for many household and other common products. This chapter hopes to develop the skill of interpreting these types of drawings as well as the skill of producing these types of drawings. The student will become familiar with dimensioning, sectioning, hatching and joining as well as the use of appropriate symbols and abbreviations.

Working Drawings

A set of working drawings includes the **detail drawings** of the component parts and the **assembly drawing** which shows these parts in their correct position relative to each other. Working drawings will also include a **parts list**, brief **annotations** and **dimensions**.

Detail Drawings

A detail drawing gives all relevant information about a component. Details of one part or a number of small parts may be given on each sheet. Detailed drawings usually show orthographic views, are fully dimensioned and show materials, finishes, tolerances and notes on manufacture. When several details are drawn on one sheet, careful consideration must be given to spacing. Ample space must be allowed around each component to allow for dimensions and notes. The same scale should be used for all details on a single sheet, if possible. When this is not practical the scale for each detail should be clearly noted under each component.

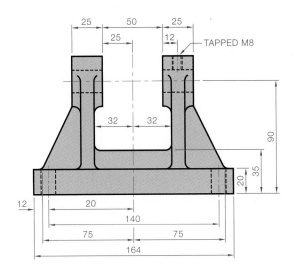

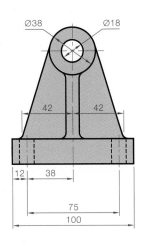

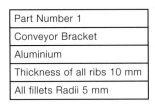

Part Number 1
Conveyor Bracket
Aluminium
Thickness of all ribs 10 mm
All fillets Radii 5 mm

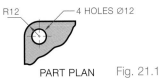

PART PLAN   Fig. 21.1

Assembly Drawing

As stated earlier, an assembly drawing shows the assembled parts in their functional positions. The views selected show how the parts fit together in the assembly and suggest the function of the entire unit. The assembly drawing does not attempt to describe the shapes of the individual parts but rather the relationship between the parts. The information on each of the parts can be found by referring to the **detail drawing**.

The views selected should be the minimum views or partial views that will show how the parts fit together. The views usually take the form of sectional views as these show more clearly how parts fit into each other or overlap each other. As a result of using sectional views, it is very rare to include hidden detail. If the clarity of the assembly can be improved by using hidden lines, then they should be used.

Dimensioning of an assembly is not necessary because all the parts have been fully dimensioned in the detail drawings. When dimensions are given, they are limited to some function of the object such as the maximum opening between the jaws or the maximum movement of a piston.

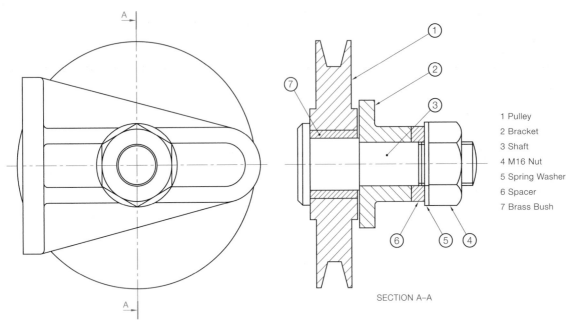

Fig. 21.2

Parts are identified in an assembly drawing by using numbers or letters which refer back to a parts table and the detailed drawings. Circles containing the part numbers are placed beside the parts with leaders ending with arrowheads touching the part. The circles should be placed in orderly, horizontal or vertical rows and should not be scattered over the sheet. The leaders should not cross each other and should be parallel or almost so. Fig. 21.2 shows an assembly drawing with parts list and identification numbers.

Sectioning of Assemblies

In the sectioning of assemblies it is important that the sectioning aids in the identification of the individual parts. Figures 21.3a, 21.3b and 21.3c show some of the principles involved when sectioning. The large area is sectioned at 45° in Fig. 21.3a. Spacings between lines should be even and judged by eye. The second large component in Fig. 21.3b is sectioned at 45° in the opposite direction. Care should be taken that the section lines do not meet on the intersection line. Additional components in Fig. 21.3c are sectioned at 30°, 60° or an odd angle. Section lines are placed closer together in smaller areas.

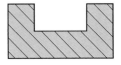

Fig. 21.3a

Some parts of an assembly section are not hatched even though they may lie on the section plane. It is standard practice to show these unsectioned or in the round.

Components not to be sectioned:

(1) Bolts	(2) Nuts	(3) Washers
(4) Rivets	(5) Shafts	(6) Keys
(7) Screws	(8) Pins	(9) Gear teeth
(10) Spokes	(11) Ribs	

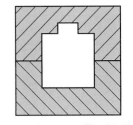

Fig. 21.3b

Sectioning of thin parts such as gaskets and sheet metal parts is both difficult and ineffective. Such parts should be shown in solid black.

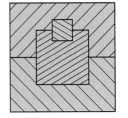

Fig. 21.3c

In the Section A–A figure the parts list reads:

1 Pulley
2 Bracket
3 Shaft
4 M16 Nut
5 Spring Washer
6 Spacer
7 Brass Bush

SECTION A–A

Sectioning of Holes, Tapped Holes, Set Screws, Nuts, Bolts, Washers and Rivets

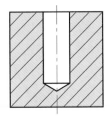

Section through a drilled hole

Fig. 21.4a

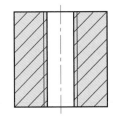

Section through a tapped hole. The sides of the hole formed by the tapping size drill are drawn dark.

Fig. 21.4b

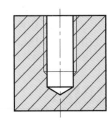

Section through a blind tapped hole. Note the section lines cross the thread to the sides of the hole.

Fig. 21.4c

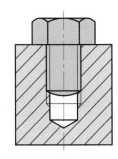

Section through a blind tapped hole with a set screw. Note the section lines are not drawn through the bolt screw thread.

Fig. 21.4d

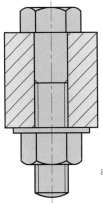

Even though the section cuts through the nut, bolt and washer they are shown in the round

Fig. 21.4e

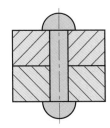

Section through a rivet. The rivet is drawn in the round.

Fig. 21.4f

Sectioning of Ribs

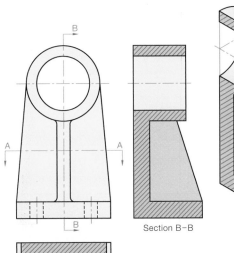

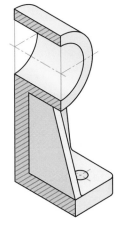

Section B–B

Section A–A

Fig. 21.5

To avoid a false sense of solidity, ribs, webs, gear teeth and other thin surfaces are not sectioned even though the section plane passes through their centre plane. Fig. 21.5 shows section plane B–B passing though the rib. Yet the rib is not hatched. When the section plane cuts across a rib or any thin member, then it is sectioned. Fig. 21.5 shows section plane A–A cutting crosswise through the rib and producing a hatched rib.

Sectioning of Spokes

Spokes, like ribs, are not sectioned. Fig. 21.6 shows a partial view of a valve wheel showing only those features that are needed for minimum representation. No further information is given by drawing the full elevation so only a small portion of it needs to be drawn.

Drawing Conventions

There are many drawing conventions used to help reduce the amount of drawing needed for a particular project yet not compromising on the amount of information provided. As a general rule, the drawing of repetitive details is avoided and every effort must be made to provide maximum information with minimum drawing.

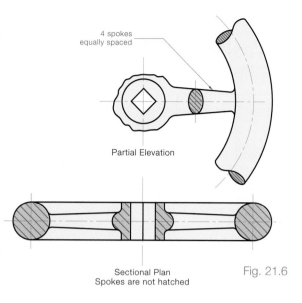

4 spokes equally spaced

Partial Elevation

Sectional Plan
Spokes are not hatched

Fig. 21.6

Symmetrical Parts

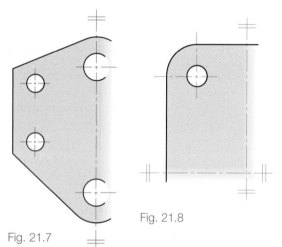

Fig. 21.7

Fig. 21.8

For symmetrical parts about one axis (Fig. 21.7) it is only necessary to draw one side of the shape. The line of symmetry is indicated by placing two parallel lines at each end of it. It is important that the outline is extended slightly past the symmetry line. Fig. 21.8 shows a metal plate with two axes of symmetry. Only a quarter of the plate needs to be drawn.

Repetitive Information

Repeated drawing of identical features is avoided by drawing one object and indicating the position of the others by using centre lines, Fig. 21.9. When holes, bolts and rivets etc. form a pattern, enough centre lines are drawn to establish that pattern (Fig. 21.10). Detailing of a small area of a pattern is often sufficient. Enough of the pattern needs to be drawn to show that it is repetitive.

The shaft support needs only to be drawn once with bolt centre lines shown to locate second bracket.

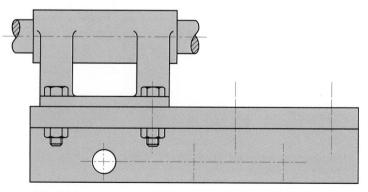

Fig. 21.9

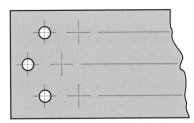

Fig. 21.10

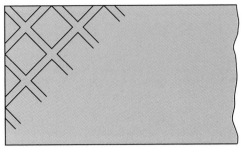

Fig. 21.11

For a regular pattern of holes, rivets etc. only the number necessary to establish the pattern are drawn. An accompanying note will provide sufficient information.

For repetitive patterns such as knurling, chequered plate, perforated sheet etc. it is sufficient to draw the pattern in a small area. A note indicating that the pattern covers a larger area will reduce the amount of drawing.

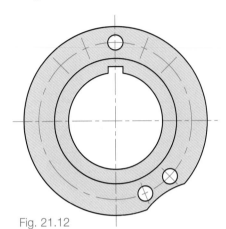

Fig. 21.12

When a special feature such as a keyway or a notch is near to a repetitive feature then the repetitive feature should be drawn in full. Fig. 21.12 shows an example. The repetitive feature, the holes, are drawn in full adjacent to the keyway and the notch.

Conventions for Breaks

In order to shorten a view of an elongated object, it is recommended to use breaks. This often allows the object to be drawn to a larger scale.

If the full object was to be drawn it might have to be scaled down to fit on the sheet.

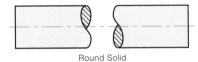

Round Solid

Fig. 21.13a

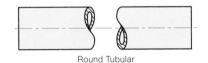

Round Tubular

Fig. 21.13b

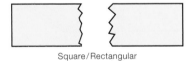

Square/Rectangular

Fig. 21.13c

Conventions for Knurling

A knurl is a roughening of a cylindrical surface, usually to give a better handgrip for tightening/loosening a thread. There are two basic types, straight knurling and diamond knurling. These are shown in Figures 22.14a and 21.14b.

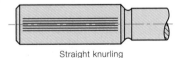

Straight knurling

Fig. 21.14a

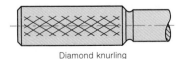

Diamond knurling

Fig. 21.14b

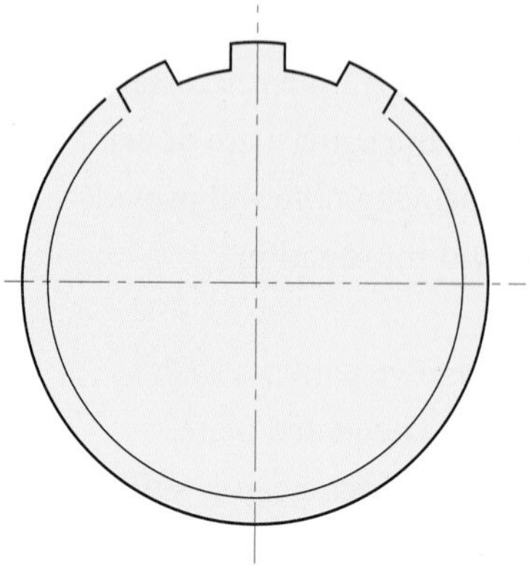

Shafts

In many cases a shaft will be machined to produce splines or serrations along its length or partially along its length. This machining is to help the shaft transfer torque to another part.

Splined Shaft
Fig. 21.15a

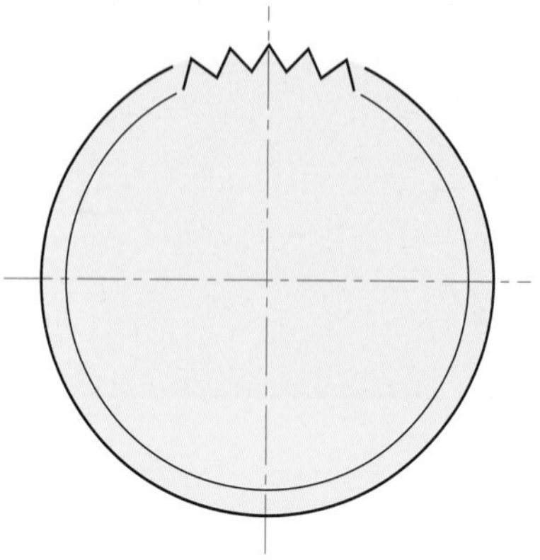

Serrated Shaft
Fig. 21.15b

Squared Shaft

The end of a cylindrical shaft will often be shaped to produce a square section to receive a handle or adjustment wheel.

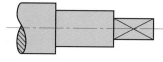

Fig. 21.16a

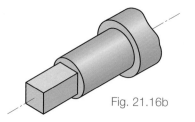

Fig. 21.16b

Shaft-fixing Devices: Keys and Keyways

One way of preventing a part from slipping on a shaft is to machine a slot, a keyway, into both pieces and to fit a third piece, the key, into this slot. The key ensures there is no relative movement between the two pieces. Figures 21.17a, 21.17b and 21.17c show a number of different types of keys and keyways.

The gib head key is easier to knock into place and to remove (Fig. 21.17a). The key itself may be parallel or tapered. A slope of 1:100 would be usual. Fig. 21.17b shows a rectangular key. Square or cylindrical keys are also used. This would be one of the more common key types. A woodruff key (Fig. 21.17c) is a segment of a disc and is often used on a tapered shaft. The size of the keys depends on the load to be carried.

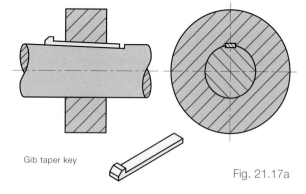

Gib taper key

Fig. 21.17a

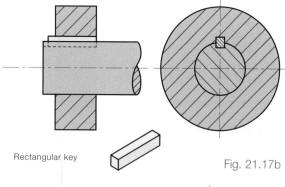

Rectangular key

Fig. 21.17b

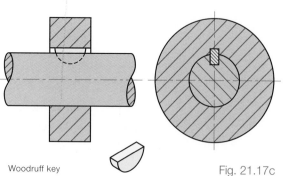

Woodruff key

Fig. 21.17c

Bearings

These are used to help to reduce friction. There are two basic types – ball bearings and roller bearings. Fig. 21.18 shows pictorials of each type. The hardened steel balls or rollers are held between an inner and outer ring. These rings are called races. Bearings are often sealed units containing the balls/rollers and a lubricant. Roller bearings are used where heavy loading occurs .

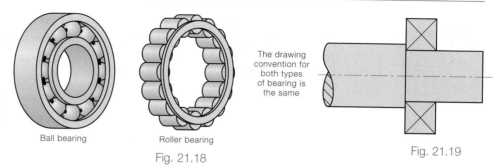

Ball bearing   Roller bearing

Fig. 21.18

The drawing convention for both types of bearing is the same

Fig. 21.19

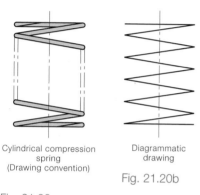

Cylindrical compression spring (Drawing convention)

Fig. 21.20a

Diagrammatic drawing

Fig. 21.20b

Springs

There are many spring shapes and sizes but they all fit into three categories according to function:

(1) compression,

(2) tension,

(3) torsion.

A few coils are drawn at either end, or the diagrammatic representation may be used.

Spur Gears

A working drawing of a spur gear is shown in Fig. 21.21. It is not necessary to show individual teeth on the drawing. The addendum and the root circles are drawn as solid circles with the pitch circle as a chain line.

In section, the teeth are not sectioned as this would give a false sense of solidity.

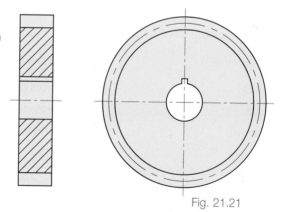

Fig. 21.21

The Drawing of Standard Bolts

Standard bolts and nuts are not shown on detail drawings but appear regularly on assembly drawings. The conventional way of drawing nuts and bolts is based on the body diameter as shown in Fig. 21.22a. the method of finding the centres for the curves on the bolt head is shown in Fig. 21.22b. Points C_1, C_2 and C_3 are all found with the 60° set-square.

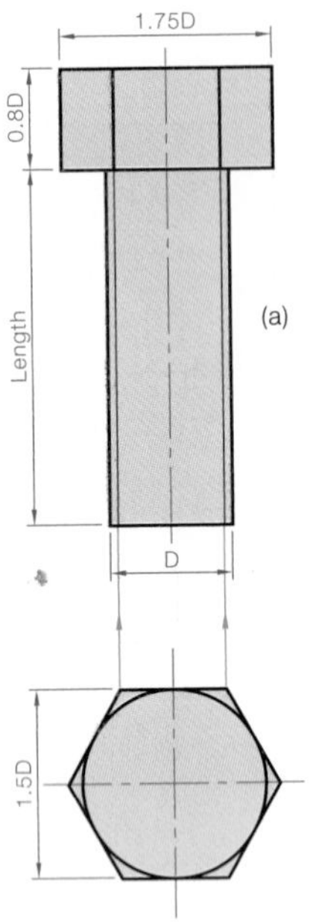

Fig. 21.22a

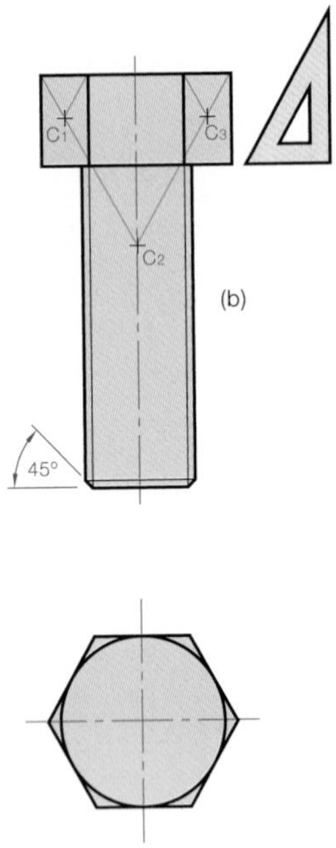

Fig. 21.22b

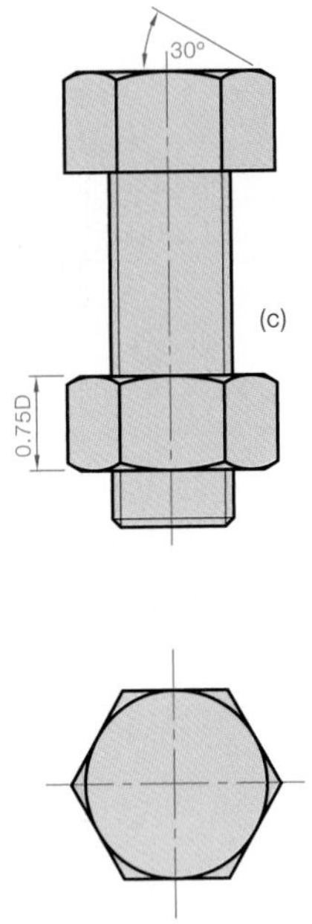

Fig. 21.22c

The inner thread lines are in line with the two inner edges of the hexagonal head. In general, bolt heads and nuts should be drawn across corners in all views, regardless of projection. This is a violation of projection rules but there are good reasons for it:

(1) It avoids confusion between hexagonal-head bolts and square-head bolts.

(2) It shows the clearance of both bolt heads and nut, in all views.

(3) It is faster to use the same construction in all views.

Bolt heads and nuts should only be drawn across the flats for a very special reason. Fig. 21.23 shows the construction convention used in such a view.

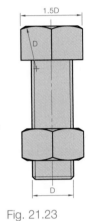

Fig. 21.23

Abbreviations and Their Uses

When producing engineering drawings there are many terms and expressions that need to be included on the drawings. Some of these are used frequently enough to justify the use of abbreviations. Many of these have been standardised.

Abbreviation	Explanation	Diagram
A/C	Across corners	
A/F	Across flats	
Hex HD	Hexagon head	
ASSY	Assembly	
CRS	Centres	
CL or ℄	Centre line	
CHAM	Chamfered	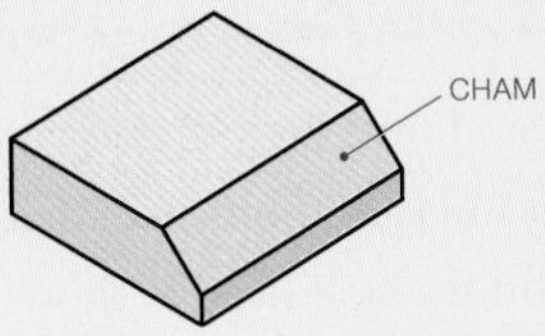

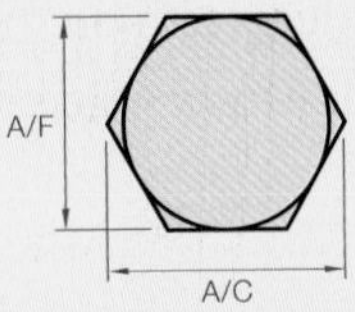

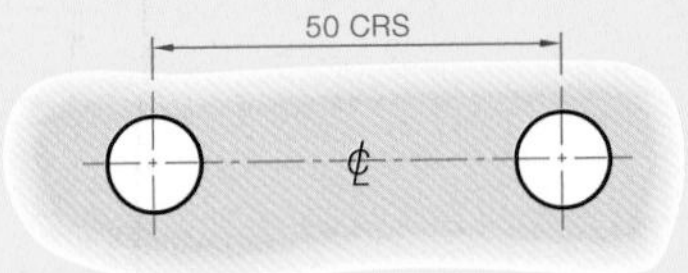

Abbreviation	Explanation	Diagram
CH HD	Cheese head screw/bolt	CH HD
CSK	Countersunk head screw or countersunk hole	CSK
C'BORE	Counterbore	C'BORE
CYL	Cylindrical	
DIA	Diameter (in a note)	
Ø	Diameter (preceding a dimension)	
R	Radius. Capital letter only.	R70 Ø26
FIG	Figure	
DRG	Drawing	
HEX HD	Hexagonal head	
INSUL	Insulated or insulation	
INT	Internal	
EXT	External	
LH	Left hand	
LG	Long	
MATL	Material	
MAX and MIN	Maximum and minimum	
No.	Number	

Abbreviation	Explanation	Diagram
PCD	Pitch circle diameter	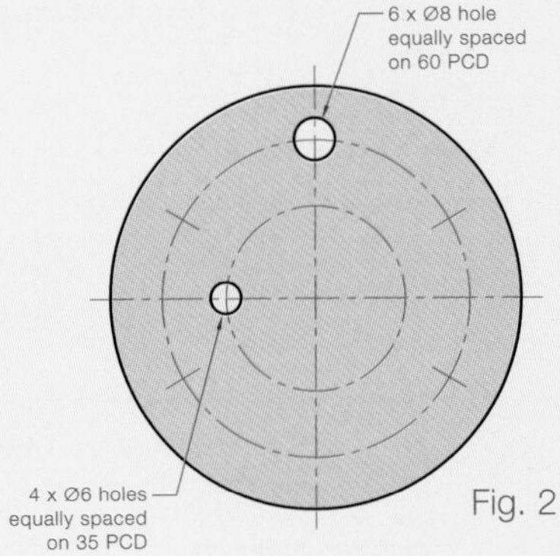 6 x Ø8 hole equally spaced on 60 PCD 4 x Ø6 holes equally spaced on 35 PCD Fig. 21.24
REQD	Required	
RH	Right hand	
RD HD	Round head	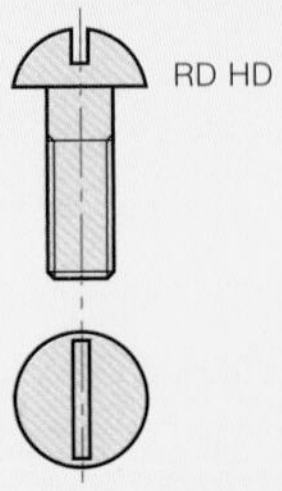 RD HD
SCR	Screwed	
SH	Sheet	
SK	Sketch	
SPEC	Specification	
SQ □	Square (in a note) Square preceding a dimension	□ 40
STD	Standard	
U'CUT	Undercut	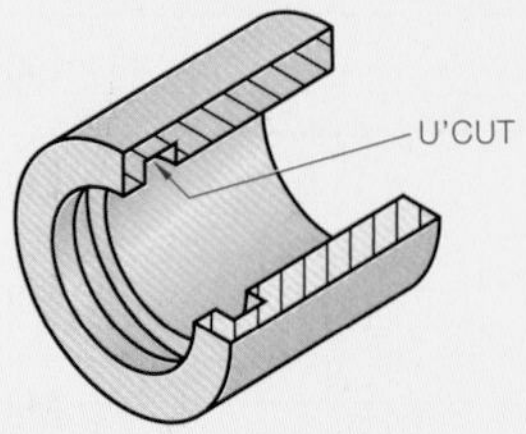 U'CUT
NTS	Not to scale	
RPM	Revolutions per minute	
FIM	Full indicated movement	

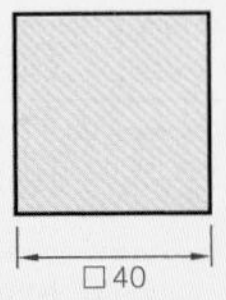

Drawings: Layout and Conventions

Title Block

Each sheet must have a title block, generally in the lower right corner. This title block will contain essential information for the identification and interpretation of the drawing. The actual layout of the title block does not matter and may be stamped on, pre-printed or drawn by hand. The following information would generally be given in the title block:

- name of firm,
- name of the object represented or assembly,
- drawing number,
- scale,
- date,
- signature(s),
- projection symbol,
- copyright clause.

As well as this information a whole body of additional information may be included such as material, quantity, treatment/hardness, finish, surface texture, screw thread forms etc.

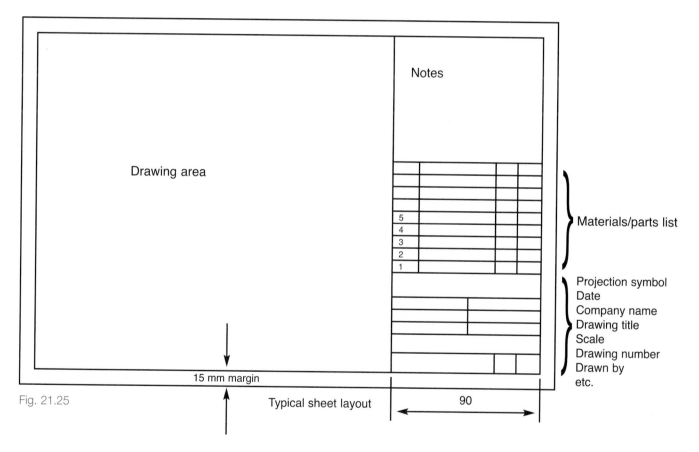

Fig. 21.25

Parts List

A parts list consists of an itemised list of the parts shown on a detail drawing or an assembly drawing. The list should contain the part number, a descriptive title, quantity needed, material used, as well as other information as deemed necessary. The parts should be listed in order of size or importance. The main castings or forgings are listed first; parts cut from cold-rolled stock are second; and standard parts such as bolts, washers and bushing are third. If the parts list is

No.	Part name	REQD	MATL
5	Pin	1	STEEL
4	Pulley	1	CI
3	Hook	1	STEEL
2	Trunnion	1	CI
1	Bracket	1	CI

Fig. 21.26

placed as shown in Fig. 21.26 then the order of parts should be from the bottom upwards so that new parts may be added to the list later if necessary.

> Standard parts such as bolts, screws and bearings are not drawn, but are listed, in the parts list.

Lines and Linework

All lines of a similar type should be consistently dense and bold throughout a drawing. Particular care should be taken with revisions of the drawing so that the new lines are not at variance with existing linework. The table below shows line types and their application.

Type of line	Example	Application of line
Thick continuous	————	Visible outlines and edges.
Thin continuous	————	Dimensions and leader lines, hatching, fictitious outlines and edges, outlines of revolved sections.
Short dashes (thin)	– – – – – – –	Hidden outlines and edges.
Chain (thin)	— · — · — · —	Centre lines, pitch circles, extreme positions of moving parts.
Chain (thin but thickened at ends and change of direction)	— · — · — · —	Cutting planes.
Continuous irregular (thin)	～～～	Limits of partial views and sections where the line is not an axis.
Thick continuous	— · — · — · —	A surface that must meet special requirements.

As a general rule, all chain lines should start and finish with a long dash. Centre lines should cross each other at solid portions of the line and should extend only a short distance beyond the feature. Centre lines should not continue through the spaces between views.

Lettering

Characters should be uniform and most importantly, legible. They should be of open form and free from serifs and other embellishments. Particular care must be taken with figures because, unlike letters, they rarely fall into patterns and must be read individually. The use of capital letters is preferred to lower case as they are less congested and, even when reduced in size, are less likely to be misread.

System of Projection

The system of projection used on the drawing must be clearly indicated by using the projection symbols.

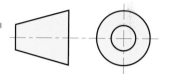

First-angle projection   Fig. 21.27

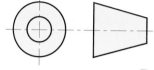

Third-angle projection   Fig. 21.28

Dimensioning

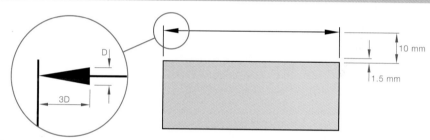

Fig. 21.29

A dimension line is a thin, solid, dark line which ends with arrowheads. The dimension line indicates the direction and extent of a measurement. The dimension nearest the object should be spaced about 10 mm away from the object outline. The extension lines 'extend' from the point on the drawing to which the dimension refers. A gap of about 1.5 mm should be left between the extension line and its reference point and it should continue past the arrowhead slightly. The arrowheads should be uniform in style and size throughout the drawing. Arrowheads should be drawn freehand and have a length and width in a ratio of 3:1.

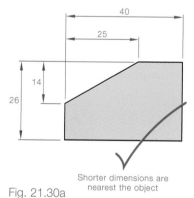

Shorter dimensions are nearest the object

Fig. 21.30a

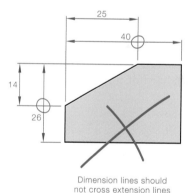

Dimension lines should not cross extension lines

Fig. 21.30b

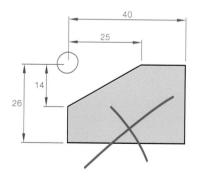

Do not shorten extension lines

Fig. 21.30c

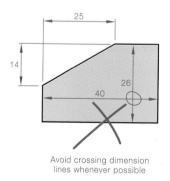

Avoid crossing dimension lines whenever possible

Fig. 21.30d

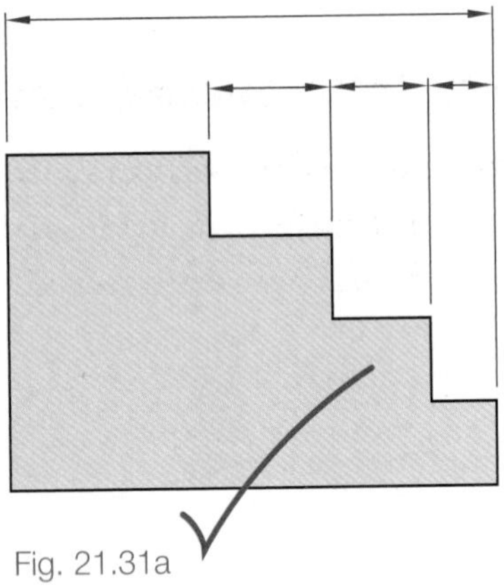

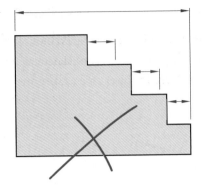

Fig. 21.31a

Fig. 21.31b

Fig. 21.31a shows how dimensions should be lined up and grouped together. The dimensioning shown in Fig. 21.31b does not show good practice

Fig. 21.32 shows a method of dimensioning which uses a datum or reference line. By referring all dimensions to a small number of reference lines/points the accumulation of slight inaccuracies can be avoided.

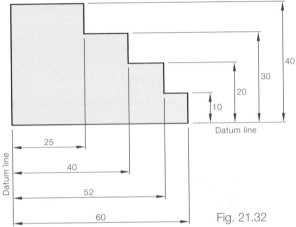

Fig. 21.32

Direction of Dimension Text

There are two accepted systems used for placing dimension text:

- The unidirectional system (preferred).
- The aligned system.

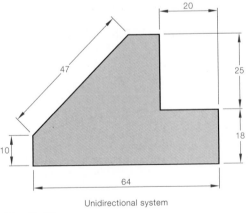

Unidirectional system

Fig. 21.33a

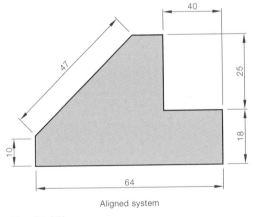

Aligned system

Fig. 21.33b

Fig. 21.33a shows a figure dimensioned using the unidirectional system. All figures and notes are lettered horizontal on the sheet and are read from the bottom of the sheet.

Fig. 21.33b shows a figure dimensioned using the aligned system. All figures are aligned with the dimension lines so that they can be read from the bottom or the right side of the sheet.

Leaders

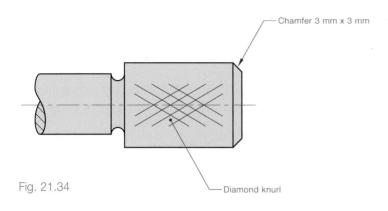

Chamfer 3 mm x 3 mm

Fig. 21.34

Diamond knurl

A leader is a line leading from a note or dimension and ending with an arrowhead or a dot touching a part. Arrowheads should always terminate on a line such as the edge of a hole, while dots should be within the outline of the object, Fig. 21.34. The leader line itself should generally be inclined and should start from the beginning or end of a note.

Leaders should cross as few lines as possible and should never cross each other. If there are a large numbers of leaders beside each other on a drawing they should be drawn parallel. When a leader points to a hole or arc it should be radial so that if extended it would pass through the centre.

Dimensioning of Circles

When dimensioning holes and circles the method used depends on the circle size. Fig. 21.35 shows four different methods. Apart from the last example they are all radial.

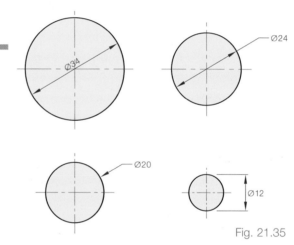

Ø34

Ø24

Ø20

Ø12

Fig. 21.35

Dimensioning Arcs

Circular arcs are dimensioned in a view showing their true shapes. The centre of the arc may be indicated by using a small cross or centre lines but this is not done for small radii.

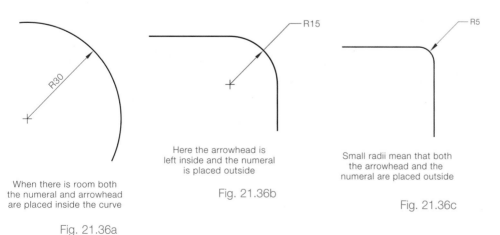

R30

When there is room both the numeral and arrowhead are placed inside the curve

Fig. 21.36a

R15

Here the arrowhead is left inside and the numeral is placed outside

Fig. 21.36b

R5

Small radii mean that both the arrowhead and the numeral are placed outside

Fig. 21.36c

Fillets on a drawing are usually of a standard size throughout and rather than dimension each one it is customary to place a note in the lower portion of the drawing. 'FILLETS R6 UNLESS OTHERWISE SPECIFIED'.

Dimensioning Angles

One of the three methods indicated in Figures 21.37a, 21.37b and 21.37c is used depending on the space inside the angle for numerals and arrowheads.

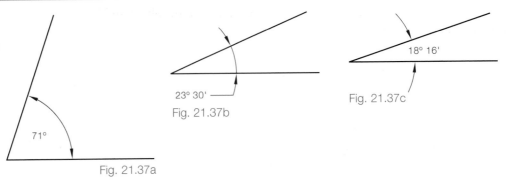

71°

Fig. 21.37a

23° 30'

Fig. 21.37b

18° 16'

Fig. 21.37c

Chamfers and Tapers

Chamfers are dimensioned by giving the length of the offset and the angle, or in the case of a 45° chamfer, usually by note, Fig. 21.38.

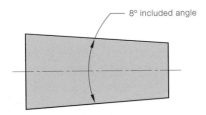

8° included angle

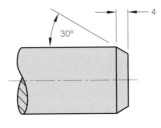

30°

4

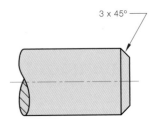

3 x 45°

Fig. 21.38

Tapers, which are conical surfaces on shafts or in holes, are used on machine spindles, shanks of tools, pins etc. They are generally indicated using either of the two methods shown in Fig. 21.39.

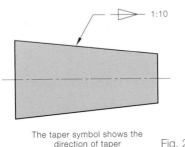

1:10

The taper symbol shows the direction of taper

Fig. 21.39

Worked Examples: Sectional Views

There are many times when the interior detail of an object cannot be seen from the outside, Fig. 21.40. We get around this, as explained earlier in the chapter, by cutting the object by a plane and showing the sectional view. In Fig. 21.40 the cutting plane A–A slices through the object. Fig. 21.41 shows how the object looks when the front material is removed. The orthographic

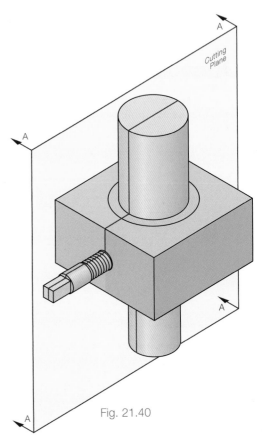

Fig. 21.40

view of this section is shown in Fig. 21.42. The shaft is shown in the round as per normal convention. The retaining screw is drawn as shown. The sectional view, Fig. 21.42, gives a clear view of the inside of the object and is easy to draw. The parts are balloon-referenced.

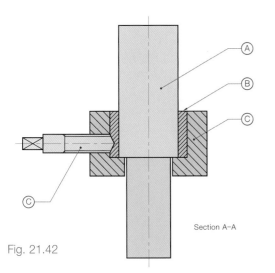

Section A-A

A Steel shaft or spindle
B Brass bush or bearing
C Cast-iron block
D Square-head retaining screw

Fig. 21.42

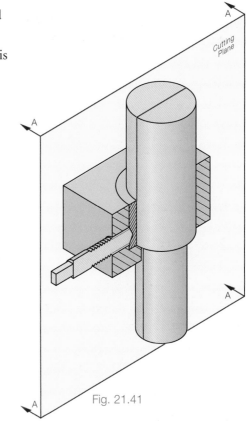

Fig. 21.41

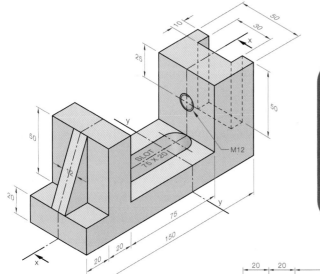

Fig. 21.43

Given the isometric projection of a machine vice body in Fig. 21.43. Draw to full-size using first-angle projection.

(i)   A sectional front elevation on X–X.

(ii) A sectional end elevation on Y–Y.

(iii) A full plan.

(iv) Insert seven leading dimensions.

There are several things to note from the solution in Fig. 21.44.

(1) The rib is not hatched in the sectional elevation X–X even though the plane passes through it.

(2) The hatch lines in the sectional elevation X–X continue through the threads for the threaded hole.

(3) The projection symbol is shown.

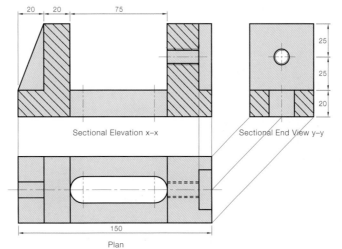

Sectional Elevation x–x

Sectional End View y–y

Plan

Fig. 21.44

MACHINE VICE BODY

Given the plan and elevation of a machined casting in Fig. 21.45.

(i) Draw the front elevation as shown.

(ii) Project a sectional plan from cutting plane A–A.

(iii) Project a sectional end view from cutting plane B–B. Insert the projection symbol, title and four leading dimensions.

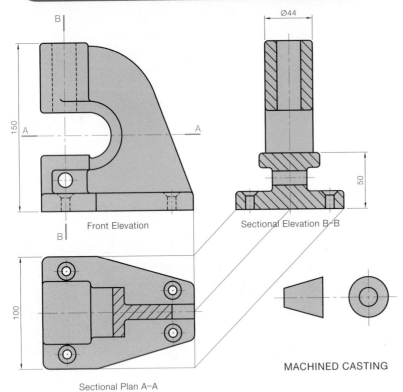

Front Elevation

Sectional Elevation B–B

Sectional Plan A–A

Fig. 21.46

MACHINED CASTING

Elevation

Plan

Fig. 21.45

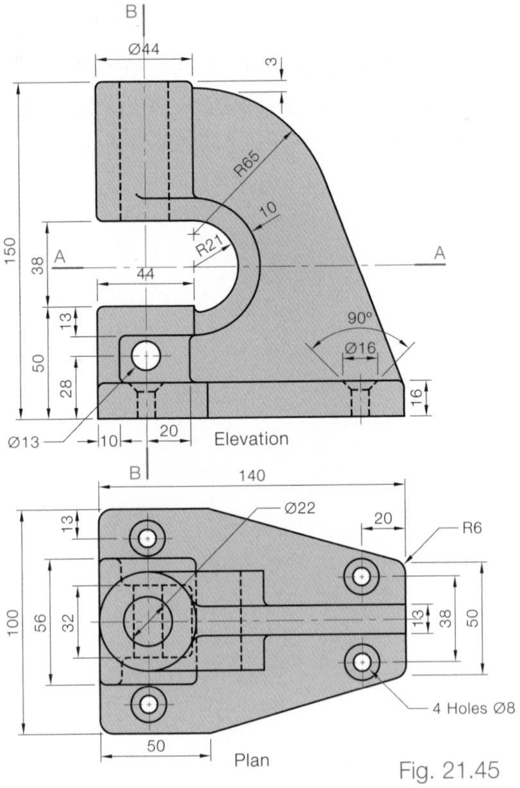

All radii not specified to be 3 mm

Generally do not show hidden detail in sectional views.

The rib is sectioned in plan because the cutting plane cuts through it perpendicularly.

Fig. 21.47 shows the plan and elevation of a vertical support bracket.

(i) Draw the given plan.

(ii) Project a sectional elevation on X-X.

(iii) Project an end view looking in the direction of arrow A.

(iv) Insert four leading dimensions and the first-angle projection symbol.

Note: No hidden detail to be shown on the end view and all undimensioned radii are 5 mm.

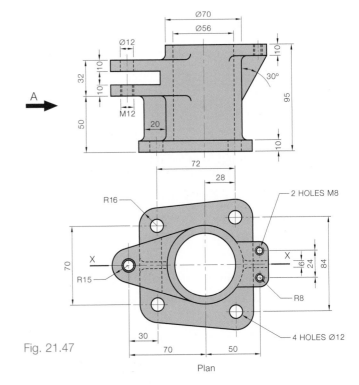

Fig. 21.47

Plan

The ribs are not sectioned even though they are cut by the section plane. Section lines run through the thread symbol. Hidden lines are not shown in the sectional view. The filleted curves are shown in the sectional view.

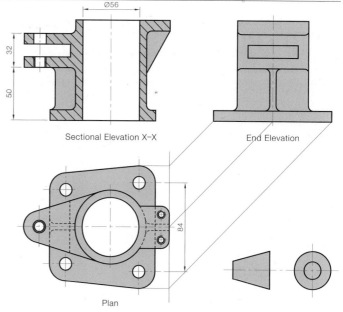

Sectional Elevation X–X   End Elevation

Plan

VERTICAL SUPPORT BRACKET   Fig. 21.48

4	NUT	MS	1
3	WASHER	MS	1
2	PIN	MS	1
1	CRANK	CI	1
REF	DESCRIPTION	MATL	QTY

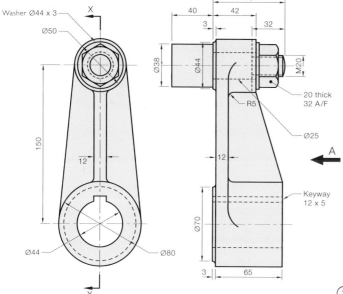

Fig. 21.49

Given the projections of a CRANK AND PIN assembly.

(i)   Draw an elevation looking in the direction of arrow A.

(ii) Draw a sectional end view on X–X.

(iii) Add the parts list, balloon reference the parts and include four main dimensions.

Use first-angle projection.

(1)   The section X–X is to be viewed from the right, so therefore the sectional view is drawn on the left.

(2)   In the sectional view the rib, pin, washer and nut are not sectioned.

(3)   Hidden detail is generally not necessary.

(4)   The keyway is not sectioned.

(5)   Try to keep the leaders for the balloon references parallel and keep the balloon circles in line vertically or horizontally.

(6)   The projection symbol must be drawn.

(7)   The parts list is numbered from bottom to top.

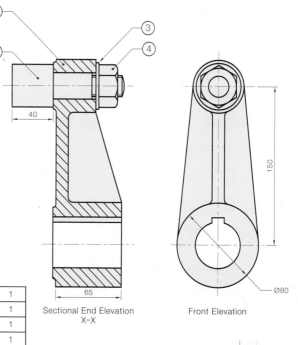

Sectional End Elevation X–X   Front Elevation

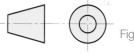

Fig. 21.50

4	NUT	MS	1
3	WASHER	MS	1
2	PIN	MS	1
1	CRANK	CI	1
REF	DESCRIPTION	MATL	QTY
CRANK AND PIN			

Worked Examples: Assemblies

Details of a Pulley Assembly are shown in Figures 21.51a to 21.51d with the parts list tabulated.

(i)   Make a sectional front elevation of the assembled parts on section plane A–A.

(ii)   Project a side elevation in the direction of arrow X.

(iii) Insert the following on the drawing:

○ Title: Pulley Assembly,   ○ ISO projection symbol,   ○ Four leading dimensions.

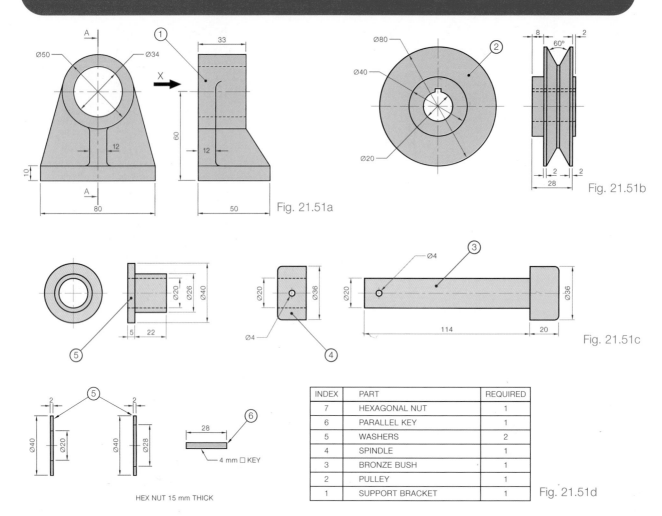

Fig. 21.51a

Fig. 21.51b

Fig. 21.51c

INDEX	PART	REQUIRED
7	HEXAGONAL NUT	1
6	PARALLEL KEY	1
5	WASHERS	2
4	SPINDLE	1
3	BRONZE BUSH	1
2	PULLEY	1
1	SUPPORT BRACKET	1

Fig. 21.51d

HEX NUT 15 mm THICK

4 mm □ KEY

Solution

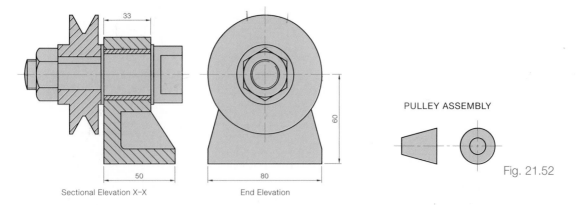

Sectional Elevation X–X

End Elevation

PULLEY ASSEMBLY

Fig. 21.52

Details of a PIVOT SUPPORT are shown in Figures 21.53a to 21.53d with parts list tabulated. Make the following drawings of the assembled parts:

(i)   A sectional elevation in the direction of arrows A–A.
(ii) A sectional end elevation in the direction of arrows X–X.
(iii) A plan projected from the front elevation.

Insert the title PIVOT SUPPORT and the ISO symbol.

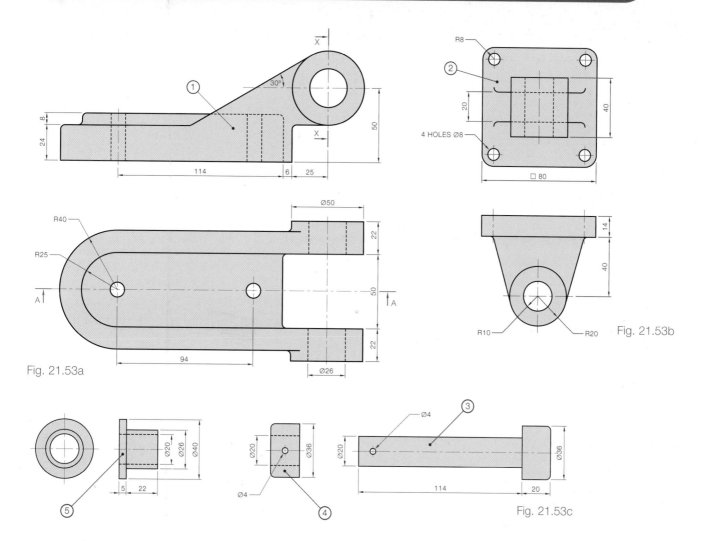

Fig. 21.53a

Fig. 21.53b

Fig. 21.53c

INDEX	PART	REQUIRED
1	BODY CASTING	1
2	SUPPORT CASTING	1
3	PIN	1
4	COLLAR	1
5	BRONZE BUSH	2
6	SPLIT PIN	1

Fig. 21.53d

Solution

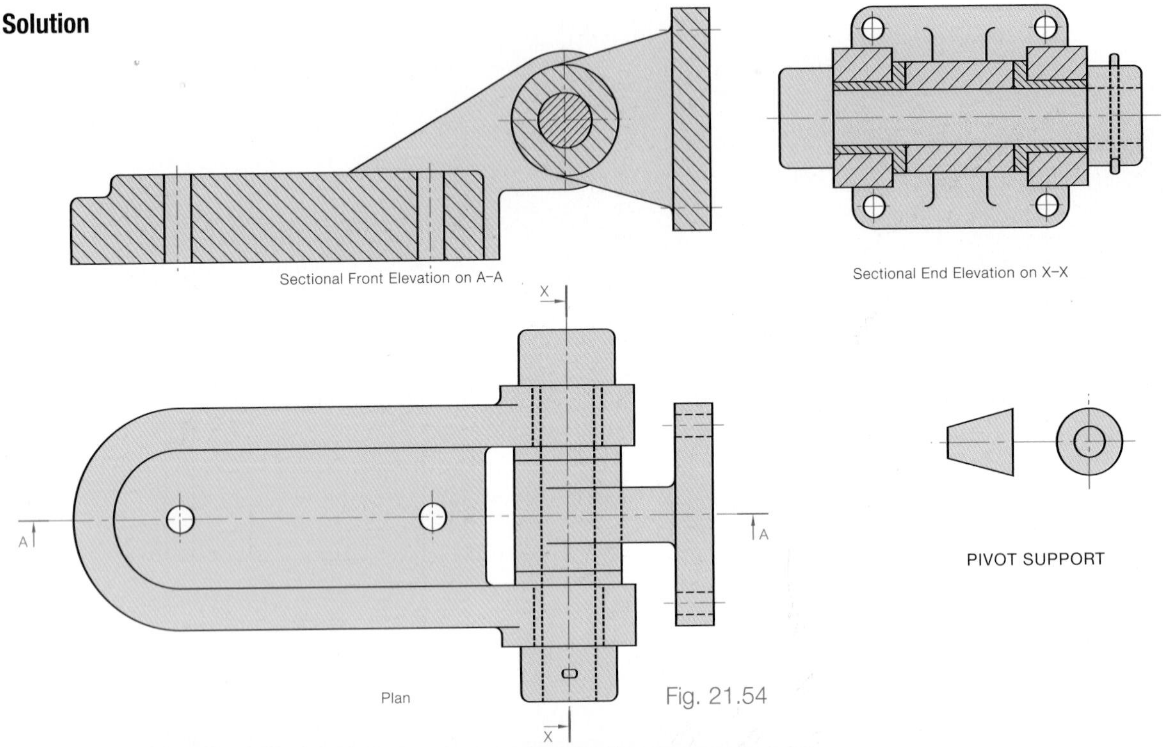

Sectional Front Elevation on A–A

Sectional End Elevation on X–X

PIVOT SUPPORT

Plan

Fig. 21.54

Given the details of a ROCKING ARM in Figures 21.55a to 21.55c with a parts list tabulated. Make the following drawings of the assembled parts with the arm resting on Q:

(i)   Sectional elevation on X–X.

(ii) Sectional plan on A–A.

(iii) An end view in the direction of arrow B.

(iv) Insert leading dimensions, the title and the ISO symbol.

REF	DESCRIPTION	QTY
1	BASE	1
2	ARM	1
3	PIN	1
4	BUSH	1
5	WASHER (Ø44 X 3 thick)	1
6	HEX NUT M22	1

Fig. 21.55a

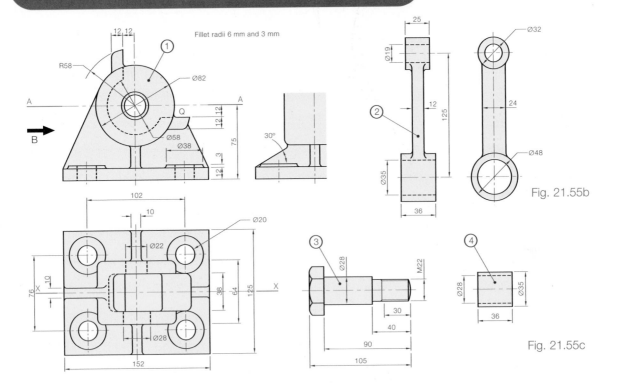

Fig. 21.55b

Fig. 21.55c

Solution

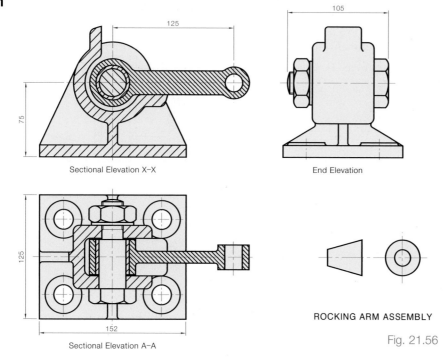

Sectional Elevation X–X

End Elevation

Sectional Elevation A–A

ROCKING ARM ASSEMBLY

Fig. 21.56

Activities

DRAWING TYPES

Q1. Explain the difference between a detail drawing and an assembly drawing.

Q2. Why is it rare to use hidden lines in an assembly drawing?

Q3. List the parts of an assembly that should not be hatched.

Q4. Explain what is meant by the following abbreviations, use diagrams where appropriate:
- A/C • A/F • ASSY • CHAM • CSK • C'BORE • CH HD
- PCD • MATL • RD HD • SQ • U'CUT • FIM • NTS

Q5. make a neat diagram of a typical sheet layout and indicate where the following information would be placed:
- projection symbol, • parts list, • name of assembly, • name of firm,
- drawing number, • date, • scale, • signature.

DIMENSIONS

Q6. Using the data below, make a fully dimensioned drawing of the machine part shown in Fig. 21.57.
1. Diameter 22, length 24.
2. Square 32, length 16.
3. Diameter 54, length 20, chamfer 3 × 3. Diamond knurl finish.
4. Taper: Max. diameter 40, min. diameter 24, length 40.
5. Undercut, length 3, diameter 16.
6. Included angle of 60°.

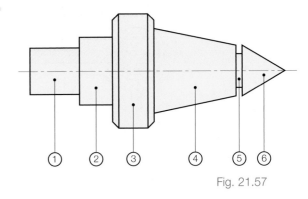

Fig. 21.57

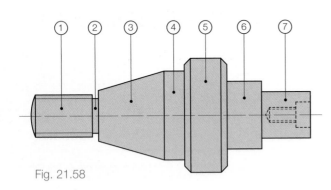

Fig. 21.58

Q7. Using the data below make a fully dimensioned drawing of the shaft shown in Fig. 21.58.
1. Screwthread: metric 20, pitch 2, length 30.
2. Undercut: length 3, diameter 16.
3. Taper: max. diameter 42, min. diameter 24, length 32.
4. Diameter 42, length 10.
5. Diameter 54, length 21, chamfer 3 × 3. Diamond knurl finish.
6. Diameter 32, length 17.
7. Square 22, length 24, hole threaded M7, 20 deep, counter-bored diameter 12, 7 deep.

Q8. Using the data given below make a fully dimensioned drawing of the machined part shown in Fig. 21.59.
1. Screw thread: M25, pitch 2, length 50 mm.
2. Undercut: length 4 mm, diameter 20 mm.
3. Taper: length 80 mm, min. diameter 28 mm, max. diameter 50 mm, woodruff keyway Ø30 depth and 6 mm × 3 mm wide.
4. Shaft: diameter 50 mm, length 100 mm, fillet radius 7 mm.
5. Flange: length 20 mm, diameter 120 mm, recess 10 mm deep and 40 mm A/F hexagonal.

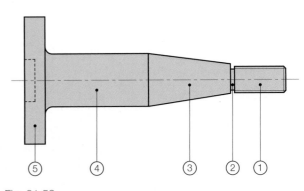

Fig. 21.59

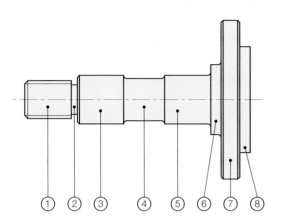

Fig. 21.60

Q9. Fig. 21.60 shows a stub axle. Using the data below draw an elevation and end view. Fully dimension the views.

1. Screwthread: M36, pitch 3, length 45.
2. Undercut: 4 mm deep × 6 mm long.
3. Diameter: 46 mm × 45 mm long, chamfer 2 mm × 45°.
4. Diameter: 40 mm × 40 mm long, fillet radius 3 mm.
5. Diameter: 46 mm × 45 mm long, fillet radii 3 mm.
6. Diameter: 66 mm × 10 mm long, fillet radii 3 mm.
7. Flange diameter 150 mm, thickness 18 mm, chamfer 2 mm × 45°, 6 × diameter 10 mm holes on 122 mm PCD.
8. Spigot diameter 100 mm × 10 mm long.

SECTIONAL VIEWS

Q10. A front elevation and plan of a casting are shown in Fig. 21.61.

(i)   Draw a sectional elevation on plane B–B.
(ii) Draw a sectional plan on plane A–A.
(iii) An end view showing all hidden detail.
(iv) Insert five leading dimensions, the first-angle projection symbol and the title 'GATE SUPPORT'.

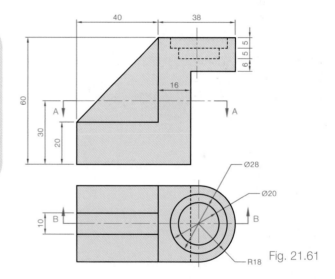

Fig. 21.61

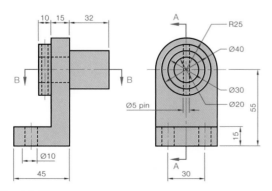

Fig. 21.62

Q11. A front elevation and end view of a ring, a shaft, a pin and a bracket.

(i)   Draw a sectional elevation on A–A.
(ii) Draw a sectional plan on B–B.
(iii) Insert four leading dimensions, the projection symbol and the title 'SHAFT SUPPORT BRACKET'.

Q12. The object shown in Fig. 21.63 is to have a 30 mm long M12 HEX HD bolt inserted in the top.

(i) Draw the given plan and elevation with the bolt included and inserted 15 mm into the threaded hole.

(ii) Draw a sectional end elevation on plane A–A.

(iii) Insert four leading dimensions, the projection symbol and the title 'BASE PLATE AND UPRIGHT'.

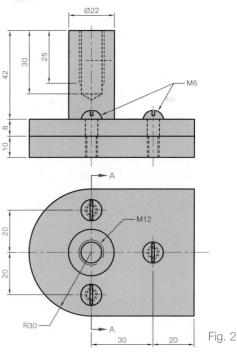

Fig. 21.63

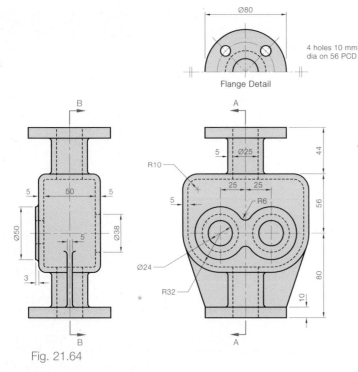

Flange Detail

4 holes 10 mm dia on 56 PCD

Fig. 21.64

Q13. Shown in Fig. 21.64 is a pump body casing.

(i) Draw a sectional end elevation on A–A.

(ii) Draw a sectional front elevation on B–B.

(iii) Draw a full plan projected from (ii).

(iv) Insert five leading dimensions, the ISO projection symbol and the title 'PUMP BODY'.

Q14. Details of a pulley assembly are given in Fig. 21.65a. The parts list is tabulated.

(1) Make the following drawings of the assembled parts:

    (i) A sectional front elevation on section plane A–A.

    (ii) A full plan projected from the front elevation.

    (iii) An end elevation in the direction of arrow B.

(2) Insert the following on the drawing:

    (i) Title: 'PULLEY ASSEMBLY'.

    (ii) ISO projection symbol.

    (iii) Five leading dimensions.

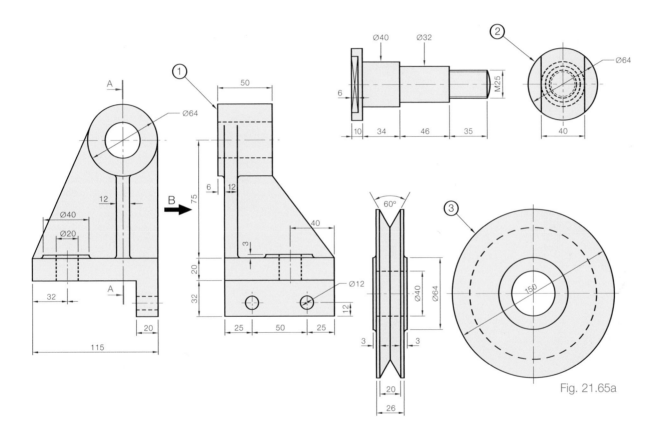

Fig. 21.65a

Index	Part	Required
1	Support Bracket	1
2	Shaft	1
3	Pulley	1
	Hex Nut M25	1
	Washer Ext Ø64, Int Ø42 1.5 mm thick	1
	Washer Ext Ø64, Int Ø28 2 mm thick	1

Fig. 21.65b

Q15. Details of a clamping device are shown in Fig. 21.66a. The parts list is tabulated.

(1)   Make the following drawings of the assembled parts:

   (i)   A sectional front elevation on section plane A–A.

   (ii) A full plan.

The movable jaw should be shown in the mid-position.

(2)   Insert the following on the drawing:

   (i)   Title: 'CLAMPING DEVICE'.

   (ii) ISO projection symbol.

   (iii) Five leading dimensions.

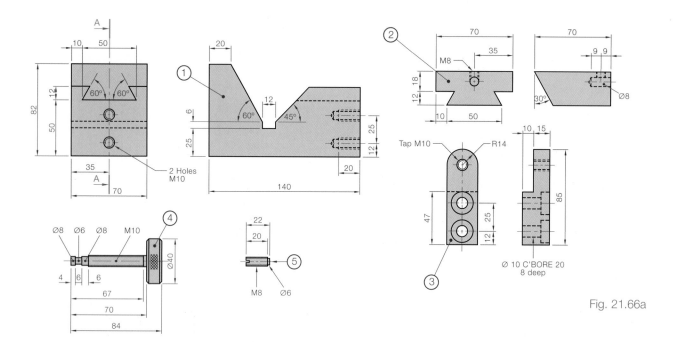

Fig. 21.66a

Index	Part	Quantity
1	Base	1
2	Sliding Jaw	1
3	End Plate	1
4	Clamping Screw	1
5	Grub Screw	1
6	Cheese Head Screw	2
	M10 x 35 mm long	

Fig. 21.66b

Q16. Details of a pulley hook assembly are shown in Fig. 21.67a. The parts list is tabulated.

(1) Make the following drawings of the assembled parts:

   (i) A front elevation viewed in the direction of arrow A.

   (ii) A sectional side elevation on section plane B–B.

(2) Insert the following on the drawing:

   (i) Title: 'PULLEY AND HOOK ASSEMBLY'.

   (ii) ISO projection symbol.

   (iii) Four leading dimensions.

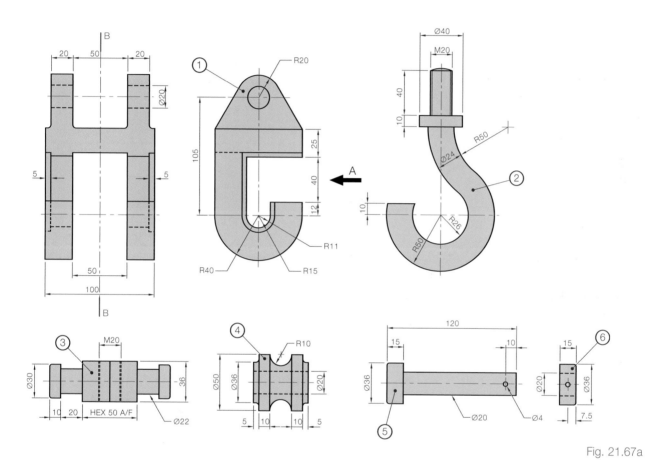

Fig. 21.67a

Index	Part	Quantity
1	Bracket	1
2	Hook	1
3	Trunnion	1
4	Pulley	1
5	Pin	1
6	Collar	1
7	Split Pin	1

Fig. 21.67b

Q17. Details of a universal joint are shown in Fig. 21.68a. The parts list is tabulated.

(1) Make the following drawings of the assembled parts.

    (i) A sectional front elevation on section plane A–A.

    (ii) An end elevation viewed in the direction of arrow B.

(2) Insert the following on the drawing:

    (i) Title: 'UNIVERSAL JOINT'.

    (ii) ISO projection symbol.

    (iii) Four leading dimensions.

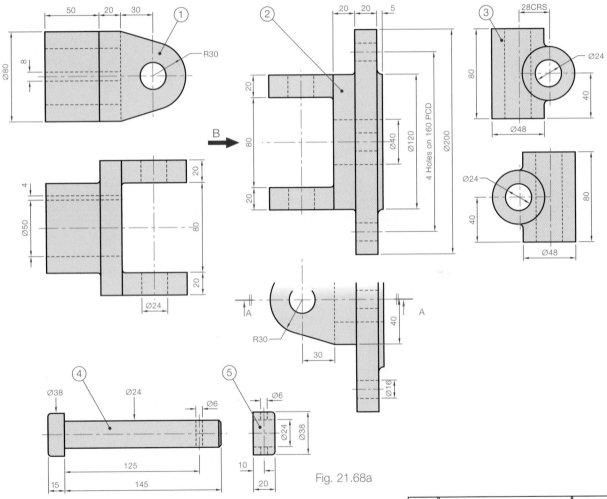

Fig. 21.68a

Index	Part	Required
1	Fork	1
2	Flange	1
3	Centre	1
4	Pin	2
5	Collar	2
6	Split Pin	2

Fig. 21.68b

Sectional Views: More Alternatives

For all the examples shown in the previous pages, single-plane sectional views have been used. There are several other useful methods of finding sectional views which we will now examine more closely.

Half Sections

These can be very useful for symmetrical objects. The cutting plane removes one quarter of the object and shows the interior of one half of the object and the exterior of the other half. The half section is at its most useful in assembly drawings where it is possible to show an internal assembly and an external construction on the same view.

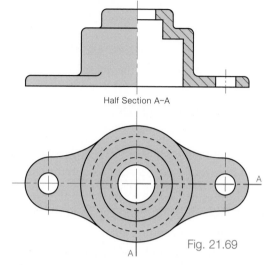

Half Section A–A

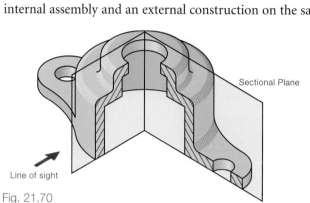

Sectional Plane

Line of sight

Fig. 21.70

Fig. 21.69

It can be seen from the pictorial, Fig. 21.70, that the section plane removes one quarter of the object. Half sections will often present difficulty when dimensioning and for this reason hidden lines are often included in the unsectioned half.

Broken-out Sections

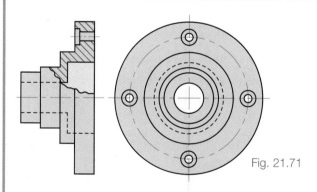

Fig. 21.71

A broken-out section is used when only a small area of the object(s) needs to be sectioned in order to explain the construction. A full section or even a half section are not necessary. The edges of a broken-out section are limited by a break line. Fig. 21.71 shows an example of a broken-out section.

Successive Sections

When an object such as a bar, spoke or arm changes shape along its longitudinal axis, this change can be shown by using successive sections as shown in Fig. 21.72.

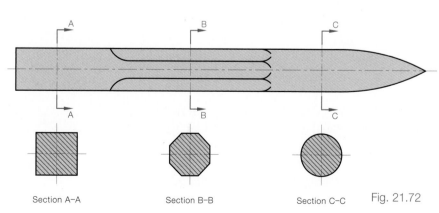

Section A–A   Section B–B   Section C–C   Fig. 21.72

Revolved Sections

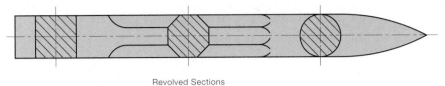

Revolved Sections

Fig. 21.73

Revolved sections show the shape of the cross-section on the actual view of the part. Such sections are made by assuming a plane perpendicular to the centre line or axis and then revolving the plane through 90° about a centre line so that the true shape of the section can be seen. The section is actually superimposed on the object and all original lines covered by it should be removed.

Offset Sections

When sectioning irregular objects it is possible to show several features in section even though they do not lie in a straight line. The cutting plane is bent or offset to pass through each of the features. The sectional view produced is called an offset section. Fig. 21.74 shows an example of an offset section. It can be seen that the cutting plane in elevation is bent twice at 90° in order to pass through the centres of the two holes, one of which can be seen in elevation and the other in plan. **The bends or offsets in the cutting plane are never shown in the sectional view.**

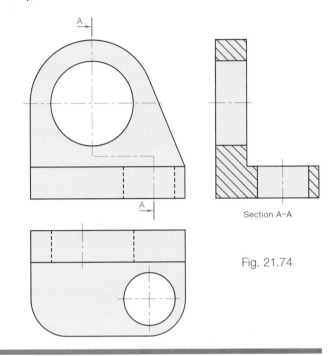

Section A–A

Fig. 21.74

Aligned Sections

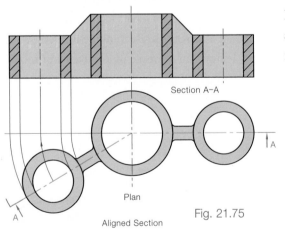

Section A–A

Plan

Aligned Section

Fig. 21.75

In an aligned section, the cutting plane is bent to pass through an angled element. The plane and section are then imagined to be revolved to align with the main direction of the cut. Fig. 21.75 shows cutting plane A–A bent to pass through the angled arm, and then rotated to a horizontal position where it is projected to the sectional elevation.

Fig. 21.76 shows a second example of an aligned section. The cutting plane is bent to include one of the drilled

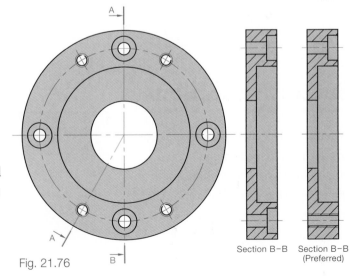

Section B–B

Section B–B
(Preferred)

Fig. 21.76

and counter-bored holes and one of the threaded holes. The aligned section A–A produces a much more informative view than does section A–B which is a vertical section taken along the centre line.

For all aligned sections the angle of revolution should always be less than 90°.

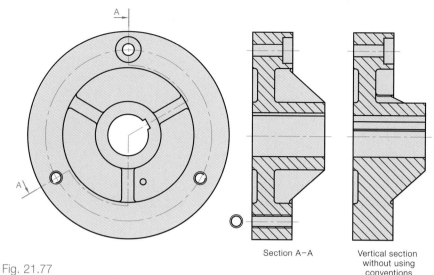

Fig. 21.77

Section A–A

Vertical section
without using
conventions

Another example of an aligned section is shown in Fig. 21.77. The cutting plane is offset in circular arc bends to include the upper counter-bored hole, the upper rib, the keyway, the centre hole, the lower rib and one of the lower threaded holes. These features are imagined to be revolved to line up vertically and then projected to give the section. It is now worth looking at the second section drawn in Fig. 21.77. This is a vertical section through the centre without using conventions, e.g. the rib is hatched. This section is less informative, confusing and takes longer to draw.

Worked Examples: Sectional Views

Figures 21.78a and 21.78b shows two views of a gear housing in third-angle projection.

(1) Make the following drawings in third-angle projection:

   (i) A sectional elevation on the cutting plane X–X.

   (ii) A sectional elevation on the cutting plane Y–Y.

   (iii) A sectional plan on cutting plane Z–Z.

Hidden details need not be shown.

(2) Insert the following on the drawing:

   (i) Title 'GEAR HOUSING'.

   (ii) ISO projection symbol.

   (iii) Four leading dimensions.

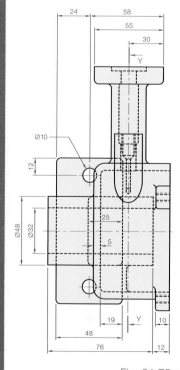

Fig. 21.78a

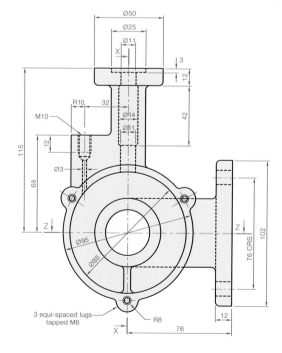

Fig. 21.78b

Solution

GEAR HOUSING

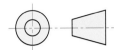

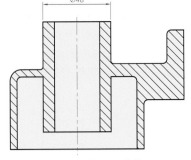

Sectional Elevation Z–Z

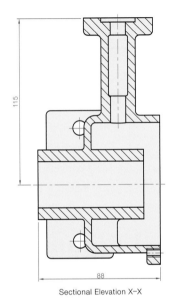

Sectional Elevation X–X

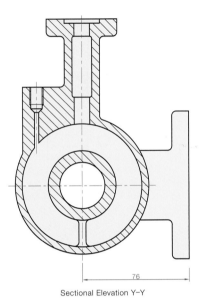

Sectional Elevation Y–Y

Fig. 21.79

Figures 21.80a and 21.80b show two elevations of a distribution casting. Draw the following views of the distribution casting in first- or third-angle projection:

(1) A front elevation by viewing the given front elevation in the direction of arrow A.

(2) A sectional plan view, through B–B, projected from the front elevation.

(3) Insert the following on the drawing:

   (i)   Title 'DISTRIBUTION CASTING'.

   (ii) ISO projection symbol.

   (iii) Four leading dimensions.

PROJECTION

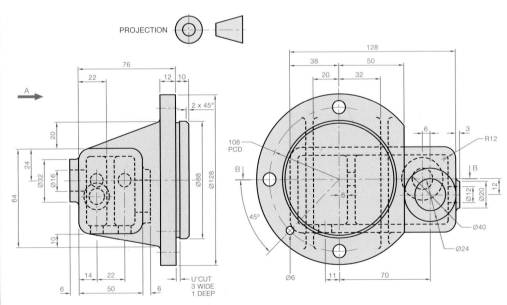

Fig. 21.80a

ALL HOLES Ø10 UNLESS STATED OTHERWISE
ALL WALLS AND WEBS 6 THICK
FILLET RADII R3

Fig. 21.80b

Solution

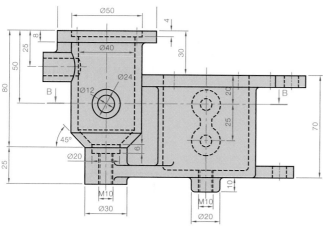

Front Elevation

Ø128

B | | B

DISTRIBUTION CASTING

PROJECTION

Ø88

50

128

Fig. 21.81

Sectional Plan B–B

HIGHER LEVEL

Ø50

4

8

25

Ø40

50

30

80

Ø24

B | | B

Ø12

45°

25

20

25

70

Ø20

6

M10

Ø30

M10

Ø20

10

ALL WALL THICKNESSES 5 mm

ALL WEB THICKNESSES 8 mm

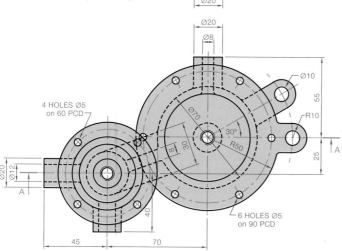

Ø20

Ø8

Ø10

4 HOLES Ø5
on 60 PCD

55

R10

Ø70

30°

Ø20

Ø12

A | | A

R50

30

40

25

6 HOLES Ø5
on 90 PCD

45

70

Fig. 21.82

Fig. 21.82 shows the plan
and elevation of a carburettor
body.

(1) Draw the following views
of the carburettor in first-
or third-angle projection:

  (i) A sectional elevation
  on A–A.

  (ii) A sectional plan on
  B–B.

(2) Insert the following on the
drawing:

  (i) Title 'CARBURETTOR
  BODY'.

  (ii) ISO projection symbol.

  (iii) Cutting and titles on
  sectional views.

  (iv) Four leading
  dimensions.

  Hidden details are not
  required.

Solution

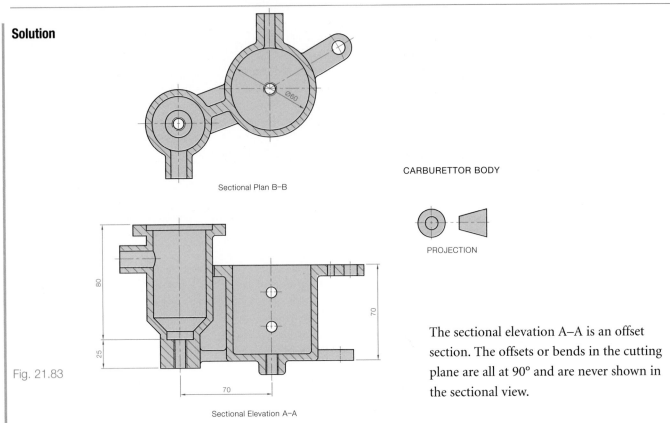

Sectional Plan B–B

CARBURETTOR BODY

PROJECTION

Fig. 21.83

Sectional Elevation A–A

The sectional elevation A–A is an offset section. The offsets or bends in the cutting plane are all at 90° and are never shown in the sectional view.

Pictorial Drawings of Sectioned Objects

It is often helpful in the representation of an object to draw the sectioned object in pictorial. Isometric projection is the most usual projection method used.

Worked Examples

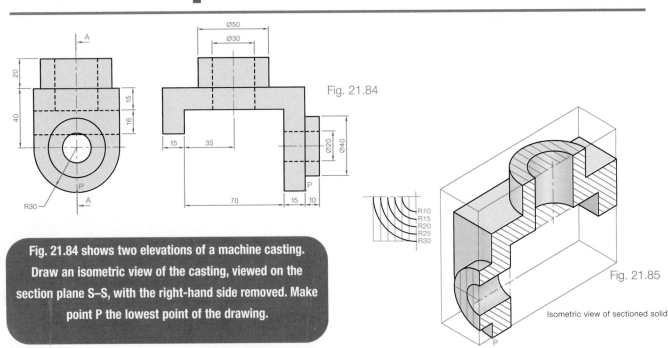

Fig. 21.84

Fig. 21.84 shows two elevations of a machine casting. Draw an isometric view of the casting, viewed on the section plane S–S, with the right-hand side removed. Make point P the lowest point of the drawing.

Fig. 21.85

Isometric view of sectioned solid

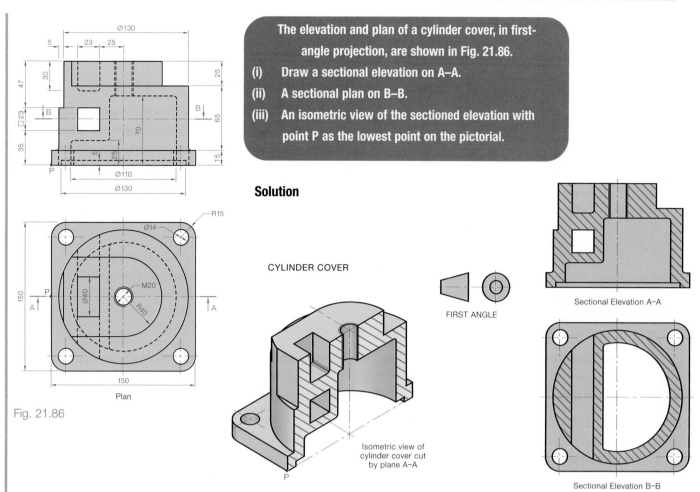

The elevation and plan of a cylinder cover, in first-angle projection, are shown in Fig. 21.86.

(i)   Draw a sectional elevation on A–A.

(ii) A sectional plan on B–B.

(iii) An isometric view of the sectioned elevation with point P as the lowest point on the pictorial.

Solution

CYLINDER COVER

FIRST ANGLE

Isometric view of cylinder cover cut by plane A–A

Sectional Elevation A–A

Sectional Elevation B–B

Fig. 21.87

Fig. 21.86

Plan

Surface Finish

Accurate control of surface quality and finish is often necessary. Engine parts, for instance, that have been accurately machined will produce less friction and less wear and will therefore last longer. The quality of finish specified must be related to the function of the surface because as the quality of finish becomes finer the cost of producing that finish increases. If the surface finish is unimportant then it should not be specified. The ideal finish is the roughest one that will do the job properly.

Fig. 21.88 shows the proportions of the standard symbol used to show finish type and quality. Fig. 21.89 gives the key to the information layout.

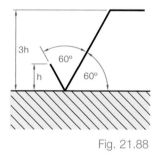

Fig. 21.88

A Roughness value
B Method of treatment
C Direction of lay
D Sampling length
E Machining allowance

Fig. 21.89

A. Roughness Value

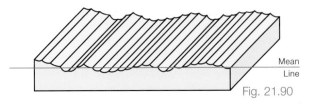

Fig. 21.90

Mean Line

This value indicates the average roughness of the surface. Even the smoothest of machined surfaces when examined under large magnification will show a series of ridges and troughs left behind by tool marks. The roughness value is calculated as the average amount of deviation of these peaks and valleys from a mean line.

Roughness is measured in microns (μm) or by a roughness number (N).

1 micron = μm = 0.0001 mm

Microns	0.025	0.05	0.1	0.2	0.4	0.8	1.6	etc
Roughness No.	N1	N2	N3	N4	N5	N6	N7	etc

Fig. 21.91

The roughness of a surface in microns and the roughness number are related as shown in the table in Fig. 21.91.

B. Method of Treatment

This refers to the method of treatment used to produce the surface finish. There are many shop processes that could be listed here, including:

(1) Sawing,
(2) Planing,
(3) Drilling,
(4) Chemical milling,

(5) Milling,
(6) Reaming,
(7) Roller burnishing,
(8) Grinding,

(9) Honing,
(10) Polishing,
(11) Lapping,
(12) Hot rolling,

(13) Forging,
(14) Extruding,
(15) Cold rolling,
(16) Die casting.

C. Direction of Lay

This indicates the direction or directions in which the finish is laid down when machining. These are indicated in Fig. 21.92.

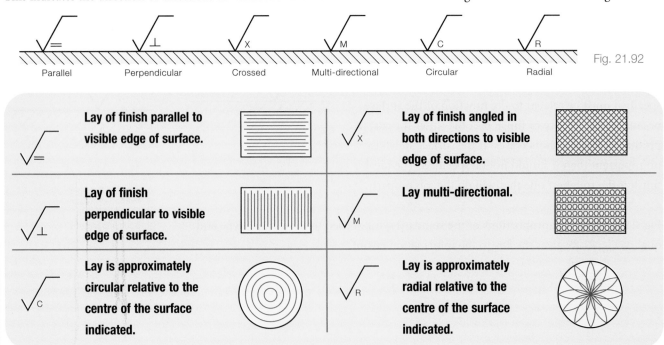

Fig. 21.92

Parallel | Perpendicular | Crossed | Multi-directional | Circular | Radial

	Lay of finish parallel to visible edge of surface.			Lay of finish angled in both directions to visible edge of surface.	
	Lay of finish perpendicular to visible edge of surface.			Lay multi-directional.	
	Lay is approximately circular relative to the centre of the surface indicated.			Lay is approximately radial relative to the centre of the surface indicated.	

Fig. 21.93

D. Sampling Length

This value is not usually necessary. It indicates the maximum allowed spacing between repetitive units of the surface pattern.

E. Machining Allowance

This is another value that is not usually necessary. It gives the amount that is to be removed from a stock or standard size.

Symbol Options

There are three symbol options shown in Fig. 21.94 which further specify the surface finish.
(1) Machined finish.
(2) Machined finish or any other finishing method may be used.
(3) Machining is not to be done. Another method of finishing must be used.

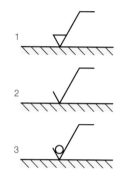

Fig. 21.94

Examples

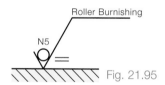

Fig. 21.95

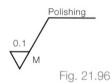

Fig. 21.96

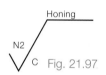

Fig. 21.97

A roller-burnished finish is to be laid parallel to the plane indicated to a roughness number of N5 (0.4 microns).

A polished finish layed down multi-directionally to a roughness value of $0.1\,\mu m$ (microns).

A honed finish layed down in a circular pattern to a roughness value of N2, 0.05 microns.

Note:
(1) When indicating surface characteristics, it is important that only those numbers which are required to specify the surface adequately for the function should be included in the symbol.
(2) The symbol is always made in the standard upright position.
(3) The symbol is never drawn at an angle or upside down. Fig. 21.98 shows examples.

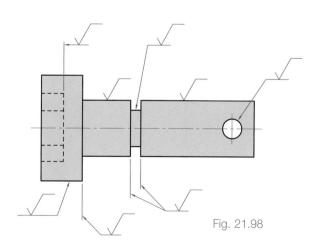

Fig. 21.98

HIGHER LEVEL

Methods of Assembly

There are many methods used to join elements of an assembly, ranging from bolts, screws and studs, rivets, folded seams and welded joints. We will look at each of these areas in a little more detail.

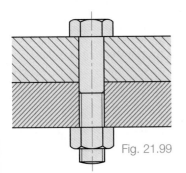

Fig. 21.99

Bolts

The term 'bolt' usually refers to a through bolt which passes through clearance holes in two or more pieces and receives a nut to tighten and hold the parts together. The head and nut are usually hexagonal but may be square.

Cap Screws

Cap screws usually pass through a clearance hole in one member and screw into another which acts as the nut. A cap screw generally has a greater length of thread than a bolt. There are a large range of head types on cap screws as shown in Figures 21.100a to 21.100i.

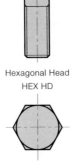

Hexagonal Head
HEX HD

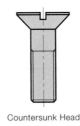

Countersunk Head
CSK HD

Pan Head
PAN HD

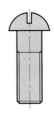

Round Head
RD HD

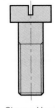

Cheese Head
CH HD

Fig. 21.100a

Fig. 21.100b

Fig. 21.100c

Fig. 21.100d

Fig. 21.100e

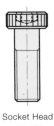

Socket Head
ALLEN

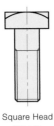

Square Head
SQ HD

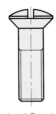

Round and Countersunk
RD CSK HD

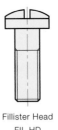

Fillister Head
FIL HD

Fig. 21.100f

Fig. 21.100g

Fig. 21.100h

Fig. 21.100i

Most of the heads of the cap screws have been shown with slots to receive a flat head screwdriver. They are also produced to accommodate other types of screwdrivers.

Stud

A stud is a steel rod which has been threaded on both ends. The stud is usually passed through a clearance hole in one member and screwed into the other member. A nut is then tightened onto the free end as shown in Fig. 21.101. The end of the stud may have a slot or an Allen key socket to aid in its insertion into the threaded hole.

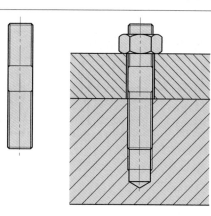

Fig. 21.101

Machine Screws

Machine screws are similar to cap screws but are much smaller. They are threaded nearly to the head and are very useful for screwing into thin material.

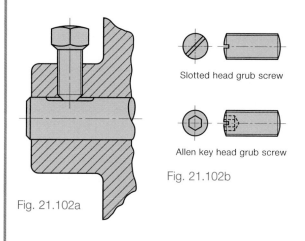

Fig. 21.102a

Slotted head grub screw

Allen key head grub screw

Fig. 21.102b

Set Screws

A set screw is used to prevent relative motion between two parts. Their most common use is to secure pulleys etc. onto their axle shafts. The set screw is screwed into one part and its point puts pressure on the other part. If a little flat area is milled onto the shaft where the set screw is to make contact with it, then a much stronger fixing is achieved. Set screws are not able to cope with heavy loads or loads that are applied suddenly. Figures 21.102a to 21.102c shows a number of set screws and some possible variations in the tip shape.

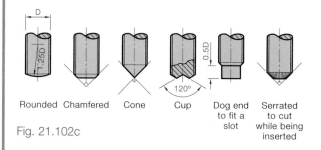

Rounded Chamfered Cone Cup Dog end to fit a slot Serrated to cut while being inserted

Fig. 21.102c

Lock Nuts and Locking Devices

There are many special nuts and devices to ensure that nuts do not work loose due to vibration during their working life. Some of the more common types are shown below in Figures 21.103a to 21.103h.

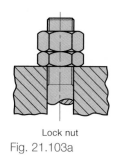

Lock nut
Fig. 21.103a

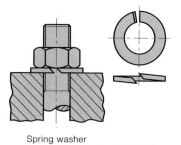

Spring washer

Fig. 21.103b

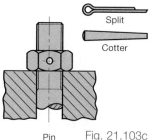

Split

Cotter

Pin   Fig. 21.103c

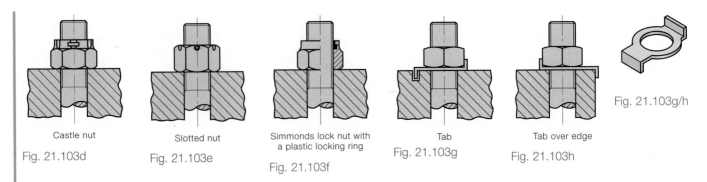

Castle nut
Fig. 21.103d

Slotted nut
Fig. 21.103e

Simmonds lock nut with
a plastic locking ring
Fig. 21.103f

Tab
Fig. 21.103g

Tab over edge
Fig. 21.103h

Fig. 21.103g/h

Rivets

Rivets are seen as a permanent method of joining sheet metal and rolled steel together. They are made from wrought iron, soft steel, copper, brass and occasionally other metals. Each rivet has one pre-formed head, the second head is formed using a hammer and a 'dolly bar' or by machine. The process of forming the second head compresses the shank of the rivet, pushing it against the sides of the hole. A number of different rivet heads are shown in Figures 21.104a to 21.104f.

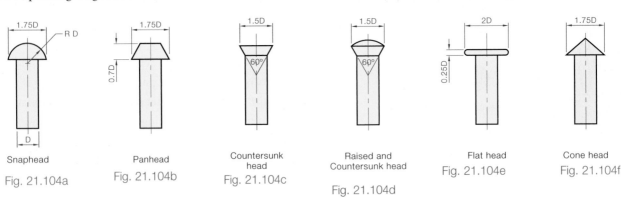

Snaphead
Fig. 21.104a

Panhead
Fig. 21.104b

Countersunk
head
Fig. 21.104c

Raised and
Countersunk head
Fig. 21.104d

Flat head
Fig. 21.104e

Cone head
Fig. 21.104f

When riveting, it is important to space the holes for the rivets carefully. If the holes are too far apart there will not be enough rivets to give the joint strength, while if they are too close together the amount of holes being drilled weakens the joint. Figures 21.105a to 21.105e shows some typical rivet layouts.

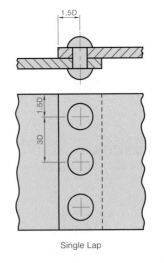

Single Lap

Fig. 21.105a

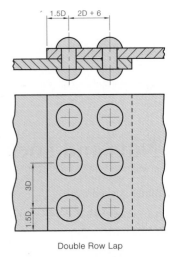

Double Row Lap

Fig. 21.105b

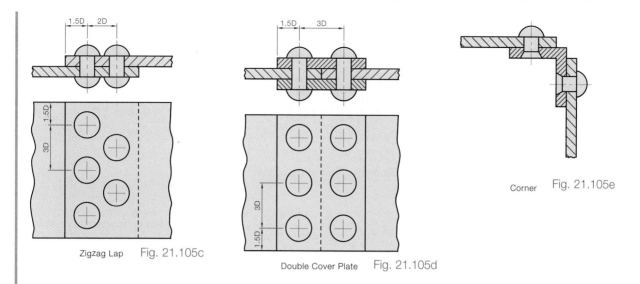

Corner   Fig. 21.105e

ZigZag Lap   Fig. 21.105c

Double Cover Plate   Fig. 21.105d

Welding

Welding is a method of joining metals by using heat to melt and fuse them together. A filler metal is usually necessary to fill the joint. Because of the range of welded joints, a system of symbols are used to display the complete welding information on a drawing in a simple and clear manner, see Fig. 21.106.

A: Joint – the joint is shown as a butt joint regardless of the type of weld joint to be used.

B: Arrow – indicates joint line.

C: Reference line.

D: Weld symbol.

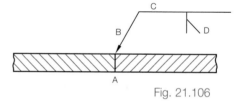

Fig. 21.106

Each of these symbols are shown below in Figures 21.107 and 21.108.

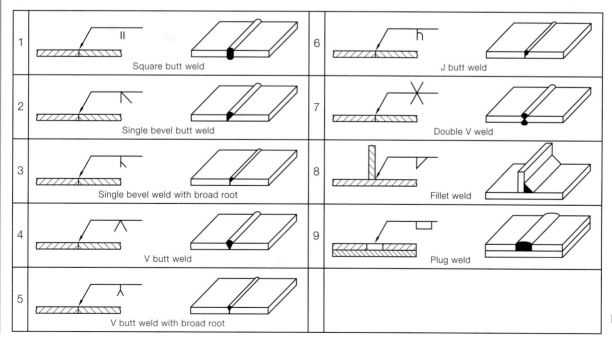

1   Square butt weld
2   Single bevel butt weld
3   Single bevel weld with broad root
4   V butt weld
5   V butt weld with broad root
6   J butt weld
7   Double V weld
8   Fillet weld
9   Plug weld

Fig. 21.107

HIGHER LEVEL

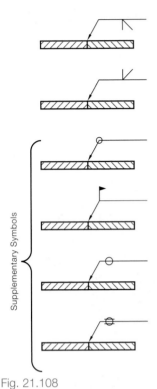

Supplementary Symbols

Weld this side. When the symbol is below the reference line the weld is to be placed where the arrow indicates.

Weld the far side. When the symbol is above the reference line the weld is to be placed on the far side of the joint that the arrow indicates.

Weld all round, e.g. welding of cylinders, pipes etc.

Weld on site.

Spot weld.

Seam weld.

Supplementary symbols are used with the main welding symbol to give additional information.

Fig. 21.108

Activities

OFFSET SECTIONS

Q1.

(i)   Draw the given elevations of the machined block as shown in Fig. 21.109.

(ii) Project an offset sectional plan A–A from the elevation.

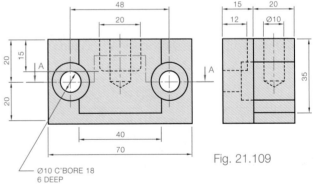

Ø10 C'BORE 18
6 DEEP

Fig. 21.109

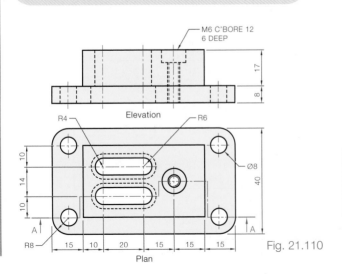

M6 C'BORE 12
6 DEEP

Elevation

R4   R6

Ø8

R8   15 10   20   15   15   15

Plan

Q2. Given the plan and elevation of a shaped block in Fig. 21.110.

(i)   Draw the given plan.

(ii) Project the offset section on section plane A–A.

Fig. 21.110

ALIGNED SECTIONS

Q3. and Q4.

In Figures 21.111 and 21.112 you are given the plan and elevation of a shaped block.

(i) Draw the given views.

(ii) Project an aligned end view on plane A–A.

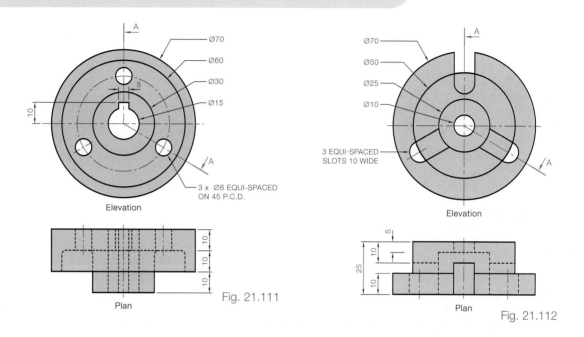

Fig. 21.111

Fig. 21.112

Q5. and Q6.

In Figures 21.113 and 21.114 the plan and elevation of a shaped block are given in first-angle projection.

(i) Draw the given views in **third-angle** projection.

(ii) Project an aligned end view on plane A–A.

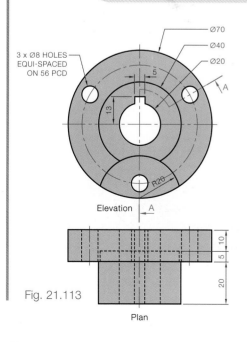

Fig. 21.113

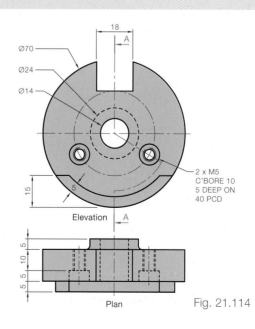

Fig. 21.114

HALF SECTIONS

Q7. and Q8.

In Figures 21.115 and 21.116 the plan and elevation of a shaped block are given.

(i)   Draw the given views.

(ii) Project a half-sectional end view on cutting plane B–B.

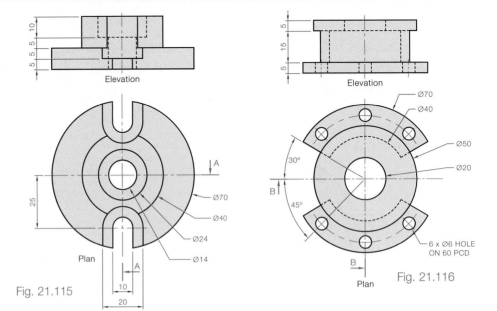

Elevation

Plan

Fig. 21.115

Ø70
Ø40
Ø24
Ø14

Ø70
Ø40
Ø50
Ø20
30°
45°
6 x Ø6 HOLE ON 60 PCD

Fig. 21.116

SECTIONS

Q9. The plan and elevation of a valve casting are shown in Fig. 21.117.

(i)   Draw the given elevation.

(ii)   Project a sectional end view on plane A–A.

(iii) Insert:
  • ISO symbol, • six leading dimensions, • the title 'VALVE CASTING'.

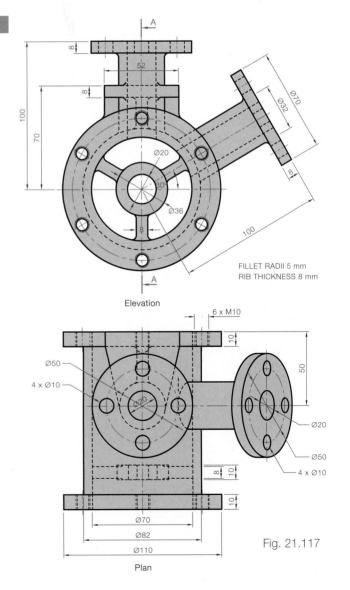

Elevation

FILLET RADII 5 mm
RIB THICKNESS 8 mm

Ø70
Ø32
Ø20
Ø36

6 x M10
Ø50
4 x Ø10
Ø20
Ø20
Ø50
4 x Ø10
Ø70
Ø82
Ø110

Plan

Fig. 21.117

Q10. The front elevation and side elevation of a Coupling Block are shown in Fig. 21.118.

(i)   Draw a sectional elevation A–A of the block.

(ii) Draw a sectional elevation B–B of the block.

(iii) Insert the following on the drawing:
   • Six leading dimensions.   • ISO projection symbol.   • Title 'COUPLING BLOCK'.   • Symbol to indicate that the top surface S must be machined on a milling machine to a surface texture N7.   • Symbol to indicate that the side surface T must be honed to a surface texture N4 with a multi-directional lay.

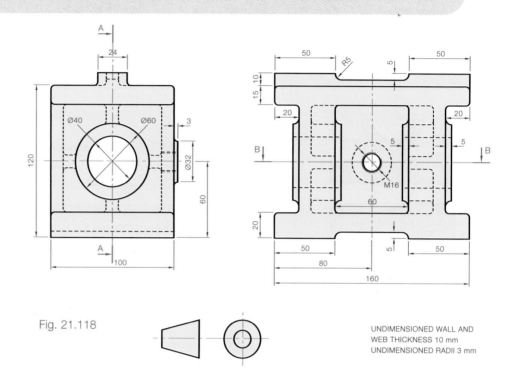

Fig. 21.118

UNDIMENSIONED WALL AND
WEB THICKNESS 10 mm
UNDIMENSIONED RADII 3 mm

SECTIONED VIEWS IN PICTORIAL

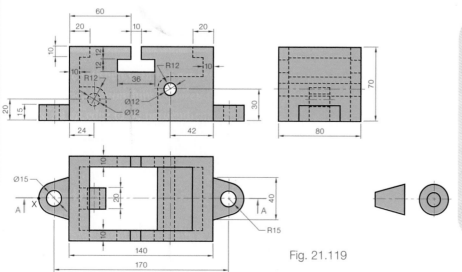

Fig. 21.119

Q11. Fig. 21.119 shows three views of an anchor block.

(i)   Draw a sectional elevation on cutting plane A–A.

(ii) Draw the full plan.

(iii) Draw an isometric view of half the block on section plane A–A and having X as the lowest point on the drawing.

Q12. Given two elevations of a vehicle rear hub.

(i) Draw the given front elevation.

(ii) Project a half section on cutting plane AAA.

(iii) Draw an isometric view of the half section showing a good view of the cut-out section.

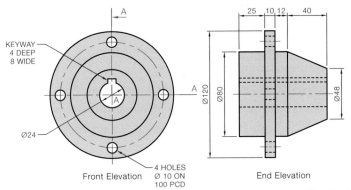

Fig. 21.120

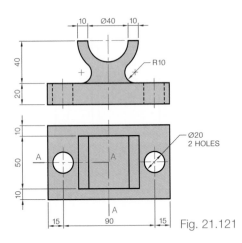

Fig. 21.121

Q13. Fig. 21.121 shows a guide shoe.

(i) Draw the given plan and project a half-sectional elevation on AAA.

(ii) Draw an isometric view of the shoe with the quadrant removed showing a good view of the cut surfaces.

Q14. The plan and elevation of a machine casting are shown in Fig. 21.122.

(i) Draw the sectional elevation AB_1 of the casting. The inclined portion of the cutting plane may be revolved onto the plane of projection.

(ii) Draw an isometric view of the half of the casting cut on the section plane BB_1.

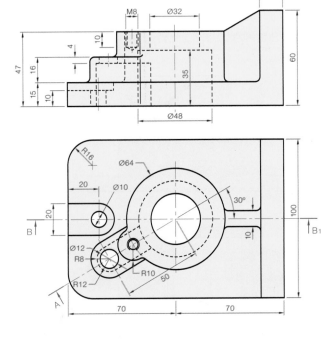

Fig. 21.122

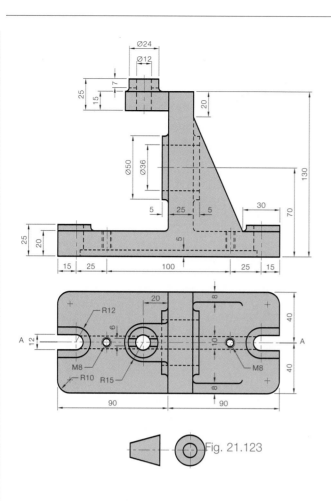

Fig. 21.123

Q15. The plan and elevation of a machine casting is shown in Fig. 21.123.

(i) Draw the given plan and project a sectional elevation on cutting plane A–A.

(ii) Draw an isometric view of half of the casting, cut on the section plane.

SURFACE FINISHES

Q16. Draw a standard symbol used to show finish type and quality. Indicate on the symbol where the five categories of information are put:

- Machining allowance.
- Direction of lay.
- Method of treatment.
- Sampling length.
- Roughness value.

Q17. Explain the following three terms:

- Roughness value.
- Direction of lay.
- Method of treatment.

Q18. For each of the following finishes, draw the correct symbol.

(i) A sawn finish, laid perpendicular to the plane indicated, to a roughness number of N9.

(ii) A milled finish, laid radially to the plane indicated, to a roughness number of N6.

(iii) A polished finish, laid multi-directionally, to a roughness number of N3.

(iv) A die cast finish to a roughness of 3.2 microns.

(v) A planed finish, laid parallel to the plane indicated, to a roughness number of N10.

FASTENING DEVICES

HIGHER LEVEL

Q19. Using notes and diagrams explain the difference in appearance and use of:
* bolts,
* cap screws,
* set screws.

Q20. Make neat diagrams (plan and elevation) of the following cap screws:
* Countersunk head (CSK HD).
* Round head (RD HD).
* Fillister head (FIL HD).
* Cheese head (CH HD).

Q21. Make a neat diagram of four different methods of locking a nut to ensure it does not accidentally work loose.

Q22. Make a neat diagram of the following rivet types:
* Pan head.
* Countersunk head.
* Snap head.

Q23. 'If you want a strong joint you put in more rivets.' Is this statement always true? Give reasons for your answer.

Q24. Make a neat diagram of a welding symbol and indicate on the symbol the important parts.

Q25. Draw weld symbols for each of the following:
(i)   Single bevel weld with broad root, weld on arrow side.
(ii)   Fillet weld on far side, weld on site.
(iii) Seam weld, double V weld.
(iv)   Spot weld, on site, square butt weld.
(v)   Plug weld on far side.
(vi)   J butt weld on far side.

ASSEMBLIES

Q26. Details of a Non-return Valve are given in Fig. 21.124b. The parts list is tabulated in Fig. 21.124a.

(i) Draw a full sectional elevation of the assembly corresponding to the given sectional elevation of the body. The valve should be in the closed position.

(ii) Insert:
- The title 'NON-RETURN VALVE'.
- Reference numbers to identify the parts.
- Four leading dimensions.
- ISO projection symbol.

Part No.	Name	Required
1	Body	1
2	Valve Seat	1
3	Valve	1
4	Cover	1
5	Seal	1

Fig. 21.124a

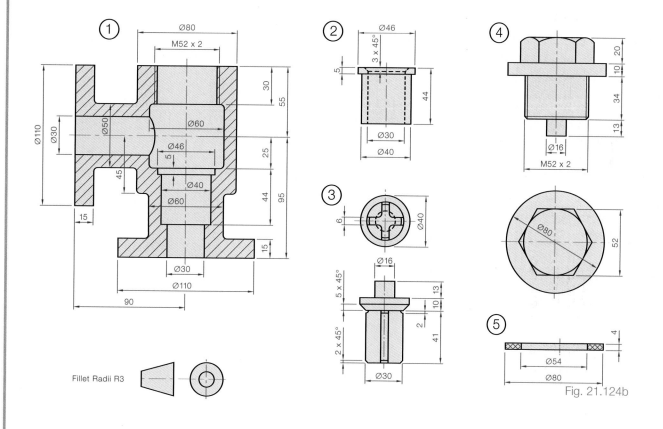

Fig. 21.124b

Q27. Details of a Welding Fixture are given in Fig. 21.125b with the parts list tabulated in Fig. 21.125a.

(i)   Draw a full-size sectional elevation S–S of the assembled parts.

(ii) Insert:
- Item reference numbers.
- ISO projection symbol.
- Title 'WELDING FIXTURE'.
- Four leading dimensions.

Part No.	Description	Required
1	Body	1
2	Hinge	2
3	Jaw	2
4	Screw	2
5	Spindle	2
6	Circlip (not shown)	2

Fig. 21.125a

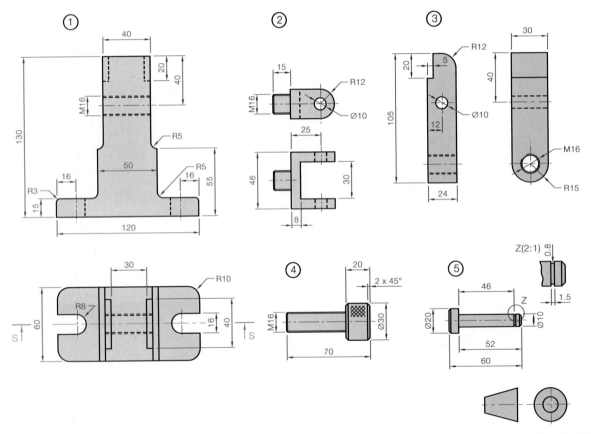

Fig. 21.125b

Q28. Details of a Cable Guide Assembly are given in Fig. 21.126b with the parts list tabulated in Fig. 21.126a.

Draw, full-size with the parts correctly assembled.

(i) A sectional front elevation on the section plane A–A in the direction indicated.

(ii) A sectional plan on the section plane B–B in the direction indicated. Insert:
- The title 'CABLE GUIDE ASSEMBLY'.
- Four major dimensions.
- ISO projection symbol.

Part No.	Description	Required
1	Roller support	1
2	Guide roller	1
3	Roller spindle	1
4	Clamping screw	1

Fig. 21.126a

HIGHER LEVEL

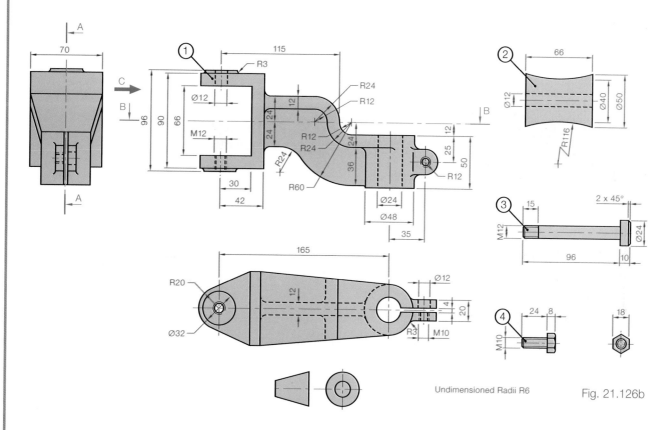

Undimensioned Radii R6

Fig. 21.126b

Q29. Fig. 21.127b shows details of a BRACKET AND GLAND ASSEMBLY. Draw the following views of the assembled pieces in first- or third-angle projection.

(i)   A sectional elevation as indicated at B–B.

(ii) A sectional end view as indicated at C–C.

(iii) Insert the following on the drawing:
  • The title 'BRACKET AND GLAND ASSEMBLY'.
  • ISO projection symbol.
  • Four leading dimensions.

Part No.	Description	Required
1	Bracket	1
2	Gland	1
3	Packing	1
4	Stud	2

Fig. 21.127a

HIGHER LEVEL

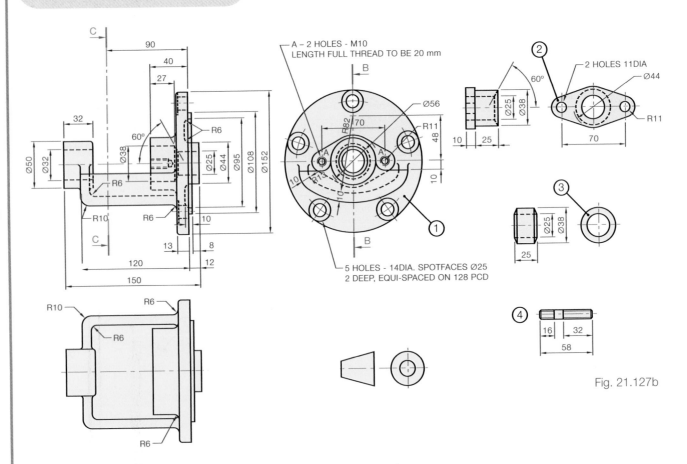

Fig. 21.127b

Q30. Details of BENCH ROLLS are given in Fig. 21.128b. The parts list is tabulated in Fig. 21.128a.

(i)   Draw a full-size sectional elevation A–A showing the parts assembled.

(ii) Insert item reference numbers to identify the parts.

(iii) Add the title 'BENCH ROLLS', the ISO projection symbol and four leading dimensions.

Part No.	Description	Required
1	Frame	1
2	Top roller	1
3	Bottom roller	1
4	Bottom bearing block	2
5	Top bearing block	2
6	Adjusting screw	2
7	Dowel	2

Fig. 21.128a

HIGHER LEVEL

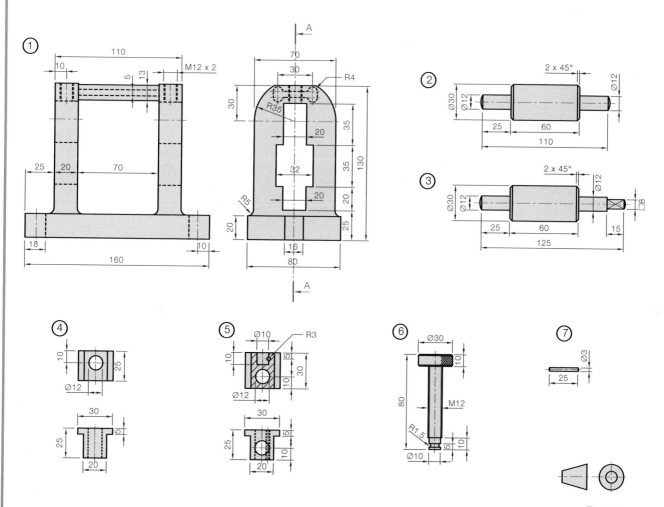

Fig. 21.128b

Q31. Details of a PIPE FLARING TOOL are shown in Fig. 21.129b with the parts list tabulated in Fig, 21.129a.

(i) Draw an elevation of the assembly showing the working parts in section and flaring a copper pipe. Pipe dimensions: outside diameter 15 mm, inside diameter 12 mm.

(ii) Balloon reference the parts and add the title 'FLARING TOOL ASSEMBLY'.

Part No.	Description	Required
1	Body	1
2	Half die	2
3	Die lock nut	1
4	Punch	1
5	Pressure screw	1
6	Handle	1

Fig. 21.129a

HIGHER LEVEL

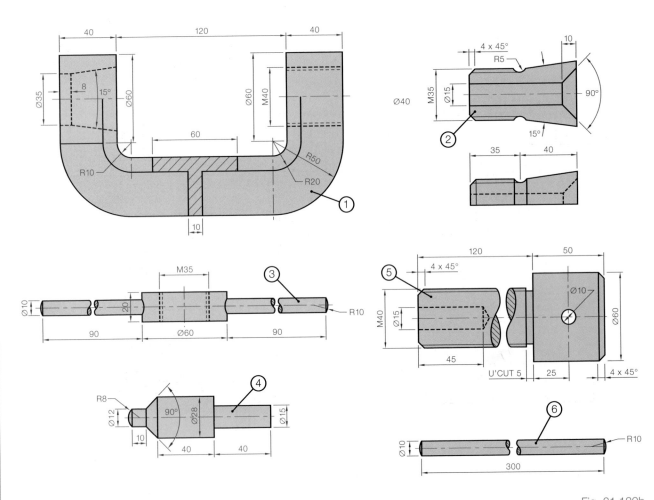

Fig. 21.129b

Q32. Details of a PIPE VICE are given in Fig. 21.130b with the parts list tabulated in Fig. 21.130a.

(i) Draw a full-size sectional elevation on cutting plane A–A showing the parts completely assembled.

(ii) Insert item reference numbers to identify the parts and add the title 'PIPE VICE'.

Part No.	Description	Required
1	Body	1
2	Clamping screw	1
3	Sliding vee	1
4	Securing screw	1

Fig. 21.130a

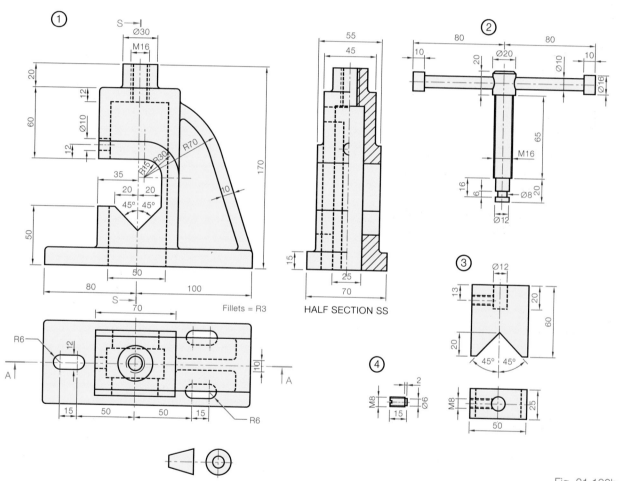

Fig. 21.130b